Social and Biological Predictors of
Nutritional Status, Physical Growth,
and Neurological Development

# Social and Biological Predictors of Nutritional Status, Physical Growth, and Neurological Development

*EDITED BY*

Lawrence S. Greene

Department of Anthropology
University of Massachusetts, Boston
Boston, Massachusetts

Francis E. Johnston

Department of Anthropology
University of Pennsylvania
Philadelphia, Pennsylvania

 1980

ACADEMIC PRESS
A Subsidiary of Harcourt Brace Jovanovich, Publishers
New York   London   Toronto   Sydney   San Francisco

ACADEMIC PRESS, INC.
111 Fifth Avenue, New York, New York 10003

*United Kingdom Edition published by*
ACADEMIC PRESS, INC. (LONDON) LTD.
24/28 Oval Road, London NW1   7DX

**Library of Congress Cataloging in Publication Data**
Main entry under title:

Social and biological predictors of nutritional status,
    physical growth, and neurological development.

    Includes bibliographies and index.
    1.  Malnutrition in children.  2.  Children--
Nutrition.  3.  Children--Anthropometry.  4.  Child
development.  I.  Greene, Lawrence S.  II.  Johnston,
Francis E. , Date  [DNLM:  1.  Child nutrition.
2.  Infant nutrition.  3.  Nutrition disorders--
In infancy and childhood.  4.  Child development--
Growth.  WS115  S674]
RJ399.M26S62    618.92'39    80--11191
ISBN  0--12--299750--6

# Contents

# List of Contributors

*Numbers in parentheses indicate the pages on which the authors' contributions begin.*

CLAIRE MONOD CASSIDY* (109), Department of Anthropology, National History Museum, Smithsonian Institution, Washington, D.C. 20560

JOAQUIN CRAVIOTO (291), Institute Nacional de Ciencias y Technologia de la Salud del Nino DIF, Mexico D. F.

ELSA DELICARDIE (291), Institute Nacional de Ciencias y Technologia de la Salud del Nino DIF, Mexico, D. F.

A. ROBERTO FRISANCHO (49), Center for Human Growth and Development and Department of Anthropology, The University of Michigan, Ann Arbor, Michigan 48109

LAWRENCE S. GREENE (223, 311), Department of Anthropology, University of Massachusetts, Boston, Boston, Massachusetts 02125

JERE D. HAAS (257), Division of Nutritional Sciences, Cornell University, Ithaca, New York 14853

GAIL GRIGSBY HARRISON (33), Department of Family and Community Medicine, Department of Pediatrics, and Department of Nutrition and Food Science, University of Arizona, Tucson, Arizona 85724

JOHN H. HIMES (9), Fels Research Institute and Department of Pediatrics, Wright State University School of Medicine, Yellow Springs, Ohio 45387

FRANCIS E. JOHNSTON (1, 291), Department of Anthropology, University of Pennsylvania, Philadelphia, Pennsylvania 19104

*PRESENT ADDRESS: 6201 Winnebago Road, Washington, D.C. 20016

SIDNEY R. KEMBERLING (61), Department of Pediatrics, Arizona Health Sciences Center, Tucson, Arizona 85724

RUDOLPH LEIBEL* (173), Department of Pediatrics, Cambridge Hospital, Harvard University Medical School, Boston, Massachusetts 02115

ROBERT M. MALINA (143), Department of Anthropology, University of Texas at Austin, Austin, Texas 78712

THOMAS J. MARCHIONE (201), Department of Anthropology, Case Western Reserve University, Cleveland, Ohio 44106

REYNALDO MARTORELL (81), Food Research Institute, Stanford University, Stanford, California 94305

BRUCE NEWMAN (291), Department of Anthropology, University of Pennsylvania, Philadelphia, Pennsylvania 19104

ERNESTO POLLITT† (173), The University of Texas, Health Science Center at Houston, School of Public Health, Human Nutrition Center, Houston, Texas 77025

FRED WILLIAM PRIOR (201), Department of Anthropology, Case Western Reserve University, Cleveland, Ohio 44106

THERESA SCHOLL (291), Department of Anthropology, University of Pennsylvania, Philadelphia, Pennsylvania 19104

WILLIAM A. STINI (61), Department of Anthropology, University of Arizona, Tucson, Arizona 85724

LINDA A. VAUGHAN (61), Department of Food and Nutrition, Arizona State University, Tempe, Arizona 85281

CHARLES W. WEBER (61), Department of Nutrition and Food Science, University of Arizona, Tucson, Arizona 85724

MORISSA WHITE (33), Bureau of Nutrition Services, Arizona Department of Health Services, Phoenix, Arizona 85007

*PRESENT ADDRESS: Rockefeller University, 1230 York Avenue, New York, New York 10021

†PRESENT ADDRESS: The University of Texas, Health Science Center at Houston, School of Public Health, Human Nutrition Center, P.O. Box 20186, Houston, Texas 77025

# Preface

Insufficient food is only one of a number of variables that influence physical growth and neurological development in human populations. Social and cultural factors usually determine the pattern of distribution of nutrients in societies. Biological differences between individuals under different nutritional and environmental circumstances also have important effects on these parameters.

The broad intent of this volume is to help clarify some issues related to the anthropometric assessment of nutritional status and to discuss recent research findings outlining the influence of social and biological factors on nutritional status, physical growth, and neurological development. Another objective is to present a number of actual clinical and population studies that evaluate the interrelationships among these variables by using novel research strategies and sophisticated statistical methods.

This volume is divided into five parts. In the Introduction, Johnston presents a brief overview of the causes of malnutrition, with emphasis on the worldwide prevalence of protein–energy malnutrition. He notes the particular importance of energy needs and reminds us that age is a major factor affecting nutritional requirements. Part I then proceeds to discuss issues involved in the anthropometric assessment of nutritional status. In Chapter 1, Himes presents an extensive discussion of the use of measures of subcutaneous fat thickness as indicators of caloric nutriture. Harrison and White in Chapter 2 then discuss the problem of the use of "population-specific" versus "reference" growth standards in assessing nutritional status in different human populations. This is an extremely important, but methodologically difficult, issue that is basic to the determination of the prevalence of protein–energy malnutrition in all human studies. In Chapter 3, Frisancho deals with the relative importance of protein and energy deficits in affecting child growth. His use of summed skinfold measurements as an estimate of caloric nutriture nicely illustrates the practical utility of this measure as was advocated by Himes in the first chapter.

The second part deals with the issues of breast-feeding, bottle-feeding, disease experience, and child growth. In Chapter 4, Stini, Weber, Kemberling, and Vaughan review the compositional, immunologic, and bacteriostatic characteristics of human milk and discuss how the choice to breast- or bottle-feed an infant may have different consequences under conditions encountered in industrialized and developing countries. Martorell in Chapter 5 then expands this discussion by considering the interaction between dietary intake and disease experience in determining nutritional status and influencing child growth. Taken together, these two chapters highlight the overall advantages of breast-feeding under conditions encountered in most developing countries.

Part III is concerned with benign neglect and its influence on nutritional status in infants and toddlers. Cassidy introduces this concept in Chapter 6 and presents extensive cross-cultural data indicating how certain weaning practices that appear to be detrimental to the individual child may serve important group functions and enhance population adaptation.

Part IV is composed of empirical studies that evaluate the relative influence of a number of social, biological, and environmental factors on nutritional status, growth, and development. Malina introduces this in Chapter 7 with an overview of factors affecting motor development, and, in Chapter 8, Pollitt and Leibel follow with a clinical study of children with failure to thrive. In Chapter 9, Marchione and Prior present a novel diachronic study evaluating the changing pattern of interrelations among a number of social and environmental factors affecting the nutritional status of 1-year-olds in Jamaica. Greene in Chapter 10 follows with a study of social and biological factors influencing nutritional status, growth, and development in an Ecuadorian highland population, where both iodine and protein–energy malnutrition are common. Haas in Chapter 11 presents an interesting study evaluating the influence of high altitude hypoxic stress on maternal adaptation and fetal growth in Bolivia. In the final chapter of Part IV, Johnston, Newman, Cravioto, DeLicardie, and Scholl employ a sophisticated statistical analysis to evaluate the relative effects of different factors influencing growth among a cohort of Mexican children between birth and 3 years of age.

In the conclusion, Part V, Greene reviews some of the issues raised throughout the volume and comments on the methodological and statistical approaches used in the empirical studies.

This volume should be of particular interest to human nutritionists, epidemiologists, biological anthropologists, developmental psychologists, community development specialists, and all other individuals in disciplines concerned with the plasticity of human development and the influence on nutritional status and child growth of a wide array of social, biological, and environmental factors. The chapters on the anthropometric assessment of nutritional status should contribute to a clarification of some of the outstanding uncertainties in this area, and the discussion of benign neglect illustrates how participation by anthropologists may greatly increase the perspective, and consequently the likelihood of success, of nutrition intervention programs. Finally, we believe that the empirical studies provide useful methodological and statistical models for future studies. Although these chapters are all of great interest in terms of their contribution to pure knowledge, we would be most gratified if the findings of these investigations were used so as to contribute substantially to the health and well-being of human populations throughout the world.

# Introduction:
# The Causes of Malnutrition

FRANCIS E. JOHNSTON

Malnutrition is one of the most serious problems confronting the human species today. The imbalances that exist between the nutrients we take in through the food we eat and the nutrients we require for the maintenance of existing tissue, the growth of new cells, and the metabolic support for the range of activities in which we participate are many, widespread, and deep-seated.

In the world's lesser developed nations, malnutrition occurs because of a deficiency of essential nutrients. Normal physiological function is not possible because there is a lack of nutrients required to support that function. In the world's industrialized nations, malnutrition is seen as the result of nutritional excess, an oversupply of nutrients which leads to impairments of health, increased morbidity, and eventually to mortality.

A large number of substances have been shown to be essential to normal function in humans, and these substances must be supplied to the body by the food we eat. These are essential nutrients. A list of nutrients which, at present, are known to be essential is given in Table I.1. This list, though lengthy, is probably not exhaustive—there are other biologically active substances which are not included because they are not yet established as essential for humans. Even with the omission of any substance not definitively shown to be essential, the list is impressive in demonstrating the many and varied substances that we must ingest regularly and, if deficient or supplied in excess, can lead to a state of malnutrition.

1

*Social and Biological Predictors of*
*Nutritional Status, Physical Growth,*
*and Neurological Development*

**TABLE I.1**

**Essential Human Nutrients**

| | | |
|---|---|---|
| Carbohydrate | | |
| Fat | | |
| Protein | | |
| Water | | |
| Minerals | | |
|   Calcium | Iron | Cobalt |
|   Phosphorus | Zinc | Chromium |
|   Potassium | Selenium | Fluorine |
|   Sulfur | Manganese | Silicon |
|   Sodium | Copper | Vanadium |
|   Chlorine | Iodine | Nickel |
|   Magnesium | Molybdenum | Tin |
| Vitamins | | |
|   A | Riboflavin | |
|   D | Niacin | |
|   E | Pyroxidine | |
|   K | Pantothenic acid | |
|   Ascorbic acid | Folacin | |
|   Thiamin | $B_{12}$ | |
|   Biotin | | |

The causes of malnutrition are incredibly complex. If we define malnutrition as a disturbed nutritional status and define nutritional status as the balance between nutrient intake and nutrient requirement, it becomes clear that malnutrition may develop in either of two ways: A person may require the same level of nutrients but may become malnourished as the dietary levels change; or a person may ingest the same amounts of nutrients but become malnourished as requirements change. To understand the problem of malnutrition, we must understand not only the issue of nutritional requirements but also the issue of nutrient availability.

But beyond this straightforward, perhaps simplistic, explanation of malnutrition, the causes are deeply enmeshed, forming a poorly defined tangle of factors which often interact with each other in complex, subtle, and as yet unrealized ways. The chapters in this volume represent the efforts of researchers to disentangle the web of factors surrounding the problem of malnutrition. The resulting picture indicates a network of correlates of malnutrition. Some components of this network are biological, growing out of the organism's changing nutritional requirements with age, or differential requirements related to gender, or increased nutrient requirements accompanying infectious disease. Some components are sociocultural. They reflect the ways in which a population's value system, social structure, and technological capabilities affect the stream of nutrients from the world of nature to the diets of individuals. Finally, some of the components of this nutritional network are transgenerational. The state of a mother's own nutrition can have significant and even long-lasting effects on the nutritional status of her offspring. Malnutrition during the period of growth may constrain the biological and intellectual functioning of individuals as adults and become manifested in their offspring.

In recent years, it has become fashionable to stress the importance of ecology, as we seek to understand our place in the world. Within the natural sciences there has been a rapid growth of the study of ecosystems, networks of interactions which affect the components of those networks. Nowhere has this orientation proved more fruitful than in the study of nutritional ecology, where scientists attempt to dissect and to understand the network of components that impinge on the satisfaction of an individual's nutrient needs. A number of researchers (e.g., Cravioto, 1970; Cravioto, Birch, DeLicardie, & Rosales, 1967; Malcolm, 1974) have dealt with the complexity of the causes of malnutrition in human populations, and of the need to understand the interrelationships among all of the factors involved.

Despite the lack of knowledge that still exists, we can make a number of statements about malnutrition which help us to understand the problem and its causes, and which perhaps help to point us in the direction of successful intervention strategies. First, the effects of malnutrition are most profoundly evident in infants, children, and youth, all of whom require additional levels of most nutrients to support the growth of new tissue and the maturation of existing systems. The effects of chronic malnutrition on growth may be permanent and, even if not permanent, may serve as a significant risk factor for the development of subsequent disease states and conditions. Overnutrition in infancy may lead to obesity which persists at least into adolescence (Johnston & Mack, 1978; Mellbin & Vuille, 1976) and which may con-

**TABLE I.2**

Relative Energy Requirements for Maintenance and Growth[a]

| Age (years) | Weight (kg) | Energy (kcal) | | |
|---|---|---|---|---|
| | | Maintenance | Growth | Ratio |
| Birth–.25 | 4.6 | 365 | 128 | 3:1 |
| .75–1.0 | 9.6 | 800 | 60 | 13:1 |
| 2.00–3.0 | 13.6 | 1020 | 30 | 34:1 |
| 9.0–10.0 | 31.1 | 1750 | 30 | 58:1 |
| 16.0–17.0 | 60.3 | 2500 | 60 | 42:1 |

[a] Data from Payne and Waterlow (1977).

**TABLE I.3**

Weighed Intakes of Protein and Energy of Weaned 1- to 2-Year-Old Children[a]

|  |  | Intake/Body weight (kg) | | | |
| --- | --- | --- | --- | --- | --- |
|  |  | Protein (gm) | | Energy (cal) | |
| Country | Child days | $\bar{X}$ | %[b] | $\bar{X}$ | %[b] |
| Ghana | 30 | 1.19 | 99 | 86 | 86 |
| Guatemala | 28 | 1.16 | 96 | 77 | 77 |
| Jamaica | 266 | 1.47 | 123 | 83 | 83 |
| Polynesia | 72 | 1.32 | 110 | 70 | 70 |
| Thailand | 54 | .61 | 51 | 52 | 52 |
| Uganda | 124 | 1.28 | 107 | 68 | 68 |
| Total | 574 | 1.30 | 108 | 75 | 75 |

[a] Data from Waterlow and Payne (1975).
[b] Percentage of FAO/WHO recommended daily intakes.

tribute to increased growth of other tissues as well (Garn, Clark, & Guire, 1975), though this needs further research.

Table I.2 indicates the relative amount of energy, expressed here as kilocalories (kcal), required for the maintenance of the body mass and for growth during the years of development. In the first three postnatal months, 23% of the energy cost is for growth, relative to maintenance. Clearly, a deficiency in energy intake during this time will significantly and adversely affect growth. In the later years, the proportion of calories for growth, relative to that for maintenance, decreases considerably, yet, when considered in the light of the chronic deficit of energy known to exist throughout the developing world, even this rather small difference can have a significant cumulative effect on growth.

Table I.3 presents data taken from Waterlow and Payne· (1975). These authors have summarized the most reliable data on energy intake of weaned 1- to 2-year-old children from various lesser developed nations; the determinations were made from weighed portions and, even though based on a small number of child days, do provide us with a picture of the magnitude of the problem. It can be seen from the table that the energy intake is quite deficient during this important period of development, averaging only 75% of the Recommended Daily Allowance (RDA) of the Food and Agriculture Organization (FAO).

Table I.4 gives figures on the prevalence of protein–energy malnutrition in children from various countries. As many as 34% of those surveyed manifested easily recognizable signs of malnutrition, categorized here as being either moderate or severe in intensity.

Next, we know that severe protein–energy malnutrition is but the tip of the iceberg. Severe malnutrition, requiring hospitalization and rehabilitation, is appallingly striking. However, it accounts for but a small proportion of infants and children who are diagnosed as malnourished. Children with chronic mild-to-moderate malnutrition suffer as well, and the long-term effects on their health and mental function may be more significant for a society than the increased mortality due to clinically severe malnutrition.

Taken on a worldwide basis, the limiting nutrient is energy. While there are areas characterized by significant deficiencies in specific nutrients such as iodine, zinc, vitamin A, and so forth, the nutritional deficit which is truly ubiquitous throughout the developing world is that of energy. Previous suggestions that the major limiting nutrient was protein seem now to be unsupported by the evidence (see e.g., Waterlow & Payne, 1975). In general, children have adequate intakes of protein, or at least only marginally inadequate, and certainly not to the extent of energy deficits.

Finally, it is clear that the root causes of nutritional deficiencies, and probably excess as well, have less to do with per capita availability on a national basis than with the distribution of food to individuals. A number of authors have presented data indicating the adequacy of available energy when considered on a national basis. Table I.5, data from Behar (1977), provides us with one example. When considered in conjunction with the intake data of Table I.3, the picture is a clear one, pointing to the importance of sociocultural factors in the incidence of malnutrition.

As a result of the preceding, it seems logical that research should be

**TABLE I.4**

**Prevalence of Protein–Energy Malnutrition in Children in 1960s[a]**

|  | Percentage | | |
| --- | --- | --- | --- |
| Country | Severe | Moderate | Total |
| Algeria | 5.9 | 16.6 | 22.5 |
| Kenya | 1.0 | 25.0 | 26.0 |
| Malawi | 3.2 | 25.8 | 29.0 |
| Tanzania | 3.2 | 17.8 | 21.0 |
| Uganda | 4.9 | 27.2 | 32.1 |
| Chile | 2.6 | 32.0 | 34.6 |
| Colombia | 1.7 | 19.3 | 21.0 |
| Costa Rica | 1.4 | 9.0 | 10.4 |
| Guatemala | 4.1 | 24.5 | 28.6 |
| Honduras | 2.0 | 22.5 | 24.5 |
| Mexico (rural) | 3.4 | 27.5 | 30.9 |
| Mexico (urban) | 1.3 | 14.8 | 16.1 |
| India | 2.3 | 16.0 | 18.3 |

[a] Data from Aylward and Jul (1975).

**TABLE I.5**

**Average per Capita Daily Supply of Energy**[a]

| Country | Energy (kcal) | Percentage of requirements |
|---|---|---|
| Japan | 2470 | 106 |
| Sweden | 2800 | 104 |
| Brazil | 2600 | 109 |
| Chile | 2460 | 101 |
| Costa Rica | 2470 | 110 |
| Mexico | 2560 | 110 |
| Micaragua | 2380 | 106 |

[a] 1970 FAO Data from Behar (1977).

devoted toward understanding those biological and social factors that influence nutritional status and the effects of variation in nutrition on health, growth, and intellectual function. Successful intervention strategies require an adequate understanding of the complexities of nutritional ecosystems. That understanding can only come from careful studies of populations, utilizing research strategies that will indicate the contribution of well-defined components to this worldwide problem of malnutrition.

## REFERENCES

Alyward, F., & Jul, M. *Protein and nutritional policy in low-income countries*. New York: Wiley, 1975.

Behar, M. Protein–calorie deficits in developing countries. *Annals of the New York Academy of Sciences*, 1977, *300*, 176–187.

Cravioto, J. Complexity of factors involved in protein–calorie malnutrition. *Bibliotheca Nutritio et Dieta*, 1970, *14*, 7–22.

Cravioto, J., Birch, H. G., DeLicardie, E. R., & Rosales, L. The ecology of infant weight gain in a pre-industrial society. *Acta Paediatrica Scandinavica*, 1967, *56*, 71–84.

Garn, S. M., Clark, D. C., & Guire, K. E. Growth, body composition, and development of obese and lean children. In M. Einick (Ed.), *Childhood obesity*. New York: Wiley, 1975. Pp. 23–46.

Johnston, F. E., & Mack, R. W. Obesity in urban black adolescents of high and low relative weight at 1 year of age. *American Journal of Diseases of Children*, 1978, *132*, 862–864.

Malcolm, L. A. Ecological factors relating to child growth and nutritional status. In A. F. Roche & F. Falkner (Eds.), *Nutrition and malnutrition, identification and measurement*. New York: Plenum, 1974. Pp. 329–352.

Mellbin, T., & Vuille, J. C. Weight gain in infancy and physical development between 7 1/2 and 10 1/2 years of age. *British Journal of Preventive and Social Medicine*, 1976, *30*, 233–238.

Payne, P. R., & Waterlow, J. C. Relative energy requirements for maintenance, growth, and physical activity. *Lancet*, 1977, *2*, 210–211.

Waterlow, J. C., & Payne, P. R. The protein gap. *Nature (London)*, 1975, *258*, 113–117.

# Part I

## THE ANTHROPOMETRIC ASSESSMENT OF NUTRITIONAL STATUS

# 1

# Subcutaneous Fat Thickness as an Indicator of Nutritional Status

JOHN H. HIMES

The problem of assessing the nutritional status of populations and individuals is of great concern to public health workers. Accordingly, many methods and approaches have been devised to evaluate the many factors that contribute to nutritional well being and to assess the varied manifestations of good nutrition (or more usually the lack of good nutrition). National and international organizations recommend that anthropometry be included in nutritional surveys along with clinical, biochemical, dietary, and other studies to evaluate the physical growth and development of individuals and populations (ICNND, 1957; WHO, 1963). Both organizations and individuals recommend measurement of subcutaneous fat thickness in the appraisal of nutritional status. Indeed, the Committee on Nutritional Anthropometry of the Food and Nutrition Board of the National Research Council has stated that "weight, height and measurement of subcutaneous fat are the irreducible basic data [Keys, 1956, p. 116]."

This chapter reviews some assumptions relevant to the use of subcutaneous fat thickness as an indicator of nutritional status and examines selected practical and theoretical considerations for their applicability and interpretation.

## RATIONALE

Subcutaneous fat refers to the *panniculus adiposus* of the *tela subcutanea*, the layer of adipose tissue just beneath the skin. Large accumulations of

9

*Social and Biological Predictors of*
*Nutritional Status, Physical Growth,*
*and Neurological Development*

adipose tissue are also found about the kidney, in the omentum, and in other tissues. Fat provides a concentrated source of energy (9.5 kcal/gm or 40 kJ/gm). Calories taken in excess of metabolic needs, activity, and growth are stored in the body as fat. Because body fat is closely associated with residual caloric balance, fatness is highly labile, and its relative contribution to the body is highly variable among individuals.

Subcutaneous fat thickness has received attention in association with nutritional studies because of its relative accessibility by noninvasive methods. The rationale for measuring subcutaneous fat thickness as an indicator of nutritional status is that the subcutaneous fat represents fairly total body fatness, and that body fat is representative of accumulated caloric nutriture. Subcutaneous fat thickness is, therefore, a morphological manifestation of nutritional status. As such, it is a measure of a specific tissue mass rather than of a heterogeneous complex, such as body weight.

## RELATIONSHIPS WITH TOTAL BODY FATNESS

One of the justifications for measuring subcutaneous fat thickness as an indicator of nutritional status is that it is valid; that is, it represents fairly total body fatness. There are few data documenting the proportion of total body fat that is located subcutaneously. Analysis of one full-term newborn infant (fat content of body 14% of body weight) revealed that 42% of the body fat was located subcutaneously (Forbes, 1962). Another study showed that 32% of total body fat was subcutaneous in a 67-year-old female who had died from carcinoma (Moore, Lister, Boyden, Ball, Sullivan, & Dagher, 1968).

Data of Garrow, Fletcher, and Halliday (1965) and Halliday (1967) allow calculation of the proportion of total body fat that is subcutaneous (plus skin) for three children whose death resulted primarily from protein–calorie malnutrition (PCM); these estimates are presented in Table 1.1. Unfortunately, there are no good data from well-nourished children for comparison. Although data for experimental animals indicate that there is little alteration with nutritional state in the relative contribution of subcutaneous fatness to total body fatness (Pitts, 1956), the results from Table 1.1 probably should not be considered as estimates for well-nourished children because of the many metabolic changes accompanying PCM. For example, considerable fatty infiltration of the liver may occur with kwashiorkor; for the child analyzed by Garrow et al. (1965) the fat in the liver comprised almost 40% of total body fat!

The weight of the skin and *tela subcutanea* as a proportion of total body weight has been determined through fetal life and into adulthood. Percentage of body weight as subcutaneous tissue increases curvilinearly through

**TABLE 1.1**

Proportion of Total Body Fat Contained in Skin and Subcutaneous Tissue

| Reference | Diagnosis | Sex | Age (months) | Percentage of subcutaneous body fat |
|-----------|-----------|-----|--------------|-------------------------------------|
| Garrow et al. (1965) | Kwashiorkor | M | 12 | 36.2 |
| Halliday (1967) | Kwashiorkor | F | 12 | 40.5 |
| Halliday (1967) | Marasmus | M | 14.5 | 27.1 |

fetal development from .8% at 5 lunar months to 13.1% at birth (Roe, 1933). Corresponding estimates for adults are 11.5% for males ($N = 13$, mean age 37 years) and 23.7% for females ($N = 2$, mean age 39 years) (Wilmer, 1940). At autopsy, subcutaneous fat thickness over the abdomen is correlated with the weight of epicardial fat in adults (Müller, 1883; Reiner, Mazzoleni, & Rodriguez, 1955); Reiner et al. (1955) reported correlation coefficients of .34 and .45 for 75 men and 62 women, respectively. Presumably similar relationships exist between subcutaneous fat thickness and other internal fat deposits.

Subcutaneous fat thickness correlates highly with total body fatness and with the percentage of body weight that is fat. Body fat is usually measured by indirect methods such as estimating body density, body water, or potassium-40 ($^{40}$K) content. Each of these methods provides a means by which the body weight can be partitioned into fat and lean components. Generally, the correlation of subcutaneous fat thickness with total body fatness ranges from .4 to .9, depending on the sites chosen and the sample, with an average of about .8 (Brožek & Keys, 1951; Pařiskova, 1961; Young, Tensuan, Sault, & Holmes, 1963).

Validity of specific sites for the measurement of subcutaneous fatness should relate to total body fatness or fatness at other sites. Suggestions that the relative value of sites for measuring subcutaneous fat thickness be based on the magnitude of correlations with body weight (Garn, Rosen, & McCann, 1971) are inappropriate. One of the central arguments in favor of using measurements of subcutaneous fatness is that they avoid the lack of specificity characteristic of gross measures such as total body weight. Moreover, why use estimates of body weight when body weight itself is generally more easily obtained?

After reviewing the relevant literature, Roche (1979) concluded that, based on validity and practicality, the preferred skinfolds to be used for measurement in children are the triceps, anterior chest, and subscapular sites; in young men, the midaxillary, paraumbilical, anterior chest, and triceps; in middle-aged men, the subscapular site; in young women, the triceps, subscapular, suprailiac, and anterior chest; and in older women, the anterior chest, paraumbilical, subscapular, and chin sites. The associations between thickness of subcutaneous fat at specific sites and measures of total body fatness have been reviewed in detail elsewhere (Keys & Brožek, 1953; Roche, 1979; Young et al., 1963).

## SUBCUTANEOUS FATNESS AND NUTRITIONAL STATUS

Many early studies of autopsy materials from starved or malnourished individuals include statements regarding qualitative observations on sub-cutaneous fat and other internal fat deposits. Although there is some varia-tion in specific internal deposits, investigators unanimously report nearly complete absence of subcutaneous fat, and virtual depletion of omental, perirenal, pericardial, and periorbital fat deposits in these individuals (En-right, 1920; Meyers, 1917; Park, 1918). In chronically malnourished or starved individuals the adipose tissue is replaced with a translucent gelatin-ous substance (Park, 1918).

Quantitative studies of subcutaneous fat thickness in severely under-nourished individuals are consistent with the above qualitative impressions, and document severely reduced subcutaneous thickness compared to well-nourished individuals (Keet, Hansen, & Truswell, 1970; Lagundoye, 1974; Shakir, Demarchi, & El-Milli, 1972). Similarly, total body fatness is de-pleted in severe PCM, as is the relative fat content of most organs and organ systems (Barac-Nieto, Spurr, Lotero, & Maksud, 1978; Garrow et al., 1965; Gopalan, Venkatachalam, & Srikantia, 1953; Himes, 1978).

On the average, children with nutritional marasmus have smaller skinfold thicknesses than those suffering from kwashiorkor-like syndromes (Jelliffe, 1966; Shakir et al., 1972). This difference in subcutaneous fat thickness does not seem to be due to the edema attending kwashiorkor because whole body analyses indicate relatively less body fat in marasmic children compared to children with kwashiorkor (Garrow et al., 1965). Nevertheless, differences between means or medians of skinfold thicknesses of marasmic children and children with kwashiorkor are, in absolute terms, small. The skinfold distri-butions for types of PCM overlap considerably, precluding classification of a single child as to type of PCM on this basis alone.

In hospitalized malnourished children, skinfold thicknesses rapidly in-crease with nutritional rehabilitation (Brooke & Wheeler, 1976); in moder-ately malnourished children, skinfold thicknesses increase with dietary supplementation (Malcolm, 1970). Similar phenomena occur in previously malnourished animals upon rehabilitation (Widdowson, 1977). Ashworth

(1969) studied $^{40}$K concentration in eight Jamaican children during recovery from PCM and found significant increases in percentage of body fat, although the absolute increases were small. It may be that fat tissue responds more quickly to nutritional rehabilitation than does lean tissue. If this is true, complete recovery from undernutrition probably should not be judged on the basis of subcutaneous fat thickness, as this measure may return to normal before deficits in lean tissue have been restored.

Lean tissue does apparently catch up completely after a time. Garrow and Pike (1967) reexamined 56 previously malnourished children 2–8 years after rehabilitative treatment. Based on measurements taken from radiographs of the calf, there were no differences in mean medial and lateral subcutaneous fat thicknesses compared to adequately nourished controls; the same was true of mean muscle and tibial widths. That subcutaneous fat thickness of previously malnourished children returns to normal after rehabilitation is clear from other data as well (Brooke & Wheeler, 1976; Keet, Moodie, Wittmann, & Hansen, 1971).

The extent to which thickness of subcutaneous fat varies with nutritional state may be seen in Figure 1.1, using triceps skinfold in boys as an example. The figure compares the unsmoothed median and extreme percentiles derived for United States white boys from the Ten-State Nutrition Survey (Frisancho, 1974) with mean triceps skinfold thickness for chronically malnourished Bundi boys from New Guinea (Malcolm, 1970), and selected means from samples of severely malnournished children. The mean thicknesses for the Bundi boys generally approximate or fall below the fifth percentile of the Ten-State reference data. Mean triceps skinfold thickness in severely malnourished children vary about the fifth percentile, although they may fall well below this level. If the thickness of skin is taken as 1 mm, the compressed double thickness of subcutaneous fat at this site for some of these malnourished children is less than 2 mm. At the other end of the spectrum, the ninety-fifth percentile (Figure 1.1) represents individuals who may have as much as six to seven times more fat over the triceps as chronically malnourished boys. While the ninety-fifth percentile may be thought of as extreme, by definition 5% of the reference population have skinfolds thicker than these values.

The precise level of fatness that defines obesity is arbitrary. Ideally, excessive fatness should be determined according to some health-related criteria. However, there is little sure knowledge concerning specific health implications of various levels of fatness, particularly in children.

Table 1.2 presents frequently cited criteria for obesity based on subcutaneous fat thickness (Seltzer & Mayer, 1965). These minimum levels are based on logarithmic means plus 1 $SD$ from a sample of unspecified provenience. These criteria were used to define obesity among adolescents in the

Ten-State Nutrition Survey (Ten-State, 1968–70); adult obesity was defined as a triceps skinfold greater than the eighty-fifth percentile for measurements of young white adults (18.6 mm in males, 25.1 mm in females). Obesity in adults included in the Health and Nutrition Examination Survey (HANES) was defined as triceps skinfold measurement greater than the eighty-fifth percentile for men and women 20–29 years of age, excluding pregnant women (Abraham, Lowenstein, & O'Connel, 1975). The actual triceps skinfold thicknesses defining obesity in this series was 17.6 mm for males and 29.7 mm for females.

Criteria of obesity based on the distribution of fatness within a population are not desirable because the levels of fatness designating obesity change from population to population, and because they assume a certain percentage of every population (in the above cases, 15 or 16%) is obese. An obvious consequence of this kind of definition of the obese state is that an individual with a stable level of fatness may become "obese" or "nonobese" simply by changing his population affiliation. The resolution of this problem is not easy

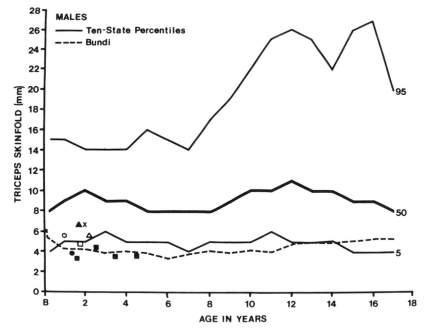

**Figure 1.1.**    Percentiles for triceps skinfold of United States white boys (Frisancho, 1974), means from chronically malnourished Bundi boys (Malcolm, 1970), and means from samples of severely malnourished children: PCM, Rao and Singh (1970) (×); Brooke and Wheeler (1976) (O); Marasmus, Shakir *et al.* (1972) (●); Keet *et al.* (1970) (□); Sastry and Vijayarghaven (1973) (■); kwashiorkor, Shakir *et al.* (1972) (▲); Keet *et al.* (1970) (△).

**TABLE 1.2**

**Minimum Triceps Skinfold Thickness Indicating Obesity**[a]

| Age (years) | Skinfold measurements (in mm) | |
| --- | --- | --- |
| | Males | Females |
| 5 | 12 | 14 |
| 6 | 12 | 15 |
| 7 | 13 | 16 |
| 8 | 14 | 17 |
| 9 | 15 | 18 |
| 10 | 16 | 20 |
| 11 | 17 | 21 |
| 12 | 18 | 22 |
| 13 | 18 | 23 |
| 14 | 17 | 23 |
| 15 | 16 | 24 |
| 16 | 15 | 25 |
| 17 | 14 | 26 |
| 18 | 15 | 27 |
| 19 | 15 | 27 |
| 20 | 16 | 28 |
| 21 | 17 | 28 |
| 22 | 18 | 28 |
| 23 | 18 | 28 |
| 24 | 19 | 28 |
| 25 | 20 | 29 |
| 26 | 20 | 29 |
| 27 | 21 | 29 |
| 28 | 22 | 29 |
| 29 | 23 | 29 |
| 30–50 | 23 | 30 |

[a] Adapted from Seltzer and Mayer (1965).

and is unlikely to occur until more information regarding health consequences of levels of fatness becomes available.

## ASSOCIATIONS WITH OTHER ANTHROPOMETRIC INDICATORS OF NUTRITIONAL STATUS

### Intercorrelations among Fat Thicknesses

Subcutaneous fat thickness measured at one site provides a good estimate of fat thickness at other sites. Correlation coefficients between subcutaneous fat thicknesses measured at various sites in children are positive, and generally range from .6 to .9, with somewhat lower correlations for fat thicknesses at corresponding sites in adults (Badora, 1975; Garn, 1954; Johnston, Hamill, & Lemeshow, 1972, 1974; Reynolds, 1951). If correlation coefficients of subcutaneous fat thickness at various sites are averaged within sites by standard $z$ transformation (Fisher, 1921), a measure of communality is obtained which expresses the degree of representativeness of a particular fat site relative to other sites. Table 1.3 presents average correlations of each of five skinfolds with four other sites, calculated from the data of Johnston et al. (1974). These data represent a large probability sample of United States youth 12–17 years of age studied by the National Center for Health Statistics.

It can be seen from Table 1.3 that there is little variation in the average correlations for these skinfolds within sexes; however, boys tend to have higher average correlations than girls, and the sites on the trunk are slightly more representative than sites on the extremities. Similar sex and site patterns in average correlations of subcutaneous fat thickness occur in adults, although, overall, correlations tend to be lower and vary more between sites in adulthood (Badora, 1975; Garn, 1957; Young, Martin, Chihan, McCarthy, Manniello, Harmuth, & Fryer, 1961). Some of the deviations from unity in correlations between sites of fat thickness are unquestionably due to measurement error; however, even when corrected for estimated measurement error, fat thicknesses at different sites do not correlate perfectly. There is considerable variation among individuals in the distribution of subcutaneous fat (Garn, 1955), and this variation in the patterning of fat tends to lower correlations among fat thicknesses at various sites.

In addition, fat patterning makes it important to measure fat thickness on the trunk and extremities (Garn, 1954, 1955; Malina, 1971; Reynolds, 1951). This differential patterning may be seen clearly in principal components

**TABLE 1.3**

Average Correlations among Five Skinfold Measurements for United States Children, 12 to 17 Years of Age[a]

| Skinfold | Boys (N = 3513) | Girls (N = 3172) |
|---|---|---|
| Triceps | .832 | .784 |
| Subscapular | .845 | .815 |
| Midaxillary | .843 | .823 |
| Suprailiac | .845 | .791 |
| Calf | .799 | .727 |

[a] Calculated from data of Johnston et al. (1974).

analyses of subcutaneous fat thicknesses that yield orthogonal components representing trunk and extremity fatness (Badora, 1975; Hammond, 1955; Tanner, 1965).

## Associations with Weight

Correlation coefficients between body weight and the sum of nine radiographic fat thicknesses (medial and lateral arm, medial and lateral forearm, medial and lateral calf, deltoid insertion, maximum hip bulge, lateral thigh) for children in the Child Research Council Longitudinal Study (Denver) are presented in Figure 1.2 (Maresh, 1966). It should be noted that the use of summed fat thicknesses causes the total fat measurement to be weighted artificially in favor of sites with thicker subcutaneous fat; nevertheless, for the present purposes the correlations plotted in Figure 1.2 can be considered representative. At most ages, correlation coefficients with weight are moderately high. The boys show a marked decline in the degree of correlation in the first 5 years of life followed by increases until prepubescence. In both sexes, although especially in boys, there is an apparent decrease in correlation coefficients about the time of pubescence. This marked decrease in boys may result from rapid increases in body weight at this time accompanied by concurrent losses in fat thickness on the extremities. Moreover, a chronological grouping of adolescent children (as in Figure 1.2) includes both early and late maturing children, and the difference in timing of the steroid-mediated changes in the relationships of fat and body weight tend to reduce the overall correlation. This is probably why the fat–weight correlations decrease in girls during pubescence.

Throughout most of childhood, subcutaneous fat thickness is more highly correlated with weight in girls than in boys (Figure 1.2), although the relative order of magnitude of correlations is reversed during infancy and pubescence. Correlations with weight of similar magnitude and pattern occur for subcutaneous fat thicknesses at other sites in other samples of children (Garn, 1958; Malina, 1972; Malina & Johnston, 1967; Reynolds, 1951; Stuart, Hill, & Shaw, 1940). In adults correlations between fat thickness and weight range from about .5 to .6 in men and from .2 to .6 in women (Badora, 1975; Keys, Fidanza, Karvonen, Kimura, & Taylor, 1972; Ward, Krzywicki, Rahman, Quaas, Nelson, & Consolazio, 1975; Young & Blondin, 1962).

From the foregoing it is clear that although subcutaneous fat thickness is usually positively correlated with weight, the general magnitude of the correlations indicates that fat thickness is somewhat independent of weight. If .5 is taken as an average correlation of fat thickness and weight, only 25% of the variance in subcutaneous fat thickness can be accounted for by variations in weight. If subcutaneous fatness is assumed to be primarily specific to caloric

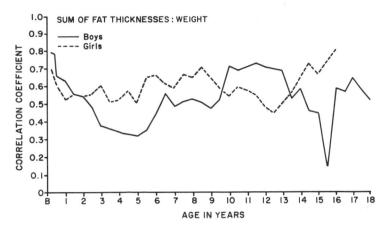

**Figure 1.2.** Correlation coefficients between body weight and the sum of nine radiographic subcutaneous fat thicknesses (drawn from data of Maresh, 1966).

nutriture, the major portion of the nutritional covariance associated with fatness is unaccounted for by body weight alone. Thus, subcutaneous fat thickness provides considerable information in addition to that provided by weight, and should be included with other anthropometric data in the assessment of nutritional status.

### Associations with Stature

It is known that children classified by various criteria as obese tend to be tall (Bruch, 1939; Fry, 1953; Wolff, 1955). Accordingly, subcutaneous fat thickness is positively correlated with stature from shortly after birth (Garn, 1958); this association continues throughout childhood and adolescence (Garn, Greaney, & Young, 1956; Maresh, 1966; Stuart et al., 1940). Age-specific correlation coefficients between stature and subcutaneous fat thickness are generally low, usually about .2 or .3, although in the first 6 years of life these correlations may reach .6 (Stuart et al., 1940). In some samples, however, correlations with stature may approach zero or even be slightly negative in later adolescence (Maresh, 1966; Reynolds, 1951). Thus, although it is clear that when samples are dichotomized into fat and lean children, the fat children are generally taller (Garn, Clark, & Guire, 1974); the exact relationships between fat thickness and stature at the less extreme levels of fatness seem less clear cut. Unlike fat thickness, which is labile, stature only increases (disregarding any statural decline in adulthood). Fat thickness thus represents a measure of short-term caloric nutriture, whereas

stature reflects the total accumulated nutriture. It is therefore not surprising that these two measures do not correlate perfectly.

The reduced correlations between fat thickness and stature in later adolescence may be due to advanced maturation in relatively fat children. Because skeletal maturity is also correlated with subcutaneous fat thickness (Chang, 1969; Garn & Haskell, 1960), the fatter children probably attain maturity earlier than their leaner counterparts, with attendant cessation of statural growth. This notion is consistent with the suggestion that obese children, though relatively tall, do not become tall adults (Lloyd & Wolff, 1961; Shuttleworth, 1937); however, data regarding this latter point are sparse and the question needs to be examined more carefully. It is clear that, in adulthood, subcutaneous fat thickness is generally unrelated to stature (Keys *et al.*, 1972; Womersley & Durnin, 1977).

## PRACTICAL AND THEORETICAL CONSIDERATIONS

### Choice of Methods

There are three practicable methods for measuring subcutaneous fat thickness in humans: soft tissue radiography, skinfold calipers, and ultrasound. Subcutaneous fat thickness has been measured by needle puncture Bullen, Quaade, Olesen, & Lund, 1965) and electrical conductivity (Booth, Goddard, & Paton, 1966); however as these methods necessitate local anesthesia and cause considerable discomfort to subjects, they are not recommended for nutritional surveys.

Among the many criteria for selecting an appropriate method for the measurement of subcutaneous fat thickness are reliability, validity, applicability, expense, ease of measurement, and appropriate reference data.

### *Reliability*

One measure of reliability of subcutaneous fat measurements is that of correlation coefficients between replicate measurements. Correlations for radiographic fat thicknesses and skinfolds, taken with calipers with recommended constant jaw pressure (10 gm/mm$^2$), approach .99 (Garn, 1961; Haymes, Lundegren, Loomis, & Buskirk, 1976), and those for ultrasound tend to be slightly lower (Bullen *et al.*, 1965; Haymes *et al.*, 1976).

In absolute terms, the standard errors of differences between observers taking replicate skinfold measurements range from 1.8 to 3 mm depending on the site measured (Edwards, Hammond, Healy, Tanner, & Whitehouse, 1955; Johnston *et al.*, 1974). In relative terms, these errors constitute from 8 to 14% of the mean measurement, with the error increasing absolutely and relatively with the thickness of the skinfold (Johnston *et al.*, 1974). The relative errors in measuring subcutaneous fat thicknesses from appropriately exposed radiographs are 3–5% (Garn, 1961; Tanner, 1965). Thus, the inherent relative measurement error for skinfold measurements is higher than for radiographic determinations and probably for ultrasound (Haymes *et al.*, 1976). These ranges of relative or percentage errors are, of course, applicable only to the means of fatness occurring in the reference samples, and thus will change inversely with the absolute size of the mean fat thickness if the absolute measurement variability remains the same.

Whittingham (1962) has stated that fat thickness measurements with ultrasound are significantly more reliable than skinfold measurements taken with Harpenden calipers—however no specific data are presented. No other relevant data regarding reliability of ultrasonic determinations of subcutaneous fat thickness are available.

## Validity

Evaluation of validity necessitates a reliable standard of reference with which methods can be compared. As previously stated, the best measure for comparison of subcutaneous fat thickness is total body fatness. While it is recognized that considerable error is inherent in the determination of total body fatness, it nevertheless provides a useful point of reference. Correlation coefficients of skinfold and ultrasonic determinations of subcutaneous fat thickness at several sites with body density determined by hydrostatic weighing (Sloan, 1967) are presented in Table 1.4. At each site, skinfold

**TABLE 1.4**

**Correlation Coefficients of Skinfold and Ultrasonic Measurements of Subcutaneous Fat with Body Density in Men $(N = 50)$[a]**

|  | Correlation coefficient | |
| --- | --- | --- |
| Site | Skinfold | Ultrasound |
| Thigh | −.80 | −.79 |
| Abdomen | −.76 | −.69 |
| Iliac | −.72 | −.68 |
| Chest | −.65 | −.62 |
| Scapula | −.74 | −.64 |
| Triceps | −.73 | −.53 |
| Buttock | −.60 | −.54 |

[a] Data from Sloan (1967).

measurements estimated body density slightly better than ultrasonic measurements; the same was true for combinations of fat thicknesses. There are few comparable data for radiographic fat thicknesses, although Brožek and Mori (1958) reported correlations of −.68 in men for triceps skinfold and body density and −.63 for body density and the comparable fat thickness determined from a radiograph. It appears that skinfold thickness has slightly higher correlations with total body fatness than the other methods, although the data are sparse.

Validity can also be assessed by associations with other reliable measures of subcutaneous fat thickness. Correlation coefficients describing associations of skinfold thickness at various sites and other measures of subcutaneous fat thickness are presented in Table 1.5. Average correlations were calculated by standard $z$ transformation for those samples reporting sample sizes. It is clear from Table 1.5 that the various methods correlate highly with skinfold measurements. Some deviations of the skinfold–fat-thickness correlations from unity are probably due to uncorrected skinfold compression as well as to measurement error.

Bullen *et al.* (1965) reported a correlation of .98 between ultrasonic and needle puncture measurement of abdominal fat thickness, and Booth *et al.* (1966) reported an $r$ of .98 between ultrasonic and electrical conductivity measurements over the abdomen. Approximately corresponding correlations of .89 for skinfolds and measurements at incision (Table 1.5), and .81 for skinfolds and electrical conductivity (Booth *et al.*, 1966), suggest that ultrasonic determinations may be more valid than skinfold measurements in estimating subcutaneous fat thickness at a particular site. Nevertheless, the data are at present insufficient to resolve the apparent conflicting conclusions that skinfold measurements estimate total body fatness slightly better than ultrasound or radiography, but do not estimate subcutaneous fat thickness per se as well as these measures.

### Applicability, Expense, and Related Factors

A double thickness of skin and subcutaneous tissue appropriate for measuring a skinfold can be elevated at many sites on the body. However, at some sites, such as medial calf, a proper fold is difficult to grasp, or may cause discomfort because of normal skin tension and firm attachment of the subcutaneous layer to the underlying tissues. Moreover, in particularly obese individuals a proper fold at some sites on the trunk is virtually unobtainable. Instead of a double fold of skin and subcutaneous tissues one can elevate only a sloping mound of flesh. As a result of this problem, and the upward limitation of the jaw openings on standard skinfold calipers (Harpenden, 55 mm; Holtain, 50 mm; Lange, 65 mm), many of the most obese

**TABLE 1.5**

**Correlations of Subcutaneous Fat Thicknesses Measured by Skinfold Calipers and Other Methods**

| Reference | N | Age (years) | Sex | Site | r |
|---|---|---|---|---|---|
| *Radiographic measurements* | | | | | |
| Baker (1955)[a] | 83 | Adult | M | Arm and thigh | .85 |
| Hammond (1955)[a] | — | Children | M | Biceps | .83 |
| | | | | Thigh | .82 |
| | | | | Triceps | .89 |
| | | | F | Biceps | .84 |
| | | | | Thigh | .89 |
| | | | | Triceps | .90 |
| Clarke *et al.* (1956)[a] | 30 | Adult | M | Biceps | .79 |
| Garn (1956) | 65 | 21–23 | M | Twelfth rib | .88 |
| Baker *et al.* (1958) | 83 | 6–14 | M | Biceps | .91 |
| | 77 | 6–14 | F | Biceps | .92 |
| Brožek and Mori (1958) | 126 | 57[b] | M | Triceps | .82 |
| Fletcher (1962) | 20 | Adult | M, F | Biceps | .61 |
| Young *et al.* (1963) | 94 | 17–27 | F | Twelfth rib | .71 |
| | | | | Suprailiac | .72 |
| | | | | Thigh | .48 |
| Hawes *et al.* (1972) | 32 | — | — | Greater trochanter | .47[c] |
| | | | | Suprailiac | .82[c] |
| Haymes *et al.* (1976) | 17 | 19–53 | M | Suprailiac | .87 |
| | | | | Triceps | .96 |
| | | | | Average: | .80 |
| *Measured at incision* | | | | | |
| Fry (1961) | 19 | 43[b] | M, F | Various | .82 |
| Fry (1962) | 13 | 41[b] | M, F | Various | .89 |
| Lee and Ng (1965) | 43 | .1–74 | M | Biceps | .83 |
| | | | | Calf | .90 |
| | | | | Cheek | .85 |
| | | | | Costal-margin | .90 |
| | | | | Forearm | .89 |
| | | | | Subscapular | .78 |
| | | | | Suprailiac | .87 |
| | | | | Thigh | .81 |
| | | | | Triceps | .87 |
| | 28 | .1–74 | F | Biceps | .86 |
| | | | | Calf | .80 |
| | | | | Costal-margin | .90 |

**TABLE 1.5** — *Continued*

| Reference | N | Age (years) | Sex | Site | r |
|-----------|---|-------------|-----|------|---|
| | | | | Face | .63 |
| | | | | Forearm | .78 |
| | | | | Subscapular | .88 |
| | | | | Suprailiac | .93 |
| | | | | Thigh | .78 |
| | | | | Triceps | .88 |
| Macků et al. (1971)[a] | 100 | 22–58 | F | Abdomen | .97 |
| | | | | Average: | .89 |
| | | | *Ultrasound* | | |
| Bullen et al. (1965) | 51 | 18–78 | M | Abdomen | .90 |
| | | | | Triceps | .80 |
| | 49 | 14–84 | F | Abdomen | .85 |
| | | | | Triceps | .80 |
| Booth et al. (1966) | 41 | 16–87 | M, F | Abdomen and subscapular | .81 |
| Haymes et al. (1976) | 17 | 19–53 | M | Abdomen | .78 |
| | | | | Subscapular | .76 |
| | | | | Suprailiac | .59 |
| | | | | Triceps | .64 |
| | 20 | 19–53 | F | Abdomen | .88 |
| | | | | Subscapular | .93 |
| | | | | Suprailiac | .92 |
| | | | | Triceps | .85 |
| | | | | Average: | .84 |
| | | | *Electrical conductivity* | | |
| Booth et al. (1966) | 41 | 16–87 | M, F | Abdomen | .81 |

[a] Used calipers other than Lange or Harpenden.
[b] Mean age.
[c] "Error-free" correlation.

individuals cannot be included in studies of obesity that include subcutaneous fatness as a variable. A distinct advantage of skinfold measurements is that standard calipers are relatively inexpensive (about $120), generally available, and easily carried about. Some prototypes of very inexpensive skinfold calipers made of durable plastic resins are currently being tested (Townsend, 1978), and the initial results regarding accuracy and reliability are very encouraging. Good reference data for several sites are available for skinfold measurements taken with standardized methods and equipment.

National reference data are available for the United States (Abraham *et al.*, 1975; Frisancho, 1974; Johnston *et al.*, 1972, 1974), Canada (Pett & Ogilvie, 1956), and England (Rona & Altman, 1977; Tanner & Whitehouse, 1975). Equations for converting measurements taken with different calipers are also available (Pařiśková & Goldstein, 1970).

Radiographs used for measurement of subcutaneous fat thickness constitute a permanent record that may be verified at a later time by subsequent measurement. As the purpose of these radiographs is to differentiate the subcutaneous fat plus skin from the underlying tissues, relatively low milliamperage exposures suffice. Even though the dosage of radiation for a soft tissue radiograph is extremely small if proper technique is used (Garn, 1961), irradiation of individuals for large nutritional surveys is difficult to justify, particularly if other methods of obtaining similar data are available. Radiographic equipment and processing are expensive and generally require individuals to be brought to some central location able to accommodate needs for power, space, developing, etc. Although portable X-ray machines and generators are available, these are still expensive and rather difficult to manage.

An appropriate soft tissue radiograph may be taken for any body part that provides a profile of the subcutaneous fat thickness shadow. This includes most areas of the body, although for certain conventional sites for skinfolds it may be difficult to obtain a satisfactory radiographic image at the same location, namely, subscapular, anterior chest, suprapubic. Available reference data for radiographic fat thickness relate mostly to limb sites, although a few trunk sites are represented (Maresh, 1966; Reynolds, 1951; Stuart & Sobel, 1946). Reference data for subcutaneous fat thicknesses determined from radiographs often have not been adjusted for radiographic enlargement; because tube-film distances vary, reference data should be adjusted on an individual basis according to standard correction formulas (Lusted & Keats, 1972).

Fat thicknesses determined by ultrasonic reflections record the distance from the probe to the first perpendicular interface substantial enough to reflect the ultrasonic echo. Often connective tissue septa in the subcutaneous fat layer are sufficient to reflect an echo (Bullen *et al.*, 1965; Haymes *et al.*, 1976); this, of course, makes interpretation of results difficult. Although little pressure is necessary to provide sufficient skin contact with the ultrasonic probe, the actual thickness of subcutaneous fat determined by ultrasound is usually smaller than the actual thickness due to the compression of soft tissues, a situation analogous to that seen with skinfolds. Finally, appropriate ultrasonic equipment is expensive and not easily transported (some portable models have been developed) (Bullen *et al.*, 1965; Moore, 1978). No good reference data are available for fat thicknesses determined by ultrasound.

## Skinfold Compression

When subcutaneous fat thickness is measured with skinfold calipers, the resultant skinfold thickness represents the compressed double layer of subcutaneous fat and skin. It has been recognized for a long time that the skinfold at a given site represents less than twice the thickness of subcutaneous tissues as measured by radiographic images or by surgical incision (Fry, 1961; Hammond, 1955)—subsequent research has confirmed these earlier findings (Lee & Ng, 1965; Macků, Doležal, Sîndelarová, & Vyhnal, 1971; Young et al., 1963).

A certain amount of compression is normal, although compression of skinfolds may vary between individuals and according to site, sex, and age (Brožek & Kinzey, 1960; Clegg & Kent, 1967; Himes, 1977; Ng, Lee, & Yuan, 1965; Young et al., 1963). In general, skinfolds of females are more compressible than those of males, and compression tends to decrease with age in adulthood, although the age changes during the growing years are unclear (Brožek &'Kinzey, 1960; Clegg & Kent, 1967; Ng et al., 1965). Variability in skinfold compressibility is probably due to differences in skin tension, distribution of fibrous tissue in the subcutaneous tissues, presence of blood vessels, etc. The variability in skinfold compressibility has been reviewed by Roche (1979).

Skinfold compressibility often has been expressed as percentage of uncompressed thickness. This use of percentages or ratios, however, is not pleasing statistically because of the probability of an inconstant ratio for varying skinfold thicknesses and a regression line that does not pass through zero (Pearson, 1899; Tanner, 1949). Although it has been claimed that for lateral thoracic fat the skinfold is reduced 35% throughout the entire range of fatness (Garn, 1956), in general, a regression approach to adjusting skinfolds for compression is preferred. The only useful regression corrections for skinfold compressibility (with Harpenden calipers) are those of Lee and Ng (1965) for Chinese people. Preliminary findings based on United States children have been presented by Himes (1977), although these data have yet to be published.

There are some aspects of skinfold compressibility that clearly seem to have theoretical implications for the applicability and appropriateness of skinfold measurements in the assessment of nutritional status. The most obvious problem in using uncorrected skinfold measurements is they are not equivalent to true fat thickness at a particular site. If .8 is taken as the representative association between skinfold measurements and subcutaneous fat thickness at the same site, a skinfold only accounts for about 64% of the variance in actual fat thickness; some of this difference is, of course, measurement error. Moreover, the differences between actual fat thickness and skinfolds are systematic due to compression. Consequently, skinfolds are always underestimates of actual thickness, although inconsistently so, depending on the site and probably sex. Underestimation of fat thickness results in an overestimation of muscle and bone areas and an underestimation of fat areas when these derived measures are calculated using upper arm circumference.

Since compressibility varies between sites and sexes, assessment of fat patterns and even sex differences may be altered when skinfold measurements have been used for such analyses.

Because there is significant similarity within individuals in average skinfold compressibility and, at least in young males, significant difference among individuals in average compressibility (Himes, 1977), it might be useful to ascertain the factors associated with compressibility. Perhaps compressibility is mediated through genetic factors or maybe it varies with nutritional status or hydration. In any case, population comparisons of skinfold measurements assume equal compressibility of skinfolds, which may not be the case.

Finally, the preceding discussions are generally theoretical implications of skinfold compressibility. Whether taking account of compressibility makes an appreciable difference in estimating total body fatness or in evaluating nutritional status are empirical questions that await further research.

### Additional Considerations

In measuring body fatness for nutritional studies one tacitly assumes that fatness is not only sensitive but specific to nutritional factors, in particular to energy balance. To a large degree this is true; however, there are some exceptions. The growth of body fatness and subcutaneous fatness at several sites has been well described in the literature (Maresh, 1966; Reynolds, 1951; Roche, 1979; Stuart & Sobel, 1946; Tanner, 1962). It is clear that individuals go through a series of changes in the thickness and distribution of subcutaneous fat as a function of age and sex. Qualitatively similar patterns of growth in subcutaneous fatness occur in all levels of nutritional adequacy; therefore, these patterns necessitate age- and sex-specific comparisons for proper interpretation of data. The fat changes occurring during adolescence are probably hormonally mediated, and proper separation of nutritional factors per se from developmental ones during this period demands the use of maturational levels or categories for comparisons rather than simply chronological age. Endocrine mediation of fatness also occurs in many disease states.

Edema is a factor that must be taken into consideration in interpreting results from subcutaneous fat measurements. The edema that accompanies some forms of clinical PCM is well recognized. The additional extracellular fluid in the subcutaneous tissues makes it difficult to measure subcutaneous fat thickness accurately. Relative body water increases in other forms of generalized undernutrition, even when ordinary clinical signs of edema are not present (Garrow *et al.*, 1965; Gopalan *et al.*, 1953; Halliday, 1967). This relative hydration due to malnutrition certainly affects the compressibility of the subcutaneous tissues, although to what degree is uncertain. The amount that skinfolds compress during a minute with the calipers in place has been suggested as an estimate of tissue hydration in neonates (Brans, Sumners, Dweck, & Cassady, 1974), although this method has neither been validated nor applied to older individuals.

Exposure of unacclimatized adult males to extreme heat (120°F) may result in increases in skinfold thickness (Newman, 1952). This swelling of skinfolds may be due to peripheral vasodilatation or accumulation of extracellular water. However, no data exist for less extreme temperatures or for other samples. This topic requires further investigation, but may have implications for assessment of nutritional status using subcutaneous fat thickness in some of the hotter climates.

## CONCLUSIONS

The widespread use of subcutaneous fat thickness as an indicator of nutritional status is justified by its validity, as determined by relationships with total body fatness and by the response of subcutaneous fat thickness to nutritional changes. As an indicator of nutritional status, subcutaneous fat thickness reflects only energy balance, and, even in this context, subcutaneous fat thickness must be interpreted considering, inter alia, endocrine normality, sex, and age.

Although each of the various methods of measuring subcutaneous fat thickness has advantages and disadvantages, skinfold thickness is the recommended method for general nutrition surveys. It is still important that care be taken in measuring skinfolds to ensure comparability and replicability of results.

## ACKNOWLEDGEMENTS

Research support was provided by Grant HD 12252 from the National Institutes of Health. Thanks are extended to Kathy Frasure for help in manuscript preparation.

## REFERENCES

Abraham, S., Lowenstein, F. W., & O'Connell, D. E. Preliminary findings of the first health and nutrition examination survey, United States, 1971–1972. In *Vital Health Statistics*. Washington, D.C.: DHEW Pub. No. (HRA) 75-1229, 1975.

Ashworth, A. Growth rates in children recovering from protein-calorie malnutrition. *British Journal of Nutrition*, 1969, *23*, 835–845.

Badora, G. The distribution of subcutaneous fat tissue in young women and men. *Studies in Physical Anthropology (Warsaw)*, 1975, No. 1, 91–108.

Baker, P. T. *Relationship of desert heat stress to gross morphology* (Tech. Rep. 3119) Natick, Mass.: United States Army, Quartermaster Research and Development Center, 1955.

Baker, P. T., Hunt, E. E., & Sen, T. The growth and interrelations of skinfolds and brachial tissues in man. *American Journal of Physical Anthropology*, 1958, *16*, 39–58.

Barac-Nieto, M., Spurr, G. B., Lotero, H., & Maksud, M. G. Body composition in chronic undernutrition. *American Journal of Clinical Nutrition*, 1978, *31*, 23–40.

Booth, R. A. D., Goddard, B. A., & Paton, A. Measurement of fat thickness in man: A comparison of ultrasound, Harpenden calipers and electrical conductivity. *British Journal of Nutrition*, 1966, *20*, 719–725.

Brans, Y. W., Sumners, J. E., Dweck, H. S., & Cassady, G. A noninvasive approach to body composition in the neonate: Dynamic skinfold measurements. *Pediatric Research*, 1974, *8*, 215–222.

Brooke, O. G., & Wheeler, E. F. High energy feeding in protein-energy malnutrition. *Archives of Disease in Childhood*, 1976, *51*, 968–971.

Brožek, J., & Keys, A. The evaluation of leanness–fatness in man: Norms and interrelationships. *British Journal of Nutrition*, 1951, *5*, 194–206.

Brožek, J., & Kinzey, W. Age changes in skinfold compressibility. *Journal of Gerontology*, 1960, *15*, 45–51.

Brozek, J., & Mori, H. Some interrelations between somatic, roentgenographic and densitometric criteria of fatness. *Human Biology*, 1958, *30*, 322–336.

Bruch, H. Obesity in childhood. I. Physical growth and development of obese children. *American Journal of Disease of Children*, 1939, *58*, 457–484.

Bullen, B. A., Quaade, F., Olesen, E., & Lund, S. A. Ultrasonic reflections used for measuring subcutaneous fat in humans. *Human Biology*, 1965, *37*, 375.

Chang, S. K. F. *Growth and development of Chinese children and youth in Hong Kong.* Privately published, University of Hong Kong, 1969.

Clarke, H. H., Geser, L. R., & Hunsdon, S. B. Comparisons of upper arm measurements by use of roentgenogram and anthropometric techniques. *Research Quarterly*, 1956, *27*, 379.

Clegg, E. J., & Kent, C. Skinfold compressibility in young adults. *Human Biology*, 1967, *39*, 418–429.

Edwards, D. A. W., Hammond, W. H., Healy, M. J. R., Tanner, J. M., & Whitehouse, R. H. Design and accuracy of calipers for measuring subcutaneous tissue thickness. *British Journal of Nutrition*, 1955, *9*, 133–143.

Enright, J. I. War oedema in Turkish prisoners of war. *Lancet*, 1920, *198*, 314–316.

Fisher, R. A. On the "probable error" of a coefficient of correlation deduced from a small sample. *Metron*, 1921, *1*, 3–32.

Fletcher, R. F. The measurement of total body fat with skinfold calipers. *Clinical Science*, 1962, *22*, 333–346.

Forbes, G. B. Methods for determining composition of the human body. (With a note on the effect of diet on body composition.) *Pediatrics*, 1962, *29*, 477–494.

Frisancho, A. R. Triceps skinfold and upper arm muscle size norms for assessment of nutritional status. *American Journal of Clinical Nutrition*, 1974, *27*, 1052–1058.

Fry, P. C. A comparative study of "obese" children selected on the basis of fat pads. *American Journal of Clinical Nutrition*, 1953, *6*, 453–468.

Fry, E. I. The measurement of subcutaneous tissue by the Harpenden caliper and by surgical incision. *American Journal of Physical Anthropology*, 1961, *19*, 98.

Fry, E. I. Subcutaneous tissue measurement by caliper and surgical incision in Hong Kong Chinese. *Proceedings of the Nebraska Academy of Sciences and Affiliated Societies*, 1962, P. 4.

Garn, S. M. Fat patterning and fat intercorrelations in the adult male. *Human Biology*, 1954, *26*, 59–69.

Garn, S. M. Relative fat patterning: An individual characteristic. *Human Biology*, 1955, 27, 75–89.

Garn, S. M. Comparisons of pinch-caliper and X-ray measurements of skin plus subcutaneous fat. *Science*, 1956, *124*, 178–179.

Garn, S. M. Selection of body sites for fat measurement. *Science*, 1957, *125*, 550–551.

Garn, S. M. Fat, body size and growth in the newborn. *Human Biology*, 1958, *30*, 265–280.

Garn, S. M. Radiographic analysis of body composition. In J. Brožek & A. Henschel (Eds.), *Techniques for measuring body composition*. Washington, D.C.: National Academy of Sciences–National Research Council, 1961. Pp. 36–58.

Garn, S. M., Clark, D. C., & Guire, K. E. Level of fatness and size attainment. *American Journal of Physical Anthropology*, 1974, *40*, 447–450.

Garn, S. M., Greaney, G. R., & Young, R. W. Fat thickness and growth progress during infancy. *Human Biology*, 1956, *28*, 232–250.

Garn, S. M., & Haskell, J. A. Fat thickness and developmental status in childhood and adolescence. *A.M.A. Journal of Diseases of Children*, 1960, *99*, 746–751.

Garn, S. M., Rosen, N. N., & McCann, M. B. Relative values of different fat folds in a nutritional survey. *American Journal of Clinical Nutrition*, 1971, *24*, 1380–1381.

Garrow, J. S., Fletcher, K., & Halliday, D. Body composition in severe infantile malnutrition. *Journal of Clinical Investigation*, 1965, *44*, 417–425.

Garrow, J. S., & Pike, M. C. The long-term prognosis of severe infantile malnutrition. *Lancet*, 1967, *1*, 1–4.

Gopalan, C., Venkatachalam, P. S., & Srikantia, S. G. Body composition in nutritional edema. *Metabolism*, 1953, *2*, 335–343.

Halliday, D. Chemical composition of the whole body and individual tissues of two Jamaican children whose death resulted primarily from malnutrition. *Clinical Science*, 1967, *33*, 365–370.

Hammond, W. H. Measurement and interpretation of subcutaneous fat, with norms for children and young adult males. *British Journal of Preventive and Social Medicine*, 1955, *9*, 201–211.

Hawes, S. F., Albert, A., Healy, M. J. R., & Garrow, J. S. A comparison of soft-tissue radiography, reflected ultrasound, skinfold calipers and thigh circumference for estimating the thickness of fat overlying the iliac crest and greater trochanter. *Proceedings of the Nutrition Society*, 1972, *31*, 91A–92A.

Haymes, E. M., Lundegren, H. M., Loomis, J. L., & Buskirk, E. R. Validity of the ultrasonic technique as a method of measuring subcutaneous adipose tissue. *Annals of Human Biology*, 1976, *3*, 245–251.

Himes, J. H. Caliper and radiographic measurement of subcutaneous fatness: Implications for assessment of nutritional status. Paper presented at *76th Annual Meetings of the American Anthropological Association*, Houston, Texas, 1977.

Himes, J. H. Bone growth and development in protein-calorie malnutrition. *World Review of Nutrition and Dietetics*, 1978, *28*, 143–187.

ICNND Interdepartmental Committee on Nutrition for National Defense. *Manual for nutrition surveys*. Washington, D.C.: U.S. National Institutes of Health, U.S. Government Printing Office, 1957.

Jelliffe, D. B. The assessment of the nutritional status of the community. *World Health Organization Monograph Series*, 1966, No. 53.

Johnston, F. E., Hamill, P. V. V., & Lemeshow, S. Skinfold thickness of children 6–11 years, United States. *Vital Health Statistics*, Series 11, No. 120, DHEW Pub. No. (HSM) 73-1602, 1972.

Johnston, F. E., Hamill, P. V. V., & Lemeshow, S. Skinfold thickness of youths 12–17 years, United States. *Vital Health Statistics*, Series 11, No. 132, DHEW Pub. No. (HRA) 74-1614, 1974.

Keet, M. P., Hansen, J. D. L., & Truswell, A. S. Are skinfold measurements of value in the assessment of suboptimal nutrition in young children? *Pediatrics*, 1970, *45*, 965–972.

Keet, M. P., Moodie, A. D., Wittmann, W., & Hansen, J. D. L. Kwashiorkor: A prospective ten-year follow-up study. *South African Medical Journal*, 1971, *45*, 1427–1444.

Keys, A. Recommendations concerning body measurements for the characterization of nutritional status. *Human Biology*, 1956, *28*, 112–123.

Keys, A., & Brožek, J. Body fat in adult man. *Physiological Reviews*, 1953, *33*, 245–325.

Keys, A., Fidanza, F., Karvonen, M. J., Kimura, N., & Taylor, H. L. Indices of relative weight and obesity. *Journal of Chronic Diseases*, 1972, *25*, 329–343.

Lagundoye, S. B. Subcutaneous fat and muscle layers in chest x-rays of children with kwashiorkor. *Journal of Tropical Pediatrics*, 1974, *20*, 287–290.

Lee, M. M. C., & Ng, C. K. Postmortem studies of skinfold caliper measurement and actual thickness of skin and subcutaneous tissue. *Human Biology*, 1965, *37*, 91–103.

Lloyd, J. K., & Wolff, O. H. Childhood obesity. A long-term study of height and weight. *British Medical Journal*, 1961, *ii*, 145–148.

Lusted, L. B., & Keats, T. E. *Atlas of roentogenographic measurement* (3rd ed.). Chicago: Year Book, 1972.

Macků, F., Doležal, A., Šindelářová, L., & Vyhnal, K. The skinfold measured by caliper and the thickness of the fat. In V. V. Novotny (Ed.), *Proceedings of Anthropology Congress dedicated to A. Hrdlička, 1969*. Prague: Academia Prague, 1971. Pp. 385–386.

Malcolm, L. A. Growth and development in New Guinea—A study of the Bundi people of the Madang District. *Institute of Human Biology*, Papua, New Guinea, 1970, No. 1.

Malina, R. M. Skinfolds in American negroes and white children. *Journal of the American Dietetic Association*, 1971, *59*, 34–59.

Malina, R. M. Skinfold–body weight correlations in negro and white children of elementary school age. *American Journal of Clinical Nutrition*, 1972, *25*, 861–863.

Malina, R. M., & Johnston, F. E. Significance of age, sex, and maturity differences in upper arm composition. *The Research Quarterly*, 1967, *38*, 219–230.

Maresh, M. M. Changes in tissue widths during growth. *American Journal of Diseases in Children*, 1966, *111*, 142–155.

Meyers, A. W. Some morphological effects of prolonged inanition. *Journal of Medical Research*, 1917, *36*, 51–78.

Moore, F. D., Lister, J., Boyden, C. M., Ball, M. R., Sullivan, N., & Dagher, F. J. The skeleton as a feature of body composition. *Human Biology*, 1968, *40*, 135–188.

Moore, W. M. Personal communication, 1978.

Müller, W. *Die Massenverhältnisse des menschlichen Herzens*. Hamburg and Leipzig: Leopold Voss, 1883.

Newman, R. W. The assessment of military personnel by 1912 height–weight standards. *Environmental Protection Branch Report No. 194*, Office of the Quartermaster General, U.S. Army, 1952.

Ng, C. K., Lee, M. M. C., & Yuan, H. M. Age influence on skinfold caliper measurements. *Far East Medical Journal*, 1965, *1*, 258–259.

Pařisková, J. Total body fat and skinfold thickness in children. *Metabolism*, 1961, *10*, 794–807.

Pařisková, J., & Goldstein, H. A comparison of skinfold measurements using the Best and Harpenden calipers. *Human Biology*, 1970, *42*, 436–441.

Park, F. S. War edema (Kriegsoedem). *Journal of the American Medical Association*, 1918, *70*, 1826–1827.

Pearson, K. Mathematical contributions to the theory of evolution—V. On the reconstruction of the stature of prehistoric races. *Philosophical Transactions of the Royal Society of London Series A*, 1899, *192*, 169–244.

Pett, L. B., & Ogilvie, G. F. The Canadian weight–height survey. *Human Biology*, 1956, *28*, 177–188.

Pitts, G. C. Body fat accumulation in the guinea pig. *American Journal of Physiology*, 1956, *185*, 41–48.

Rao, K. V., & Singh, D. An evaluation of the relationship between nutritional status and anthropometric measurements. *American Journal of Clinical Nutrition*, 1970, *23*, 83–93.

Reiner, L., Mazzoleni, A., & Rodriguez, F. L. Statistical analyses of the epicardial fat weight in human hearts. *Archives of Pathology*, 1955, *60*, 369 373.

Reynolds, E. L. The distribution of subcutaneous fat in childhood and adolescence. *Monographs of the Society for the Research of Child Development*, 1951, *14*, No. 2 (Serial No. 52).

Roche, A. F. Postnatal growth of adipose tissue in man. *Studies in Physical Anthropology (Warsaw)* 1979, 5:53–74.

Roe, H. E. The weight of the skin and tela subcutanea of the human fetus. *The Anatomical Record*, 1933, *55*, 127–137.

Rona, R. J., & Altman, D. G. National study of health and growth: Standards of attained height, weight and triceps skinfold in English children 5 to 11 years old. *Annals of Human Biology*, 1977, *4*, 501–523.

Sastry, J. G., & Vijayaraghavan, K. Use of anthropometry in grading malnutrition in children. *Indian Journal of Medical Research*, 1973, *61*, 1225–1232.

Seltzer, C. C., & Mayer, J. A simple criterion of obesity. *Post Graduate Medicine*, 1965, *38*, A101–A107.

Shakir, A., Demarchi, M., & El-Milli, N. Pattern of protein-calorie malnutrition in young children attending an outpatient clinic in Baghdad. *Lancet*, 1972, *2*, 143–146.

Shuttleworth, F. K. Sexual maturation and the physical growth of girls age six to nineteen. *Monographs of the Society for the Research of Child Development*, 1937, *2*, No. 5 (Serial No. 12).

Sloan, A. W. Estimation of body fat in young men. *Journal of Applied Physiology*, 1967, *23*, 311–315.

Stuart, H. C., Hill, P., & Shaw, C. The growth of bone, muscle and overlying tissues as revealed by studies of roentgenograms of the leg area. *Monographs of the Society for the Research of Child Development*, 1940, 5, No. 3 (Serial No. 26).

Stuart, H. C., & Sobel, E. H. The thickness of the skin and subcutaneous tissue by age and sex in childhood. *Journal of Pediatrics*, 1946, *28*, 637–647.

Tanner, J. M. Fallacy of per-weight and per-surface area standards and their relation to spurious correlation. *Journal of Applied Physiology*, 1949, *2*, 1–15.

Tanner, J. M. *Growth at adolescence* (2nd ed.). Oxford: Blackwell Scientific Publications, 1962.

Tanner, J. M. Radiographic studies of body composition in children and adults. In J. Brožek (Ed.), *Human body composition*. Oxford: Pergamon Press, 1965. Pp. 211–236.

Tanner, J. M., & Whitehouse, R. H. Revised standards for triceps and subscapular skinfolds in British children. *Archives of Disease in Childhood*, 1975, *50*, 142–145.

Ten-State Nutrition Survey 1968–1970. *Clinical, anthropometry and dental Ten-State nutrition survey* (Vol. III). DHEW Pub. No. (HSM) 72-8131, 1968–1970.

Townsend, E. Comparison of a new skinfold caliper to Lange and Harpenden calipers. *American Journal of Physical Anthropology*, 1978, *48*, 433.

Ward, G. M., Krzywicki, H. J., Rahman, D. P., Quaas, R. L., Nelson, R. A., & Consolazio, C. F. Relationships of Anthropometric measurements to body fat as determined by densitometry, potassium-40, and body water. *American Journal of Clinical Nutrition*, 1975, *28*, 162–169.

Whittingham, P. D. G. V. Measurement of tissue thickness by ultrasound. *Aerospace Medicine*, 1962, *33*, 1121–1128.

WHO. Expert committee on medical assessment of nutritional status. *World Health Organization Technical Report Series*, 1963, *258*.

Widdowson, E. M. Undernutrition and retarded growth before and after birth. *Nutrition and Metabolism*, 1977, *21*, 76–87.

Wilmer, H. A. Quantitative growth of skin and subcutaneous tissue in relation to human surface area. *Proceedings of the Society for Experimental Biology and Medicine*, 1940, *43*, 386–388.

Wolff, O. H. Obesity in childhood. *Quarterly Journal of Medicine*, 1955, *24*, 109–123.

Womersley, J., & Durnin, J. V. G. A. A comparison of the skinfold method with extent of 'overweight' and various weight–height relationships in the assessment of obesity. *British Journal of Nutrition*, 1977, *38*, 271–284.

Young, C. M., & Blondin, J. Estimating body weight and fatness of young women. *Journal of the American Dietetic Association*, 1962, *41*, 452–455.

Young, C. M., Martin, M. E. K., Chihan, M., McCarthy, M., Manniello, M. J., Harmuth, E. H., & Fryer, J. H. Body composition of young women. *Journal of the American Dietetic Association*, 1961, *38*, 332–340.

Young, C. M., Tensuan, R. S., Sault, F., & Holmes, F. Estimating body fat of normal young women. *Journal of the American Dietetic Association*, 1963, *42*, 409–413.

# 2

# Overweight in Arizona Infants: Relation to Birthweight and Ethnic Group

GAIL GRIGSBY HARRISON AND MORISSA WHITE

## INTRODUCTION:
## THE QUESTION OF GROWTH STANDARDS

The use of reference standards for assessment of growth and their application to assessment of nutritional status is of concern to the clinician and the public health worker as well as to the student of human variation. For clinical use in following the growth of an individual child, any of the existing standards may be used without major difficulty because one is looking for significant deviations from a pattern, using the child as his/her own control. For cross-sectional evaluation of nutritional status in populations and for determining who is nutritionally at risk and therefore eligible for various intervention programs, the issue of appropriateness of the standards used becomes more important.

The International Union of Nutritional Sciences recommended the development of an international series of anthropometric reference standards based on "studies [to] be carried out in as large a variety of countries as possible. Each country's own standards must be derived from carefully selected samples representing children growing in an optimal environment

*Social and Biological Predictors of Nutritional Status, Physical Growth, and Neurological Development*

for that country. Genetic and racial factors must be defined and appropriately represented in the sample [Falkner, 1972, p. 218]." Aside from the practical problem of defining such a group of children in any country, the idea of population-specific standards has been criticized on the grounds that the resources required to develop them would be enormous. Furthermore, the problems of defining the optimal environment for growth are not easily solved (Haas and Harrison, 1977).

Nevertheless, it does seem possible to begin to unravel some of the major factors associated with variation in normal growth patterns and to adjust growth standards accordingly. It is clear that American black and white children grow differently, with black children being lighter and shorter at birth but taller by the preschool years (Garn & Clark, 1976; Owen & Lubin, 1973; Robson, Larkin, Bursick, & Perri, 1975). For older children, the need for adjustment of standards for parental size has been pointed out (Garn & Rohmann, 1967; Tanner, Goldstein, & Whitehouse, 1970).

Garn, Shaw, and McCabe (1977) have analyzed data from the Collaborative Perinatal Project of the National Institute of Neurological and Communicative Disorders and Stroke, in which more than 20,000 black and white children were longitudinally studied from birth to age 7. They conclude that for both males and females and for both black and white children, size at birth is a significant predictor of future development, at least up to the age of 7 years. Infants in the lower percentiles at birth for length, weight, and head circumference tended to be in the lower percentiles for these dimensions at age 7; those in the higher percentiles at birth tended to be in the higher percentiles at age 7. There was considerable variability, but size at birth was a stronger predictor of relative size at age 7 years than was maternal size. On the basis of these data the authors suggest that, at least for children up to age 7, birthweight-specific growth standards would be appropriate.

Alvear and Brooke (1978) have published anthropometric data on newborns of three racial groups in Britain, carefully matched for socioeconomic status, maternal smoking, maternal age, gestational age, parity, and sex. They conclude that the Asian infants (from the Indian subcontinent) were significantly smaller in several dimensions than North European or Negro infants, independent of the above factors. They point out that racial differences in growth may be genetic in origin or may reflect the intergenerational effects of environmental factors such as malnutrition, but state that "if it takes generations of improved nutrition before fetal size alters materially, the boundaries between environmental and racial influences on fetal growth become blurred and it is no longer important to differentiate between them; in either case special growth standards are necessary [p. 30]."

## ASSESSMENT OF LENGTH AND WEIGHT
## IN ARIZONA INFANTS

In this chapter, we analyze the relationship of a widely used growth standard (National Center for Health Statistics, 1977) to lengths and weights of infants of three ethnic groups and varying birthweights.

In Arizona, the nutrition program of the Department of Health Services includes among its objectives a reduction in the prevalence of overweight, underweight, and low height for age in children from birth to 5 years (Arizona Department of Health Services, 1977). Among these, overweight is by far the most prevalent condition. The Arizona nutrition program defines "overweight" as weight-for-length or weight-for-height at or above the ninty-fifth percentile with respect to the National Center for Health Statistics reference standard. Several limitations of this definition are recognized. First, the weight-for-length is not a precise index of fatness for infants. Analysis of data on weight, height, and triceps fatfold thickness from the Ten-State Nutrition Survey in the United States shows that, up to age 6 or 7 years, the use of weight for height tends to result in an underestimate of fatness, so that some children who are no more than 10% "overweight" may actually be obese by the criterion of the triceps fatfold measurement (Garn, Clark & Guire, 1975). There is no doubt that fatfold measurements are the best available anthropometric indicators of obesity, but both the expense of reliable skinfold calipers and the difficulty of training and quality control to obtain valid data from many workers have so far precluded their widespread use in public health programs.

A second limitation of the definition of "overweight" used in the Arizona program is the racial and ethnic heterogeneity of the population served. Mexican–American, American–Indian and Caucasian children make up the largest proportions of the target population, and each of these groups is genetically heterogeneous. While current national growth standards may be assumed to be reasonably appropriate for Arizona Caucasian children, they may not be so for the other groups. Little is known about normal growth of Mexican–American and American–Indian children in comparison to white and black American children. Bleibtreu, Meany, and Taylor have longitudinally studied growth patterns in Tucson school children and have concluded that there are identifiable differences in patterns of growth among white, black, Mexican–American, American–Indian, and Oriental children ages 6–13 years (Meany, 1977). Adams and Niswander (1968) documented heavier mean birthweights in American Indian infants than in other groups. We have gathered anthropometric data on several hundred Caucasian and Mexican–American newborns in Tucson in 1976–78, and found no significant differences in birthweight, length, head circumference, or fatfold measurements between the two groups, although there are differences in sexual dimorphism for some characteristics between the two groups (Harrison & Morrow, 1979; Harrison & Udall, in press). A third limitation of the weight-for length criterion has to do with the probable association of size at birth with weight and length later in infancy. It may be that size at birth, independent of the postnatal nutritional environment, reflects factors that influence a child's chance of being classified as "overweight."

## METHODOLOGY

To explore the interrelationships between ethnic background, size at birth, and weight-for-length in later infancy, we analyzed cross-sectional data on length and weight for length of 4085 Caucasian ("Anglo"), Mexican–American, and American–Indian infants. Subjects were infants aged 13 to 24 months attending county health department clinics, Indian Health Service Clinics, or WIC (women, infants, and children supplemental feeding program) clinics in Arizona in 1974, 1975, and 1976. The population is almost entirely low income. Subjects included 1554 Mexican–American, 1639 American–Indian, and 829 Anglo infants. The Indian population was drawn from a number of tribes. Two hundred fifty-two black infants are not included in this analysis because of the small size of that group relative to the others; 258 infants of "other" ethnic groups or unknown ethnic background are also excluded.

As part of the nutrition screening and surveillance program of the Arizona Department of Health Services, length and weight were obtained by a

TABLE 2.1

Number of Infants in Each Ethnic Group and Birthweight Category

| Birthweight (gm) | White | | Mexican–American | | American–Indian | | Total | |
|---|---|---|---|---|---|---|---|---|
| | N | (%) | N | (%) | N | (%) | N | (%) |
| <2500 | 84 | (9.4) | 160 | (10.3) | 128 | (7.8) | 372 | (9.1) |
| 2500–2999 | 191 | (21.4) | 359 | (23.1) | 404 | (24.6) | 954 | (23.4) |
| 3000–3499 | 328 | (36.8) | 582 | (37.5) | 629 | (38.4) | 1539 | (37.7) |
| 3500–3999 | 207 | (23.2) | 339 | (21.8) | 361 | (22.0) | 907 | (22.2) |
| >4000 | 82 | (9.2) | 114 | (7.3) | 117 | (7.1) | 313 | (7.6) |
| Total | 892 | (100.0) | 1554 | (100.0) | 1639 | (100.0) | 4085 | (100.0) |

paraprofessional community health worker under the supervision of a public health nutritionist. All of the paraprofessionals were trained and supervised under the state health department program, so that methods and recording procedures were standardized. Weight was measured with outer clothing and shoes removed, and was recorded to the nearest 1/4 lb. Recumbent length was determined with the infant supine and the legs fully extended, and recorded to the nearest 1/8 in. Ethnic group was as identified by the mother. Birthweight was estimated by history from the mother, and when possible was checked against hospital records. When such records were not available, the recollection of the mother was accepted. Reported birthweight was converted to grams and classified into 500-gm increments. The numbers of infants in each ethnic group and birthweight category are shown in Table 2.1.

## RESULTS

The Arizona infants are compared with the reference population (hereafter referred to as the NCHS standard) in Figures 2.1–2.4 as follows: The sex-specific and age-adjusted percentiles of the NCHS standard (tenth, twenty-fifth, fiftieth, seventy-fifth, and ninetieth percentiles) are plotted as straight lines. The data for the Arizona children, specific for ethnic group and birthweight category, are superimposed upon this grid. Thus for each of Figures 2.1–2.4, the distribution of data for the Arizona infants is compared to the age- and sex-appropriate percentile of the NCHS standard. We would expect, therefore, to see no deviation from the NCHS percentiles *if* length and weight-for-length were distributed in the Arizona population similarly to the reference population and if there were no relationship between birthweight and length or weight-for-length in the second year of life.

With regard to the distribution of lengths, we do see very nearly such a match (Figure 2.1). There are very slight excesses of children in the Arizona population over the ninetieth percentile and below the tenth percentile of the reference standard for length. The twenty-fifth, fiftieth, and seventy-fifth percentiles are very similar to the NCHS standard. There is no significant effect of reported birthweight or of ethnic group on the distribution of values for length. Unfortunately, data on length at birth are not available for these infants, so the relationship of birth length to length in the second year of life cannot be ascertained.

The distribution of weight for length, however, shows significant differences between the Arizona infants and the NCHS standards (Figures 2.2–2.4). For all three ethnic groups, the distributions of the tenth, twenty-fifth, and fiftieth percentiles are markedly altered by birthweight, with chil-

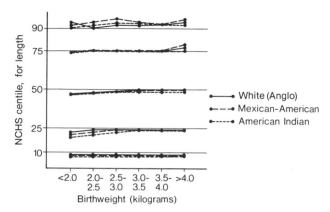

**Figure 2.1.** Percentiles of body length (adjusted for age and sex) by birthweight for Arizona infants compared to percentiles of NCHS reference population.

dren who were light at birth tending to be lighter for length in the second year than children who were heavy at birth. The effect of birthweight is less marked for the seventy-fifth percentile in Mexican–American and American–Indian children, and seems not to be present at the extremes of weight for length (third, ninetieth, and ninety-seventh percentile) for any group. For all ethnic groups, but especially for Mexican–American and

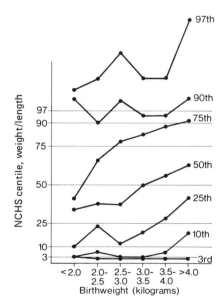

**Figure 2.2.** Percentiles of weight for length (adjusted for age and sex) by birthweight for white (Anglo) infants compared to percentiles of NCHS reference population.

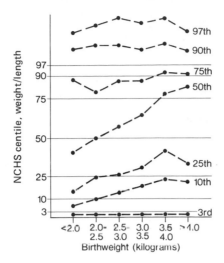

**Figure 2.3.**  Percentiles of weight for length (adjusted for age and sex) by birthweight for Mexican–American infants compared to percentiles of NCHS reference population.

American–Indian children, there is an excess, relative to the NCHS standard, of infants over the ninetieth percentile of weight for length.

The tenth, fiftieth and ninetieth percentiles for each ethnic group are compared in Figure 2.5. Anglo infants tended to be the lightest for length and American–Indian infants the heaviest for length. The distribution of

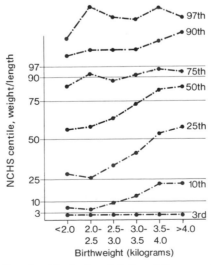

**Figure 2.4.**  Percentiles of weight for length (adjusted for age and sex) by birthweight for American–Indian infants compared to percentiles of NCHS reference population.

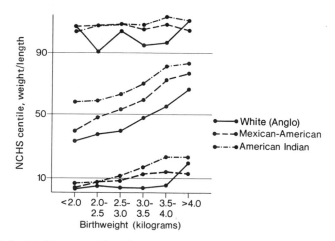

**Figure 2.5.** Median, ninetieth and tenth percentiles of weight for length (adjusted for age and sex) by birthweight for Arizona infants compared to the NCHS reference population.

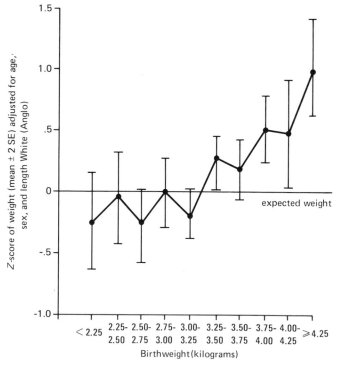

**Figure 2.6.** Z-score of weight (adjusted for age, sex, and length) for white (Anglo) infants by birthweight, compared to expected weight (fiftieth percentile of NCHS standard).

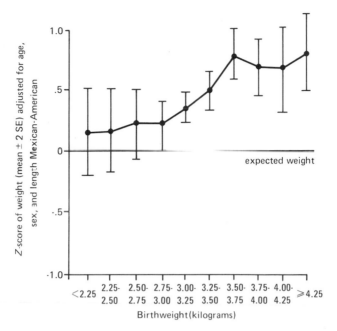

**Figure 2.7.**   Z-score of weight (adjusted for age, sex, and length) for Mexican–American infants by birthweight, compared to expected weight (fiftieth percentile of NCHS standard).

median values is consistent with the probable genetic distances among the three populations.

Figures 2.6–2.8 show the mean Z-score of weight, adjusted for age, sex, and length, by birthweight category for each of the three ethnic groups. The brackets indicate the distance of plus or minus two standard errors from the mean. Thus where the brackets do not cross the zero line (representing the fiftieth percentile of the appropriate NCHS standard), we may conclude that the mean Z-score is significantly different ($p < .05$) from the reference standard. It can be seen that both ethnic group and birthweight affect the mean Z-score. For Anglo infants, those whose birthweights were in excess of 3750 gm differ significantly from the reference standard; Mexican–American infants are significantly heavier for length than the reference standard if birthweights were over 3000 gm, and American–Indian infants differ from the NCHS reference population at all birthweights over 2500 gm.

Figure 2.9 compares mean Z-scores for age and sex-adjusted weight for length for the three ethnic groups within each category of estimated birthweight. The relative positions of each ethnic group are consistent over the range of birthweights between 2250 and 4250 gm.

These data suggest that weight relative to length in the second year of life is significantly related both to ethnic group and to size at birth. American–Indian infants, in our population, were heavier for length than Anglo infants at age 13–24 months within every category of reported birthweight. Mexican–American infants were, over most of the birthweight range, intermediate, i.e., heavier for length than Anglo infants and lighter than American–Indian infants. Within each ethnic group, birthweight was related to weight for length in the second year, with heavier birthweights associated with greater weight for length at age 13–24 months.

When compared with the NCHS reference population, it is evident that the reference population differs significantly in this age range from the Mexican–American and American–Indian infants in our study with regard to

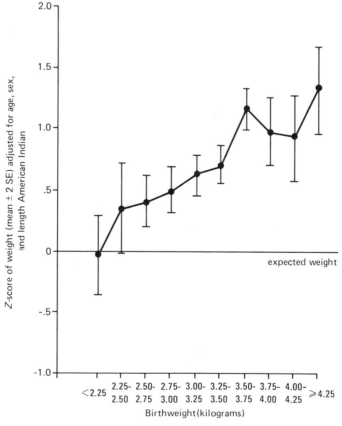

**Figure 2.8.** Z-score of weight (adjusted for age, sex, and length) for American–Indian infants by birthweight, compared to the expected weight (fiftieth percentile of NCHS standard).

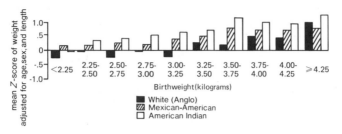

**Figure 2.9.** Mean Z-score of weight (adjusted for age, sex, and length) for Anglo, Mexican–American, and American–Indian infants within categories of birthweight.

weight for length. Since the Arizona infants of all three ethnic groups are very similar to the NCHS reference population with regard to length for age, we may conclude that these differences reflect greater lean mass, greater adiposity and/or differences in body proportions (such as the trunk-to-leg ratio) in the Arizona infants of Mexican–American and American–Indian background. As the present data base does not include either fatfolds or crown–rump length measures, the relative contributions of these factors cannot be estimated.

In terms of immediate practical implications, it is clear that Mexican–American and American–Indian infants are at higher risk than Anglo infants of being classified as "overweight" by the program definition of being at or above the ninety-fifth percentile of weight for length on the sex-appropriate NCHS standard.

The positive association of weight for length in the second year with birthweight is consistent with the observations of others (Dine, Gartside, Glueck, Rheimes, Green, & Khoury, 1979; Garn *et al.*, 1977) that there is significant "tracking" or channelization of growth with regard to relative weight in the first few years of life.

## DISCUSSION AND IMPLICATIONS

Understanding the influences of prenatal growth experience and genetic variability on postnatal growth patterns is important if we are to assess the adequacy of postnatal growth.

Influences on prenatal growth can be thought of as either genetic or environmental, and it has been shown that the latter is the more important in determining the variability in birthweight within populations (Morton, 1955; van Valen & Mellin 1967). The prenatal environment can be conceptualized as including factors in the immediate environment (such as maternal nutrition or smoking during pregnancy), factors determined by the genotype of the mother, and factors established through environmental influences during the mother's own period of growth and development (intergenerational factors). Factors in the immediate prenatal environment have received the most attention. Thus we know that high parity, high maternal weight for height at conception, high maternal weight gain during pregnancy, and maternal diabetes are correlated with relatively high birthweights, and that maternal malnutrition during pregnancy, low parity, and various complications of pregnancy are associated with low birthweights. Cigarette smoking during pregnancy has long been associated with lower birthweights. Yerushalmy (1971, 1972) questioned the assumption based on a prospective study of more than 15,000 pregnancies of women enrolled in a prepaid health plan in California. He found that while mothers who smoked during pregnancy had a greater proportion of low-birthweight babies than nonsmokers, mothers who were nonsmokers during the pregnancy but *later* became smokers also had an increased proportion of low-birthweight babies. Yerushalmy concluded that biological or life-style characteristics of the *smoker*, rather than smoking itself, may exert the observed effect on birthweight (van den Berg, 1977). However, Garn, Shaw, and McCabe (1978) found, in analyzing data from the Collaborative Perinatal Study, that maternal smoking was associated not only with lower birthweights, but with lower maternal weight and lower weight gains. Thus maternal smoking may exert its effects partly through the intermediate variable of maternal nutritional status. Intergenerational influences on pregnancy outcome are just beginning to be explored, but there is reason to believe that undernutrition and hypoxia during the mother's period of growth and development may affect birthweight and/or functional characteristics of the infant (Weinstein & Haas, 1977).

At some critical periods, development is a one-way process. Once a certain developmental pathway has been taken, other possible pathways may be closed and development may have to proceed along the chosen line. Thus environmental stresses such as malnutrition which occur very early in life are more effective in changing the adult phenotype than those which occur later (Weinstein & Haas, 1977). However, stresses which occur at less critical periods in development may be corrected at a later time with relatively little change in the adult phenotype. Waddington (1957) termed this buffering against developmental aberration "canalization" of the development pattern and the well-canalized pathways "epigenetic." Catch-up growth after a period of malnutrition is an expression of this phenomenon (correction of an earlier disturbance due to environmental stress).

Sorting out the degree to which early growth-patterns program or channel future growth and the extent to which aberrant early patterns are corrected for in the development process is complex. It is known that the relative risk of becoming an obese adult is somewhat high for the obese child, even though most adult obesity does not have its onset in childhood (Weil, 1977). Whether developmental patterns established *in utero* will continue in infancy and later depends at least in part on whether and how strongly the postnatal environment reinforces or operates counter to the pattern established earlier.

It is well accepted that low birthweight infants are a heterogeneous group, with the small-for-gestational-age infant quite a different organism from the appropriately grown but prematurely born neonate (Ounsted & Taylor, 1971). The difference has functional significance beyond the immediate postnatal period, as small-for-gestational-age infants tend to persist in their small size relative to age mates more than appropriate-for-gestational-age children who were born prematurely (Baszo, Karmazsin, & Gelei, 1964). Recently attention has begun to focus on the heterogeneity of the group of infants classified as heavy for gestational age. We are obtaining anthropometric measurements, including fatfolds, on a large group of healthy term neonates and their mothers. Our own data illustrate that variability in fatness among heavy-for-gestational-age newborns is great (Harrison & Udall, in press; Udall *et al.*, 1978). The consequences of relative fatness or thinness at birth for later growth in these heavy infants is yet unknown.

## SUMMARY

The data presented here indicate that the high-birthweight infant, the Mexican–American infant, and the American–Indian infant are at relatively high risk of exceeding the ninety-fifth percentile of weight for length on national reference standards during the second year of life. Whether this pattern has any functional consequence is not known.

## ACKNOWLEDGMENTS

The authors wish to thank James B. Goldsby, Center for Disease Control, U.S. Public Health Service, Atlanta, Georgia, for data handling and Cole Thies, Division of Biostatistics and Computer Services, Arizona Health Sciences Center, for data processing and statistical consultation. This work was supported by Biomedical Research Grant 3150-80 from the National Institutes of Health RR05675, and by Grant #540 from The Nutrition Foundation, Inc.

## REFERENCES

Adams, M. S. & Niswander, J. D. Birthweight of North American Indians. *Human Biology*, 1968, *40*, 226–234.

Alvear, J., & Brooke, O. G. Fetal growth in different racial groups. *Archives of Disease in Childhood*, 1978, *53*, 27–32.

Arizona Department of Health Services, Bureau of Nutrition Services. *1977–78 Program Plan*. Phoenix: Arizona Department of Health Services, 1977.

Bazo, J., Karmazsin, L., & Gelei, K. Observations on the physical and mental development in newborn infants of intra-uterine growth retardation. In J. Oster (Ed.), *Proceedings of the international Copenhagen conference on the scientific study of mental retardation*. Copenhagen: Statens Andssvageforsorg, 1964. P. 411.

Dine, M. S., Gartside, P. S., Glueck, C. J., Rheines, L., Green, G., & Khoury, P. Where do the heaviest children come from? A prospective study of white children from birth to 5 years of age. *Pediatrics*, 1979, *63*, 1–7.

Falkner, F. The creation of growth standards: A committee report. *American Journal of Clinical Nutrition*, 1972, *25*, 218–220.

Garn, S. M., & Clark, D. C. Problems in the nutritional assessment of black individuals. *American Journal of Public Health*, 1976, *66*, 262–267.

Garn, S. M., Clark, D. C., & Guire, K. E. Growth, body composition and development of obese and lean children. In Myron Winick (Ed.), *Childhood obesity* (Vol. 3). New York: Wiley, 1975. P. 23.

Garn, S. M., & Rohmann, C. G. "Midparent" values for use with parent-specific, age-size tables when parental stature is estimated or unknown. *Pediatric Clinics of North America*, 1967, *14*, 283–284.

Garn, S. M., Shaw, H. A., & McCabe, K. D. Birth size and growth appraisal. *Journal of Pediatrics*, 1977, *90*, 1049–1051.

Garn, S. M., Shaw, H. A., & McCabe, K. D. Maternal smoking as a nutritional variable. *Ecology of Food and Nutrition*, 1978, *7*, 143–146.

Haas, J. D., & Harrison, G. G. Nutritional anthropology and biological adaptation. *Annual Review of Anthropology*, 1977, *6*, 69–101.

Harrison, G. G. and Morrow, G., III. Differences in sexual dimorphism for body size in Mexican–American and Anglo–American newborns. *American Journal of Physical Anthropology*, 1979, *50*, 447 (Abstract).

Harrison, G. G., & Udall, J. N. Effects of maternal obesity on fetal growth. *Studies in Physical Anthropology (Warsaw)*, in press.

Meany, F. J. *Factors influencing physical growth of Tucson school children*. Unpublished doctoral dissertation, University of Arizona, 1977.

Morton, N. E. The inheritance of human birthweight. *Annals of Human Genetics*, 1955, *20*, 125–134.

National Center for Health Statistics. *NCHS growth curves for children birth-18 years, United States*. DHEW Publication No. (PHS) 78-1650. Hyattsville, Md.: NCHS, 1977.

Ounsted, M., & Taylor, M. E. The postnatal growth of children who were small-for-dates or large-for-dates at birth. *Developmental Medicine and Child Neurology*, 1971, *13*, 421–434.

Owen, G. M., & Lubin, A. H. Anthropometric differences between black and white preschool children. *American Journal of Diseases of Children*, 1973, *126*, 168–169.

Robson, J. R. K., Larkin, F. A., Bursick, J. H., & Perri, K. P. Growth standards for infants and children: A cross-sectional study. *Pediatrics*, 1975, *56*, 1014–1020.

Tanner, J. M., Goldstein, H., & Whitehouse, R. H. Standards for children's height at ages 2–9 years allowing for height of parents. *Archives of Disease in Childhood*, 1970, *45*, 755–762.

Udall, J. H., Harrison, G. G., Morrow, G., III, Vaucher, Y., & Walson, P. D. Interaction of maternal and neonatal obesity. *Pediatrics*, 1978, *62*, 17–21.

van den Berg, B. J. Epidemiologic observations of prematurity: Effects of tobacco, coffee and alcohol. In D. M. Reed & F. J. Stanley (Eds.), *The epidemiology of prematurity*. Baltimore: Urban and Schwarzenburg, 1977.

van Valen, L., & Mellin, G. W. Selection in natural populations, New York babies. *Annals of Human Genetics*, 1967, *31*, 109–127.

Waddington, C. H. *The strategy of the gene*. New York: Macmillan, 1957.

Weil, W. B., Jr. Current controversies in childhood obesity. *Journal of Pediatrics*, 1977, *91*, 175–187.

Weinstein, R. S., & Haas, J. D. Early stress and later reproductive performance under conditions of malnutrition and high altitude hypoxia. *Medical Anthropology*, 1977, *1*, 25–54.

Yerushalmy, J. The relationship of parents' cigarette smoking to outcome of pregnancy—Implications as to the problem of inferring causation from observed association. *American Journal of Epidemiology*. 1971, *93*, 443–456.

Yerushalmy, J. Cigarette smoking and low-birthweight babies. *American Journal of Obstetrics and Gynecology*, 1972, *114*, 571–573.

# 3

# Role of Calorie and Protein Reserves on Human Growth during Childhood and Adolescence in a Mestizo Peruvian Population

A. ROBERTO FRISANCHO

## INTRODUCTION

The determination of the relative role of calories and protein in influencing, or improving, growth is important to biologists and public health workers concerned with correcting growth retardation in children. Several studies have indicated that protein supplementation produced marked increases in height, weight, and skeletal maturation of children (Corry-Mann, 1926; Guzman, 1975; Guzman, Rohmann, Flores, Garn, & Scrimshaw, 1964; Leighton & Clark, 1929; Orr, 1928), while other investigations found either minimal or no improvement in growth and maturation (Becroft & Bailey, 1965; King, Sebrell, Severinghaus, & Stovick, 1963; MacWilliams & Dean, 1965; Scrimshaw & Guzman, 1953; Subrahmanyah, Joseph, Doraiswamy, Narayanarao, Sankaran, & Swarinathan, 1957).

Malcolm (1970) found that protein supplementation among Bundi children in New Guinea produced significant gains in height and weight relative to controls, while the supplementation of extra calories led only to an increase in weight and body fat. In contrast, investigations among Indian preschool children indicated that calorie supplementation improved rates of growth in

Social and Biological Predictors of
Nutritional Status, Physical Growth,
and Neurological Development

height and weight (Gopalan, Swamminathan, Kumari, Rao, & Vijayaraghavan, 1973); similar studies among Guatemalan preschool children indicated that the effects of calorie supplementation on rates of growth in height and weight were similar to those derived from combined protein and calorie supplements (Martorell, Lechtig, Yarbrough, Delgado, & Klein, 1978). These findings, and estimates of protein and calorie requirements, have led several investigators to postulate that the protein–calorie malnutrition affecting children of developing nations is not due to protein deficiency, but is principally the consequence of a shortage of energy (Gopalan *et al.*, 1973; Payne, 1975; Martorell *et al.*, 1978). However, other investigators have questioned the extrapolation of these findings to all populations (Hegsted, 1978; Rosenfield, 1975). Thus, at present, the relative impact of calorie and protein deficiency on growth is unclear. As a contribution toward this goal, we have evaluated the relationship between subcutaneous fat thickness and arm muscle mass and height in a sample of *mestizo* children living in the eastern Peruvian lowlands.

## METHODS

### Sample

The subject population was drawn from the town of Lamas in the Department of San Martin, Peru. The 1961 Peruvian census indicates that the population of the district of Lamas was 12,866, of which 7139 inhabitants were located in the central town of Lamas and 5727 people were distributed among the aggregated native-owned settlements. The town of Lamas is 1320 m above sea level, making it one of the highest populated locations in the Province of Lamas. The climate is that of moderate heat stress, the average annual temperature being about 27°C with a relative humidity of about 50%.

The population of the town consists of two distinct and separate ethnic groups: the indigenous Quechua and the *mestizos*. The *mestizos* are descendants of Spanish-speaking inhabitants who settled in the region during the Colonial period and founded the town of Lamas in 1650. *Mestizos* from the Peruvian coast and highlands have also contributed to the population of the town. This *mestizo* population is of a variable Spanish and indigenous admixture.

The sample for this study, 680 *mestizo* boys and girls ranging in age from 6 to 17 years, was derived from the elementary and secondary schools of the town of Lamas. The ages of all subjects were derived from birth records provided by the school officials in Lamas.

## Anthropometric Measurements

The subjects were measured using standard anthropometric techniques (Weiner & Lowrie, 1969). These included measurements of height (cm), weight (kg), sitting height (cm), leg and arm length (cm), chest circumference (cm), calf and upper arm circumference (mm), and skinfold thicknesses (mm). The latter measurements were taken at triceps, subscapula, midaxillary, and calf sites. Following previous investigations, measurements of the upper arm circumference and triceps skinfold thickness were used to calculate the upper arm muscle area (Frisancho, 1974; Frisancho, Klayman, & Matos, 1977a, 1977b). The thickness of skinfolds at the four sites were added to give the sum of skinfold thickness. The relationship between a child's height and his/her summed skinfold thickness and upper arm muscle area is evaluated.

## Indices of Nutritional Status

Subjects of each sex were divided into two age groups (males: 6.0–11.9 and 12.0–17.9 years; females: 6.0–11.9 and 12.0–14.9 years). Age- and sex-specific means were determined for summed skinfold thickness and upper arm muscle area and the subjects were classified into four nutritional status subgroups based on whether their sum of skinfold thickness and upper arm muscle area were greater than or less than the age- and sex-specific mean values for these respective measurements. These groups are: (a) high-muscle–high-fat; (b) high-muscle–low-fat; (c) low-muscle–high-fat; (d) low-muscle–low-fat. The mean height of each nutritional status subgroup was then adjusted for an equal projected age derived by analysis of covariance.

It is assumed that individuals with high-muscle and high-fat measurements have high protein and high calorie reserves, while individuals with high-muscle and low-fat measurements have high protein and low caloric reserves. Conversely, individuals with low-fat and low-muscle measurements have low reserves of both calories and protein. This assumption is based on the fact that previous investigations of humans have shown that subcutaneous fat and body muscle are positively associated with advanced dimensional growth and advanced maturation under conditions of both good and poor nutrition (Dugdale, Chen, & Hewitt, 1970; Frisancho & Garn, 1971a, 1971b; Frisancho, Garn, & McCreery, 1971; Frisancho, et al., 1977a, 1977b; Garn, Clark, & Guire, 1975; Keet, Hansen, & Truswell, 1970). Furthermore, investigations have shown that under conditions of nutritional restriction, body fat and body muscle are utilized by the organism as a source of calories and amino acids for the production of energy and the synthesis of essential proteins (Arroyave & Castellanos, 1961; McFie & Welbourn, 1962; Standard, Wills, & Waterlow, 1959; Waterlow, 1968). For these reasons, the amount of body fat and body muscle is considered as the organism's reserves of calories and proteins (Dugdale *et al.*, 1970; Jelliffe, 1966; Frisancho, 1974; Stini, 1972).

## RESULTS AND DISCUSSION

The mean and standard deviations for height, sum of skinfold thickness and upper arm muscle area of the *mestizo* boys and girls are given in Table 3.1. These data show that until the age of 12 years boys and girls exhibit similar heights, but thereafter males are taller than females, but females are fatter and less muscular than males at all ages.

In Table 3.2 the subjects in the different nutritional status groups are compared for differences in height, and Figure 3.1 illustrates the regression lines describing the relationship between height and age in the four nutritional status categories among *males* age 6–11 and 12–17 years.

**TABLE 3.1**

**Mean and Standard Deviations in Height, Sum of Skinfold Thickness, and Upper Arm Muscle Area of Mestizo Children Living in the Peruvian Eastern Lowland**

| Year | N | Height (cm) Mean | SD | Sum of skinfolds (mm) Mean | SD | Upper arm muscle area (mm$^2$) Mean | SD |
|---|---|---|---|---|---|---|---|
| | | | | *Males* | | | |
| 6.0–7.9 | 48 | 110.3 | 5.1 | 24.3 | 4.6 | 1270.1 | 180.7 |
| 8.0–9.9 | 60 | 118.7 | 6.9 | 24.8 | 4.8 | 1459.0 | 209.1 |
| 10.0–11.9 | 80 | 128.2 | 6.4 | 26.3 | 5.9 | 1692.8 | 252.3 |
| 12.0–13.9 | 53 | 133.7 | 4.9 | 27.1 | 7.2 | 1835.3 | 224.5 |
| 14.0–15.9 | 69 | 147.1 | 9.1 | 27.6 | 6.2 | 2329.7 | 387.4 |
| 16.0–17.9 | 53 | 155.4 | 8.9 | 32.0 | 8.2 | 2916.0 | 519.4 |
| | | | | *Females* | | | |
| 6.0–7.9 | 59 | 108.6 | 5.5 | 31.4 | 6.2 | 1135.0 | 157.8 |
| 8.0–9.9 | 73 | 118.2 | 6.1 | 28.1 | 6.4 | 1356.9 | 209.4 |
| 10.0–11.9 | 65 | 127.5 | 7.1 | 32.5 | 6.4 | 1564.1 | 329.1 |
| 12.0–13.9 | 53 | 137.4 | 6.4 | 37.1 | 8.7 | 1769.0 | 370.2 |
| 14.0–15.9 | 67 | 145.2 | 7.3 | 54.7 | 8.6 | 2066.3 | 329.3 |

**TABLE 3.2**

**Comparison of Age-adjusted Heights (cm) and Regression Equations of Mestizo Samples from Lamas (Classified into Four Nutritional Status Groups)**

### Males

Age = 6.0–11.9 Years; N = 186

| Nutritional status | Mean | S.E. | Regression equation | Contrast groups | F test |
|---|---|---|---|---|---|
| 1. High-muscle-High-fat | 122.9 | 0.7 | Ht = 77.6 + 4.9 (age) | 1vs2 | 1.26 |
| | | | | 1vs3 | 31.1** |
| 2. High-muscle-Low-fat | 121.7 | 0.9 | Ht = 71.8 + 5.3 (age) | 1vs4 | 27.76** |
| | | | | 2vs3 | 14.60** |
| 3. Low-muscle-High-fat | 117.1 | 0.8 | Ht = 66.9 + 5.4 (age) | 2vs4 | 9.07* |
| | | | | 3vs4 | 1.00 |
| 4. Low-muscle-Low-fat | 118.2 | 0.7 | Ht = 74.9 + 4.6 (age) | | |

Age = 12.0–17.9 Years; N = 173

| Nutritional status | Mean | S.E. | Regression equation | Contrast groups | F test |
|---|---|---|---|---|---|
| 1. High-muscle-High-fat | 151.1 | 0.9 | Ht = 70.4 + 5.4 (age) | 1vs2 | 6.12* |
| | | | | 1vs3 | 29.31*** |
| 2. High-muscle-Low-fat | 147.7 | 0.9 | Ht = 62.9 + 5.7 (age) | 1vs4 | 67.98*** |
| | | | | 2vs3 | 8.38* |
| 3. Low-muscle-High-fat | 143.8 | 0.9 | Ht = 66.6 + 5.2 (age) | 2vs4 | 32.65*** |
| | | | | 3vs4 | 8.13* |
| 4. Low-muscle-Low-fat | 139.9 | 0.9 | Ht = 71.3 + 4.6 (age) | | |

### Females

Age = 6.0–11.9 Years; N = 190

| Nutritional status | Mean | S.E. | Regression equation | Contrast groups | F test |
|---|---|---|---|---|---|
| 1. High-muscle-High-fat | 121.4 | 0.8 | Ht = 74.9 + 5.11 (age) | 1vs2 | 0.18 |
| | | | | 1vs3 | 9.25** |
| 2. High-muscle-Low-fat | 119.9 | 0.8 | Ht = 76.5 + 4.8 (age) | 1vs4 | 37.74*** |
| | | | | 2vs3 | 2.64* |
| 3. Low-muscle-High-fat | 118.1 | 0.7 | Ht = 71.6 + 5.2 (age) | 2vs4 | 23.33*** |
| | | | | 3vs4 | 12.42*** |
| 4. Low-muscle-Low-fat | 114.4 | 0.8 | Ht = 76.4 + 4.2 (age) | | |

Age = 12.0–14.9 Years; N = 80

| Nutritional status | Mean | S.E. | Regression equation | Contrast groups | F test |
|---|---|---|---|---|---|
| 1. High-muscle-High-fat | 141.7 | 1.2 | Ht = 125.3 + 1.21 (age) | 1vs2 | 0.94 |
| | | | | 1vs3 | 0.71 |
| 2. High-muscle-Low-fat | 139.6 | 1.7 | Ht = 107.7 + 2.35 (age) | 1vs4 | 15.88*** |
| | | | | 2vs3 | 0.02 |
| 3. Low-muscle-High-fat | 139.9 | 1.6 | Ht = 141.9 + 0.12 (age) | 2vs4 | 5.56* |
| | | | | 3vs4 | 6.84* |
| 4. Low-muscle-Low-fat | 134.4 | 1.3 | Ht = 120.1 + 1.1 (age) | | |

Heights are adjusted for age, and the significance of the difference between means and regression equation is derived from covariance analysis.
*Significant at 0.05 level.
**Significant at 0.01 level.
***Significant at 0.001 level.

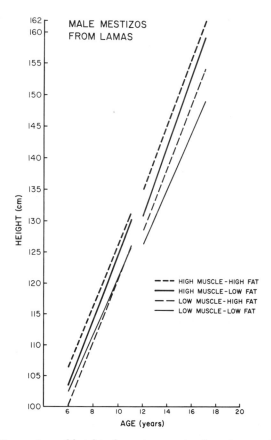

**Figure 3.1.** Comparison of height of *mestizo* samples from Lamas, classified into four nutritional status groups. Children with high-protein and high-calorie reserves (high-muscle–high-fat) during childhood and adolescence are significantly taller than their counterparts with low-protein and low-calorie reserves (low-muscle–low-fat); subjects with high-protein reserves (high-muscle–low-fat) are much taller than those who have high-calorie reserves (low-muscle–high-fat).

Among the 6–11 year age group of *males* the following trends are evident:

1. Subjects with high-muscle–high-fat have heights similar to subjects with high-muscle–low-fat.
2. Subjects with high-muscle–low fat are significantly taller ($P < .01$) than subjects with low-muscle–high-fat.
3. Subjects with low-muscle–high-fat have heights similar to subjects with low-muscle–low-fat.

The 6–11 year age group of *females* are characterized by the following:

1. Girls with high-muscle–high-fat are as tall as their counter-parts with high-muscle–low fat.
2. Girls with high-muscle–low-fat are significantly taller ($p < .05$) than those with low-muscle–high-fat.
3. Subjects with low-muscle–high-fat are significantly taller ($p < .01$) than their counterparts with low-muscle–low-fat.

The 12–17 year age group of *males* exhibit the following characteristics:

1. High-muscle–high-fat subjects are significantly taller ($p < .05$) than subjects with high-muscle–low fat.
2. Boys with high-muscle–low-fat are significantly taller ($p < .05$) than subjects with low-muscle–high-fat.
3. Low-muscle–high-fat boys are significantly taller ($p < .05$) than their counterparts with low-muscle–low-fat.

Among the 12–14 year age group of *females* the following are evident:

1. High-muscle–high-fat subjects are significantly taller ($p < .001$) than subjects with low-muscle–low-fat.
2. High-muscle–high-fat (or high-muscle–low-fat) girls do not differ in stature from their counterparts with low-muscle–high-fat.

In conclusion, the present findings demonstrate that among preadolescent and adolescent males differences in calorie and protein reserves are associated with significant differences in stature, so that subjects with high-muscle and low-fat are taller than their peers with low-muscle and low-fat. An important finding is the fact that an increase in protein reserves (high-muscle–low-fat) is associated with greater statures than an increase in calorie reserves (low-muscle–high-fat). These observations are in agreement with studies relating maternal nutritional status to prenatal growth (Frisancho *et al.*, 1977a, 1977b). They are also in agreement with studies of nutritional supplementation among Bundi schoolchildren from New Guinea, which indicated that protein supplementation produced a greater gain in height than did calorie supplementation (Malcolm, 1970). Furthermore, it was found that the growth increments among these Bundi schoolchildren showed a positive linear relationship to the level of protein supplementation (Lampl, Johnston, & Malcolm, 1978). These findings together demonstrate the role of increased protein stores in promoting growth. On the other hand, studies on nutritional supplementation indicate that calorie supplementation alone results in increased birth weight and improved rates of growth in height and weight among undernourished Indian and Guatemalan children (Gopalan,

Swamminathan, Kumari, Rao, Vijayaraghavan, 1973; Martorell, Lechtig, Yarbrough, Delgado, & Klein, 1978; Habicht, Lechtig, Yarbrough, & Klein, 1974; Lechtig, Yarbrough, Delgado, Habicht, Martorell, & Klein, 1975). These findings, besides their contribution to basic research, have implications for applied human nutrition research and for the formulation of public policy with respect to nutritional intervention and nutritional education programs. These data suggest that in undernourished populations increasing the *reserves* of calories and protein effectively improves growth of children.

## SUMMARY

Anthropometric measurements were made on a sample of 680 *mestizo* boys and girls age 6–17 years in the Province of Lamas in the eastern Peruvian lowlands. The subjects were classified into four nutritional status categories based on age- and sex-specific mean values of sum of skinfold thickness and upper arm muscle area. These data indicate that during childhood and adolescence individuals with high protein and calorie reserves (high-muscle–high-fat) show significantly greater heights when compared to peers with poor protein and calorie reserves (low muscle–low-fat). Increased protein reserves (high-muscle–low-fat) are associated with greater stature than increased calorie reserves (low-muscle–high-fat). Furthermore, female subjects with increased calorie reserves (low-muscle–high fat) showed greater stature than subjects with low reserves of both calories and protein (low-muscle–low-fat).

## ACKNOWLEDGMENTS

I thank the schoolchildren, directors, and teachers of the schools of the province of Lamas for their cooperation in this study. I also acknowledge assistance of my colleagues Drs. William Babler, Gary Borkan, Jane Klayman and Anthony Way, and Dr. Jorge Sanchez of the Department of Anthropology of the University of Cuzco, Peru in the collection of the data. We also thank Ken Guire, Robert Wainwright, Margaret Owen, and Nancy Becker for their assistance in manuscript preparation. The investigation has been supported in part by Grant GS-37524X of the National Science Foundation.

## REFERENCES

Arroyave, G., & Castellanos, H. Role of the adrenal cortical system in the response of children to severe protein malnutrition. *American Journal of Clinical Nutrition*, 1961, 9, 186–195.

Becroft, T., & Bailey, K. V. Supplementary feeding trial in New Guinea highland infants. *Journal of Tropical Pediatrics*, 1965, *11*, 28–34.

Corry-Mann, H. C. *Diets for boys during the school age*. Special Reports Series, Medical Research Council of London, no. 105, 1926.

Dugdale, A. E., Chen, S. T., & Hewitt, G. Patterns of growth and nutrition in childhood. *American Journal of Clinical Nutrition*, 1970, *23*, 1280–1287.

Frisancho, A. R. Triceps skinfold and upper arm muscle size norms for assessment of nutritional status. *American Journal of Clinical Nutrition*, 1974, *27*, 1052–1058.

Frisancho, A. R., & Garn, S. M. Skinfold thickness and muscle size: Implications for developmental status and nutritional evaluation of children from Honduras. *American Journal of Clinical Nutrition*, 1971, *24*, 541–546.(a)

Frisancho, A. R., & Garn, S. M. The implications of skinfolds and muscle size to developmental and nutritional status of Central American children. III. Guatemala. *Tropical and Geographical Medicine*, 1971, *23*, 167–172.(b)

Frisancho, A. R., Garn, S. M., & McCreery, L. D. Relationship of skinfolds and muscle size to growth of children. I. Costa Rica. *American Journal of Physical Anthropology*, 1971, *35*, 85–90.

Frisancho, A. R., Klayman, J. E., & Matos, J. Newborn body composition and its relationship to linear growth. *American Journal of Clinical Nutrition*, 1977, *30*, 704–711. (a)

Frisancho, A. R., Klayman, J., & Matos, J. Influence of maternal nutritional status on prenatal growth in a Peruvian urban population. *American Journal of Physical Anthropology*, 1977, *46*, 265–274. (b)

Garn, S. M., Clark, D., & Guire, K. E. Growth, body composition and development of obese and lean children. In M. Winick (Ed.), *Childhood obesity*. New York: Wiley, 1975.

Gopalan, C., Swamminathan, M. C., Kumari, V. K. K., Rao, D. H., & Vijayaraghavan, K. Effect of calorie supplementation on growth of undernourished children. *American Journal of Clinical Nutrition*, 1973, *26*, 563–566.

Guzman, M. A. Bone maturation in children recovered from malnutrition. In *Proceedings of the Ninth International Congress of Nutrition, Mexico*, 1972, (Vol. 2). Basel: Karger, 1975. Pp. 276–279.

Guzman, M. A., Rohmann, C., Flores, M., Garn, S. M., & Scrimshaw, N. S. Osseous growth of Guatemalan children fed a protein-calorie supplement. *Federation Proceedings*, 1964, *23*, 338.

Habicht, J-P., Lechtig, A., Yarbrough, C., & Klein, R. E. Maternal nutrition, birth weight and infant mortality. In *Size at birth*, Amsterdam: Ciba Foundation Symposium, 27, ASP, 1974.

Hegsted, D. M. Assessment of nitrogen requirements. *American Journal of Clinical Nutrition*, 1978, *31*, 1669–1677.

Jelliffe, D. B. The assessment of the nutritional status of the community. *WHO Monograph*, 1966, *53*, 228.

Keet, M. P., Hansen, J. D. L., & Truswell, A. S. Are skinfold measurements of value in the assessment of suboptimal nutrition in young children? *Pediatrics*, 1970, *45*, 965–972.

King, K. W., Sebrell, W. H., Severinghaus, E. L., & Stovick, W. D. Lysine fortification of wheat bread fed to Haitian school children. *American Journal of Clinical Nutrition*, 1963, *12*, 36–48.

Lampl, M., Johnston, F. E., & Malcolm, L. A. The effects of protein supplementation on the growth and skeletal maturation of New Guinean school children. *Annals of Human Biology*, 1978, *5*, 219–227.

Lechtig, A., Yarbrough, C., Delgado, H., Habicht, J-P., Martorell, R., & Klein, R. E. Influence of maternal nutrition on birth weight. *American Journal of Clinical Nutrition*, 1975, *28*, 1223–1233.

Leighton, D., & Clark, C. L. Milk consumption and the growth of schoolchildren. *Lancet*, 1929, *i*, 40.

MacWilliams, K. V., & Dean, R. F. A. The growth of malnourished children after hospital treatment. *East African Medical Journal*, 1965, *42*, 297–304.

Malcolm, L. A. *Growth and development in New Guinea. A study of the Bundi people of the Madang District*. Madang: Institute of Human Biology, 1970.

Martorell, R., Lechtig, A., Yarbrough, C., Delgado, H., & Klein, R. E. Energy intake and growth in an energy deficient population. *Ecology of Food Nutrition*, 1978, *7*, 147–154.

Mcfie, J., & Welbourn, H. F. Effect of malnutrition in infancy on the development of bone, muscle and fat. *Journal of Nutrition*, 1962, *76*, 97–105.

Orr, J. B. Milk consumption and the growth of schoolchildren. *Lancet*, 1928, *i*, 202.

Payne, P. R. Safe protein-calorie ratios in diets: The relative importance of protein and energy intake as causal factors in malnutrition. *American Journal of Clinical Nutrition*, 1975, *28*, 281–286.

Rosenfield, D. Protein-calorie alleviation of malnutrition. *American Journal of Clinical Nutrition*, 1975, *28*, 1–3.

Scrimshaw, N. S., & Guzman, M. A. The effect of dietary supplementation and the administration of vitamin B, the aureomycin on the growth of schoolchildren. *Nutrition Symposia*, series no. 7, pp. 101–117.

Standard, K. L., Wills, V. G., & Waterlow, J. C. Indirect indications of muscle mass in malnourished infants. *American Journal of Clinical Nutrition*, 1959, *7*, 271–279.

Stini, W. Reduced sexual demorphism in upper arm muscle circumference associated with protein deficient diet in a South American population. *American Journal of Physical Anthropology*, 1972, *36*, 341–352.

Subrahmanyah, V., Joseph, K., Doraiswamy, T. R., Narayanarao, M., Sankaran, A. N., & Swarinathan, M. The effect of a supplementary multipurpose food on the growth and nutritional status of children. *British Journal of Nutrition*, 1957, *11*, 382–388.

Waterlow, J. C. The adaptation of protein metabolism to low protein intakes. In R. A. McCance and E. M. Widdowson (Eds.), *Calorie deficiencies and protein deficiencies*. London: Churchill. Pp. 61–72.

Weiner, J. S., & Lourie, J. A. *Human biology: A guide to field methods*. Oxford: Blackwell Scientific Publications, 1969.

# Part II

## BREAST-FEEDING, BOTTLE-FEEDING, AND DISEASE EXPERIENCE

# 4

# Lean Tissue Growth and Disease Susceptibility in Bottle-fed versus Breast-fed Infants

WILLIAM A. STINI, CHARLES W. WEBER,
SIDNEY R. KEMBERLING, AND LINDA A. VAUGHAN

## INTRODUCTION

One of the fundamental social factors affecting postnatal nutrition is the decision by the mother as to whether she will breast-feed her infant or resort to one of a variety of supplemental feeds. These are conscious decisions by mothers that are usually strongly influenced by social, economic, and maternal nutritional factors. However, the consequence of these decisions varies according to the particular environmental setting. This chapter will briefly review some of the unique characteristics of human milk and then discuss the relative efficacy of human milk, formula, and cow's milk in promoting growth under conditions commonly encountered in less-developed and industrialized nations. We will also consider the important issue of the nutritional adequacy of human milk as a function of length of lactation and the advancing age of the infant.

## COMPOSITION OF HUMAN MILK

The composition of human milk has been the object of considerable investigation. Early work concentrated on the major constituents, fat, protein,

*Social and Biological Predictors of*
*Nutritional Status, Physical Growth,*
*and Neurological Development*

lactose, and total ash usually being the only determinations made (Macy, 1949; Macy, Nims, Brown, & Hunscher, 1931; Nims, Macy, Brown, & Hunscher, 1931). It was a number of years before the analysis of major and minor minerals, of specific amino acids, and of individual fatty acids could be accurately reported. A National Academy of Sciences Publication (Macy, Kelly, & Sloan, 1953) summarized the available data and noted large discrepancies in published values for each of the major constituents. Many of these inconsistencies arose from a lack of standardization in milk-collection procedures. It is now known that composition values for human milk are applicable only under the specific conditions of a particular study.

### Colostrum, "Transitional," and "Mature" Milk

The composition of human milk, as well as the milk of other species, undergoes significant changes during the transition from colostrum to mature milk (Ajans, Sarrif, & Husbands, 1965; Barltrop & Hillier, 1974; Belavady & Gopalan, 1959; Cockburn, Brown, Belton, & Forfar, 1973; Hefnawi, Badraoui, Younis, & Hassib, 1972; Lonnerdal, Forsum, & Hambraeus, 1976a, 1976b; Read & Sarrif, 1965; Underwood, Hepner, & Abdullah, 1970). Colostrum is usually defined as milk produced during the first 5 days postpartum (Ajans *et al.*, 1965; Barltrop & Hillier, 1974; Fomon, 1974; Lonnerdal *et al.*, 1976a; Macy, 1949). An additional "transition" period, from Day 5 to Day 10 (Macy, 1949; Macy *et al.*, 1953; Nims *et al.*, 1931), may also be identified. Confusion arises from the fact that some investigators label all samples simply as "milk," with no specification as to "colostrum," "transitional," or "mature" (Cavell & Widdowson, 1964; Cockburn *et al.*, 1973; Hytten, 1954a; McLeod & Robinson, 1972; Prinsloo, Wittmann, Strydom, de Villiers, Wehmeyer, Laubscher, & Botha, 1970).

Human colostrum contains an average of 2.29 gm protein/100 ml whereas human milk averages 1.1 gm/100 ml (Fomon, 1974; Macy, 1949). Fat increases from 2.95 gm/100 ml in colostrum to 3.52 gm/100 ml in the transition period, and reaches an average of 4.54 gm/100 ml in the mature state (Fomon, 1974; Macy, 1949). Lactose levels increase slightly during the change from colostrum to mature milk, from 6.4 gm/100 ml to an average of 7.1 gm/100 ml (Macy, 1949). Total ash declines from 308 mg/100 ml in colostrum, to 267 mg/100 ml in transitional milk, to 202 mg/100 ml in mature milk (Fomon, 1974; Macy, 1949).

### Composition Changes with Increased Duration of Lactation

Protein levels decline as the duration of lactation progresses (Belavady & Gopalan, 1959; Fomon, 1974; Kader, Bahgat, Aziz, Hefnawi, Badraoui,

Younis, & Hassib, 1972; Underwood *et al.*, 1970). Absolute concentrations and rate of decline vary from one study to another. The total nitrogen content in breast milk decreases rapidly during the first 20 days. Further decreases occur more slowly thereafter. Nonprotein nitrogen remains fairly constant throughout lactation. The $\alpha$-lactalbumin and lactoferrin fractions, both hormonally controlled, decrease during lactation (Lonnerdal, Forsum, & Hambraeus, 1977).

The total amino acid composition of milk differs little between women of different ethnic origin (Svanberg, Gebre-Medhin, Ljumgqvist, & Olsson, 1977) and concentration changes little throughout lactation (Karmarkar, Kapur, Deodhar, & Ramakrishnan, 1959). Fat levels have the highest variability of any constituent of human milk, but they have not been shown to change significantly with duration of lactation (Belavady & Gopalan, 1959; Fomon, 1974; Hagyard, 1972; Underwood *et al.*, 1970). No consistent pattern of change with duration of lactation has been shown for lactose concentration (Hagyard, 1972; Kader *et al.*, 1972). The data on total milk output are also not entirely clear. Hanafy, Seddick, and Habib (1972) report that the daily yield of milk from healthy mothers increases slightly as lactation proceeds from Month 1 to Month 12; while Hefnawi *et al.* (1972) found that milk yield increases significantly from the second month postpartum to a maximum at the seventh month, after which there is a gradual decline. The lack of agreement between these studies may stem from the use of subjects who were not of the same age, parity, race, health status, or interdelivery stage. More importantly, the authors did not measure milk yield in the same manner. One study used a mechanical pump for direct measurement of the amount of milk obtained (Hefnawi *et al.*, 1972), while the other weighed the infant before and after a test feed (Hanafy *et al.*, 1972).

## Effect of Dietary Factors on Human Milk Composition

Besides the effect of time on human milk composition other factors influence both its quality and quantity. Dietary intake, whether expressed in terms of overall adequacy or defined for specific nutrients, can alter the composition of human milk (Ajans *et al.*, 1965; Bourges, Martinez, & Chavez, 1977; Fomon, 1974; Gebre-Medhin, Vahlquist, Hofvander, Uppsall, & Vahlquist, 1976; Guthrie, Picciano, & Sheehe, 1977; Hagyard, 1972; Hanafy *et al.*, 1972; Karmarkar & Ramakrishan, 1960; Lindblad & Rahimtoola, 1974; Lonnerdal, Forsum, Gebre-Medhin, & Hambraeus, 1976; Matoth, Pinkas, & Sroka, 1965; Potter & Nestel, 1976; Prinsloo *et al.*, 1970; Read & Sarrif, 1965; Schou & Amdisen, 1973). Several studies report that women who are chronically undernourished produce milk that is qualitatively similar to milk from well-nourished women (Fomon, 1974; Lindblad &

Rahimtoola, 1974; Prinsloo *et al.*, 1970). However, not all reports agree with these findings. Hanafy *et al.* (1972) found that chronically malnourished women produced less milk and that the milk was lower in protein, lactose, and fat content.

Karmarkar and Ramarkrishan (1960) studied the relationship between dietary intake of protein, fat, carbohydrate, and selected minerals and the milk levels of these same nutrients. They found a general increase in milk protein level as dietary protein increased. The association was maintained only up to a certain point, beyond which further increases in dietary protein produced no changes in milk protein. As dietary fat increased, so did the level of milk fat, again only up to a certain point. No significant correlation was found between dietary carbohydrate and the lactose content of human milk, nor was there a relationship between dietary and milk levels of calcium, phosphorus, or iron. Bourges *et al.* (1977) recently reported that dietary supplementation with a high-protein, milk-based beverage resulted in a higher daily output of milk (650 versus 550 ml in nonsupplemental women). There was, however, a general dilution effect, so that the concentration of most nutrients actually declined.

A number of studies have shown that dietary fat and carbohydrate have a marked influence on the fatty acid composition of human milk (Guthrie *et al.*, 1977; Hagyard, 1972; Insull, Hirsch, James, & Ahrens, 1959; Read, Lutz, & Tashjian, 1965a, 1965b; Read & Sarrif, 1965; Underwood *et al.*, 1970). A striking increase has been observed in the linoleic acid content of human milk sampled in the 1970s compared to milk sampled two to three decades earlier. This is apparently the consequence of an increased intake of polyunsaturated oils and a decreased use of saturated fats over this period of time (Guthrie *et al.*, 1977; Insull *et al.*, 1959; Macy *et al.*, 1953).

## Maternal Adaptation for Pregnancy

During the period preceding menarche, the human female experiences a substantial alteration in body composition. During this time the amount of fat representing stored calories increases rapidly. Frisch (1972, 1974, 1978) has argued that this alteration of body composition, and the lowered metabolic rate associated with it, trigger hormonal changes that ultimately initiate menarche. The accumulation of a caloric reserve of 80,000 to 90,000 calories is sufficient to carry a woman through her first pregnancy even though her nutritional intake is only adequate enough to supply her own metabolic requirements (Blackburn & Calloway, 1976a, 1976b). Thus, the human female will not usually enter reproductive life without possessing the capacity to support her fetus, even when her intake of nutrients is limited. It is likely that throughout the history of our species, there were many times when food was too scarce to provide additional food for pregnant women. Thus, the capacity to reproduce successfully during alternating periods of feast and famine was probably highly advantageous. This capacity is a consequence of the mother's ability to divert stored amino and fatty acids to the growing fetus and to the production of breast milk.

Thus, for a time the human female may consume a high carbohydrate diet, yet produce milk supplying her newborn with amino acids, fatty acids, immunoglobins, vitamins, and minerals. This is done by utilizing the mother's stores of these nutrients (Naismith & Ritchie, 1975; Ritchie & Naismith, 1975). It is a tribute to human adaptation that with a reasonably adequate nutritional intake, a woman can accomplish this feat repeatedly. It should come as no surprise, however, that, when births occur at close intervals and when nutrition is inadequate, the system is overwhelmed and both the mother and child can be adversely affected.

The significant point is that a human female can and usually does replenish her reserve sufficiently to permit successful pregnancy and breast-feeding if given a modest amount of appropriate nutritional supplements. The amount needed varies, and many factors, including the state of health and the activity level of the woman, will influence the quality and quantity of the supplementation required. In many parts of the world, the kind of supplementation needed to carry a human baby through the first months of life without breast milk is simply not possible. Adequate quantities of milk or balanced formulas that simulate the composition of mothers' milk require resources beyond those at hand. While carbohydrate sources are sometimes available in suitable quantities, high-protein foods are expensive everywhere, and, more often than not, prohibitively so. Thus, it is much more difficult to supplement the diet of a newborn who is prematurely weaned than to supplement the mother who could then continue breast-feeding. More than that, early supplementation of the mother's diet during her pregnancy can reduce the likelihood of her giving birth to an undersized infant. Since the prognosis for undersized newborns is especially poor, and their supplementation requirements are particularly demanding, there is additional reason to direct the allocation of scarce resources to the mother.

## Effect of Disease on Human Milk Composition

A number of disease states may influence the composition of human milk (Abdel Kader, Abdel Hay, El-Safouri, Abdel Aziz, Saad El-Din, Kamal, Hefnawi, Ghoneim, Talaat, Younis, Tagui, & Abdalla, 1969; Barsivala & Virkar, 1973; Sevy, 1971). Acute emotional stress resulted in a 400% rise in the sodium content of a woman's breast milk (Sevy, 1971), and women hospitalized for acute breast infections exhibited higher concentrations of ash, slightly lower total solids content, and a significantly lower concentration of lactose, fat, and total protein in their milk than healthy lactating women of the same racial and economic background (Barsivala & Virkar, 1973).

## BREAST-FEEDING, BOTTLE-FEEDING, AND GROWTH

Comparisons of the growth of breast-fed and bottle-fed infants have produced a confusing variety of conclusions. This is a consequence of a large number of factors which tend to obscure the relationships between nutritional intake and attained growth. A brief consideration of several of these factors is necessary to clarify the problems and to develop guidelines for addressing them.

### Studies in Developing Countries

Much of the work comparing breast-fed and bottle-fed infants has been done in developing countries. Under the conditions prevailing in many such populations, nutritional level is inextricably intertwined with disease experience. Thus, the observation that bottle-fed babies are smaller and weigh less than breast-fed babies in many developing countries (Puffer & Serrano, 1973) implies that nutritional factors alone account for these differences in growth. However, contamination of the nipples, bottles, and milk in the absence of adequate sanitation and sterilization leads to high rates of infectious disease. Available nutrients are then diverted from the growth process to support the immune response or are consumed in sustaining the elevated metabolic rate characteristic of pyrogenic diseases or injury (Burman, Perham, & Ward, 1976). Under such circumstances, growth differences between breast-fed and bottle-fed infants are obviously not the consequence of nutritional adequacy alone. These differences do, however, reflect the apparent superiority of breast-feeding in sustaining growth under many conditions encountered by human populations. This dual ability of human milk to provide adequate nutrition and to minimize the possibility of infectious disease (which would have an adverse effect on nutritional level) is undoubtedly the consequence of long-term selective pressures.

Bottle-feeding as practiced in many parts of the world involves low-grade nutrients which fall far short of satisfying the requirements of a growing infant. Rice water, crushed bananas, sugar water, and starch are all used as bottle feeds. All have serious nutritional deficiencies. More widespread than any of these milk substitutes is the feeding of dilute cow's or goat's milk. The degree of dilution depends upon the degree of scarcity of milk, and it is not uncommon to see babies feeding from a bottle which appears to contain nothing more than cloudy water. The probability that the highly dilute solution is also highly contaminated makes it even more unlikely that these infants will achieve their potential growth.

Thus, convincing evidence from developing countries indicates that bottle-fed babies are generally smaller and less viable than breast-fed infants (Puffer & Serrano, 1973). But such observations most often apply to growth in the first 6 months or so in life. Other factors predominate the later half of infancy.

Total reliance upon breast-feeding for a year or more postpartum is becoming less common, but is still practiced in parts of Africa, Asia, and Latin America. Prolonged breast-feeding by undernourished mothers is sometimes associated with the occurrence of nutritional marasmus in the infant. (In general, marasmus is a condition of earlier onset than kwashiorkor and, because of its occurrence during a period of rapid growth and myelinization of the brain, potentially the cause of enduring neurological deficit [Winick, 1976].) So it is sometimes true that prolonged breast-feeding will produce a smaller 1-year-old than bottle-feeding. The decrease in milk flow after 6 months postpartum which underlies the marasmic state is most precipitous in undernourished mothers, the very ones least likely to have access to appropriate supplements. Thus, we see that in undernourished populations, breast-fed 1-year-olds are smaller than bottle-fed 1-year-olds (Martinez & Chavez, 1971), with the latter group quite probably representing a subsample of survivors capable of adapting to a high carbohydrate diet and repeated exposure to pathogens.

It should be recognized that where sufficient supplements are unavailable to the mother, it is unlikely that the demanding requirements of the newborn could be satisfied through use of indigenous resources. Thus, the choice of breast-feeding under conditions of general nutritional inadequacy, in most cases, is beneficial for the newborn in view of the limited options available.

## Comparisons in Industrialized Countries

Comparisons with the situation in more affluent populations yield further inconsistencies. For example, pediatricians concerned with the comparative growth performance of infants during the first 4 months of life have generally concluded that their breast-fed patients show superior growth. Again, infectious disease is the apparent confounding variable, with bottle-fed babies averaging 3.9 infections during their first 9 months while breast-fed infants averaged 2.6 (Woodruff, Latham, & McDavid, 1977).

It has long been known that certain factors in human milk assist in the establishment of the immune response of the fetus. In the immediate post-partum period, colostrum transmits a number of antibodies. In mature milk, passive IgA antibodies provide an important defense against gastrointestinal infections (Stiehm, 1977). Even in the industrialized countries, it has been shown that breast-fed infants have a lower incidence of neonatal sepsis (Winberg & Wessner, 1971). The factors responsible for the immunological benefits of mature human milk are not entirely understood (György, 1971), but a comparison of the incidence of respiratory and gastrointestinal infections of breast- and bottle-fed infants of similar socioeconomic backgrounds during the first 9 months of life supports the contention that some factor or factors are at work.

Because of its high lactose content, human milk tends to support the growth of *Lactobacillus bifidus*. The proliferation of this particular intestinal flora yields benefits in terms of enhanced vitamin and amino acid availability derived from metabolic processes possessed by these bacteria and lacking in humans (Dubos, 1965). The competitive exclusion of pathogenic bacteria and the symbiotic relationship between host and intestinal flora early in the breast-fed infant do not arise as a normal outcome of bottle-feeding.

## Comparative Advantages and Disadvantages

In the absence of sustained suppression, human growth is target seeking and delays due to infection are usually followed by a period of acceleration so that the advantage of breast-fed babies has disappeared by age 9 months, perhaps even as early as 6 months. From the ninth month onward, bottle-fed infants appear to grow faster then breast-fed ones (Neumann & Alpaugh, 1976). So, depending upon the time of measurement, the population, and the history of the sample involved, it is possible to draw virtually any conclusion one is predisposed to make concerning the comparative growth performance of breast-fed and bottle-fed infants.

It must be stressed that even when well-controlled matched comparisons are made (an accomplishment which still lies in the future) it will be necessary to determine the nature of the differences, if any, in body composition. While it may be found that mean weights, lengths, and other anthropometric variables are similar, the ratio of lean body mass to fat may differ. Whereas obesity has often been cited as an undesirable consequence of bottle-feeding, this has not been demonstrated so far. That is not to say that the inducement of high growth velocity through the use of formulas of high biologic value may not have its own undesirable consequences such as an enhancement of nutrient demand through increased lean body mass. There is abundant evidence that early nutrition can have a profound effect on the volume of lean tissue present. Animal breeders have applied this principle with considerable success and the principles underlying their methods remain valid when applied to humans.

One general observation that can be made concerning the effect of volume per se on the growth process arises from Adolph's (1972) observation that both pigs and dogs given a forced excess of nitrogen intake will retain 90% of it, mostly in the form of lean body mass. According to the process described by Winick, Brasel, and Rosso (1972), this high level of retention does not involve the production of new muscle fibers. What does increase is the number of nuclei within the fiber along with fiber size. Lowrey (1973) has observed similar retention in human children, recording that by simply increasing the protein content of the diet, a substantial increase in nitrogen retention is induced. Increased retention can be maintained for prolonged periods. Neither in infants nor older children is there any consistent correlation between such increases in nitrogen retention and increases in height or weight. Clearly, the consequence of overfeeding need not always be obesity.

The beneficial effects of breast-feeding appear to extend into many aspects of human physiology. Furthermore, early nutritional patterns play an important role in determining the level of adult nutrient requirements. Breast-feeding yields important advantages in both affluent and impoverished populations. But the nature of the benefits derived differs according to degree of affluence. In the areas of the world where food is abundant, leading causes of death are heart disease and cancer. Both are nutritionally related. For the most part, nutritional overabundance and an acquired appetite for a diet high in animal proteins and fats constitute the leading risk-enhancing factors in affluent nations. Recognition of nutritional needs as a product of long-term evolutionary trends is a necessary step in determining actual needs. Supply of the proper nutrients in quantities appropriate to the stage of development of the newborn is generally the natural outgrowth of successful breast-feeding. In a properly nourished mother, an average daily milk flow of 850–900 ml supplies the necessary nutrients in the proper balance without forcing a surplus of any dietary constituent to be ingested. Bottle-feeding has the potential of including both oversupply and imbalance in terms of amino acid versus fatty acid and sugar intake. The result is the stimulation of growth in excess of that which breast-feeding would produce. Thus, tendencies toward obesity are realized and muscle growth is accelerated before any functional justification for it exists.

The problem of overfeeding of protein-rich cow's milk is aggravated by behavioral factors. Overfeeding of bottle-fed infants often occurs as a form of maternal compensation. Often, a baby responding to the excess of sodium contained in cow's milk will be thirsty. Since additional milk will assuage the thirst temporarily, a pattern of frequent feedings to satisfy what is perceived as hunger often emerges (Burman, 1976). This, of course, only serves to force-feed the infant further. And since each liter of cow's milk is loaded with three times the amount of protein found in human milk, much of the excess is in the form of animal protein, and much of that is casein. In affluent populations, bottle-fed babies, whether given cow's milk or prepared formula, grow faster during the first 9 months of life than breast-fed ones. By the time they have reached the age of 1 year, they have acquired a predisposition for a peculiar type of diet for a primate, with animal protein and fat yielding nearly half of daily caloric requirements. Moreover, the infant subjected to a year of ad libitum feeding of high-protein milk or formula is the possessor of a substantial bulk of both lean body mass and adipose, neither of which can be functionally justified. This is maximization and not optimization of growth.

## SPECIFIC NUTRITIONAL CHARACTERISTICS OF HUMAN MILK

Human milk has certain unique characteristics which distinguish it from its common substitutes (Table 4.1). It is relatively low in protein (particularly casein protein) and high in both carbohydrate and lipid. Thus, during lactation the demand made on maternal reserves involves more lipid and less total amino acid than in most other species. Nevertheless, the aggregate demand on maternal amino acid reserves is substantial when the length of time breast-feeding may be sustained in humans is taken into account. To accommodate this demand a woman acquires between 1 and 1.5 kg of lean tissue during the last half of pregnancy. This tissue serves as an amino acid reservoir, and eventually certain of these amino acids will become part of the protein fraction of milk.

The high lipid content of human milk places a strain on maternal lipid reserves. The amino acid alanine aids in the maintenance of these reserves. This nonessential amino acid is the primary endogenous glucogenic substrate released by muscle and extracted by the liver in times of need. Alanine is quantitatively one of the most abundant amino acids in human plasma and, in its role as an energy source, conserves fat reserves making up the lipid pool. The maintenance of these reserves allows the lipid composition of human milk to be kept reasonably constant in the face of a variety of challenges. As stated earlier, fluctuations in milk composition do occur, even within the span of a single day and, perhaps more importantly, within a single breast-feeding. There are even differences in the composition of milk drawn from one or the other breast during the same feeding. All of these variations notwithstanding, the composition of human breast milk is highly

**TABLE 4.1**

**Mature Human Milk versus Cow's Milk[a]**

| Composition | Human milk | Cow's milk |
|---|---|---|
| Water per 100 ml | 87.1 | 87.3 |
| Energy (kcal/100 ml) | 75 | 69 |
| Total solids (gm/100 ml) | 12.9 | 12.7 |
| Protein (%) | 1.1 | 3.3 |
| Fat (%) | 4.5 | 3.7 |
| Lactose (%) | 6.8 | 4.8 |
| Ash (%) | 0.21 | .72 |
| Proteins as percentage of total protein | | |
| Casein | 40 | 82 |
| Whey proteins | 60 | 18 |
| Ash, major components per liter | | |
| Calcium (mg) | 340 | 1250 |
| Phosphorus (mg) | 140 | 960 |
| Vitamins per liter | | |
| Vitamin A (IU) | 1898 | 1025 |
| Thiamin | 160 | 440 |
| Riboflavin | 360 | 1750 |
| Niacin | 1470 | 940 |
| Vitamin C (mg) | 43 | 11 |

[a] From S. V. Fomon. *Infant nutrition.* Philadelphia: Saunders, 1967.

resistant to changes arising from deterioration of the nutritional status of the mother. When adjustments do occur they are more often volumetric than compositional.

Perhaps the most poorly understood and potentially one of the most significant characteristics of human milk, however, is the remarkable bioavailability of its nutrient content for the human infant. Perhaps the best known evidence of superior bioavailability of the nutrients of breast milk compared to even the best commercial formulas is seen in the uptake and incorporation of iron by the human infant. Woodruff *et al.* (1977) have shown that although the actual intake of iron during the first 9 months of life is lower for breast-fed than for bottle-fed infants, their levels of hemoglobin, serum iron, and transferrin saturation are as high or higher. Since the boiling of milk under conditions which destroy lactoferrin does not alter iron absorption, it appears that this protein is not responsible for the superior iron absorption characterizing human milk. A number of trace minerals exhibit a similar pattern. A common element of these patterns is a combination of maternal parsimony in uptake and allocation of trace minerals and efficient transfer to the infant. In their aggregate, these factors define availability.

## HUMAN BREAST MILK: THE PRODUCT OF LONG-TERM NATURAL SELECTION FOR HUMAN INFANTS

Because of its immediate and direct influence on reproductive success, the characteristics of maternal milk of a species has certainly been greatly influenced by the process of natural selection. Pregnancy wastage occurring after a full gestational period is particularly disadvantageous since it removes the mother from the pool of potential parents for an extended period without any compensating benefit. Thus, any modification of milk composition which conveys even the slightest advantage will stand a good chance of becoming part of a species genetic composition. Empirical evidence supporting the foregoing statement is found in the enormous range of variability that exists among the milk compositions of mammalian species. The unique requirements of the newborn of each species are so varied, so complex, and so vitally interrelated, that the biochemistry of milk has been a focal point of evolutionary fine tuning. We cannot now and perhaps never will be able to discover all the factors involved in the millions of years of evolution leading to the various forms of mother's milk that exist today. However, their very differences can yield important clues to the requirements that gave rise to the specific milk composition of various species.

Understanding the needs experienced by newborn humans compared to newborns of other species will permit an assessment of what is a normal nutritional intake and what type of growth this intake implies. Dietary supplementation during the early months of postnatal life is a recent phenomenon (in evolutionary terms). Thus, the nutrients supplied by the species' own unique milk composition provide an accurate guide to the pace of growth which should characterize that period. Viewed from this perspective, human milk composition is notable more for what it seems to lack than for what it contains. This can be seen in Table 4.2, which compares human milk with milk of several other species with respect to its protein composition.

In the case of cow's milk, the most widely used substitute for breast milk in industrialized nations, the water:solid ratio is similar; although within the solid component, some highly informative differences emerge. The percentage of protein in cow's milk is three times as great as in human milk, while human milk is substantially richer in fat and sugar (lactose). Of the total protein, cow's milk has double the casein found in human milk, while whey

**TABLE 4.2**

Comparison of Milk Protein Content and Time to Double Birthweight in
Several Mammalian Species

| Species | Days required to double birthweight | Percentage protein content in milk |
|---------|-------------------------------------|------------------------------------|
| Humans  | 180 | 1.6 |
| Horse   | 60  | 2.0 |
| Cow     | 47  | 3.5 |
| Goat    | 19  | 4.3 |
| Pig     | 18  | 5.9 |
| Sheep   | 10  | 6.5 |
| Dog     | 8   | 7.1 |
| Rabbit  | 6   | 10.4 |

proteins are three times greater in the protein component of human milk. In terms of overall composition this translates into a casein protein content six times greater in cow's milk than in human milk, while the whey proteins are present in similar quantities. Calcium and phosphorous are also much more abundant in cow's milk.

Table 4.2 compares the amount of time required to double birthweight in several different species. These data indicate that the protein content of milk increases as the birthweight doubling time decreases (growth is more rapid). This makes good sense evolutionarily, since early attainment of an independent capacity to forage requires rapid growth and maturation in most mammals. However, humans, unlike most mammals, have an extremely long period of dependency during which time an enormous amount of learning takes place. To facilitate this learning central nervous system growth has high priority during the first year of life, while muscle growth has low priority. The composition of human milk reflects these priorities. A high-fat and lactose content supply the unique requirements of early growth of the human nervous system. At the same time, a relatively modest protein content reveals the most unique aspect of this pattern of human growth, namely, the attainment of independence by the human infant is delayed to an extraordinary extent. Humans are, in a very real sense, the most mammalian of mammals because of this extended period of dependency.

Another characteristic of human milk is also of interest. The enzyme cystathionase is absent from the liver of the human fetus and premature newborn (György, 1971). This means that the capacity to metabolize the amino acid methionine is also absent. As a consequence, the human fetus and premature newborn must rely upon cystine as the essential sulfur-bearing amino acid. In human milk, the methionine:cystine ratio is the lowest among all sources of animal protein. Thus, while cow's milk, meat, and most other animal proteins have a methionine:cystine ratio of 2.5:1, in human milk the ratio is slightly greater than 1:1, favoring cystine. Evolutionary fine tuning can be seen in this uniquely human ratio (Macy, 1953; Hagyard, 1972).

Fatty acid absorption is superior in human milk compared to cow's milk (György, 1971). Fatty acids are important energy sources and are needed for myelinization of the central nervous system which is rapidly proceeding during the first year of life. Human milk also contains a significantly different balance of nucleotides than does cow's milk, associated with enhanced nitrogen uptake when protein intake is low. Thus, the evolutionary process has provided the breast-fed human infant with substantially greater efficiency in utilization of the relatively low proportion of protein present in its nutrient intake.

## CONCLUSIONS

What is the significance of the decline in breast milk volume and mineral concentrations exhibited by human mothers? The decline in calcium and zinc levels in the milk of *well-fed* women bottoms out at about 9 months postpartum. This is a time when milk volume also attains a low stable level. Calculations of estimated milk flow in a number of *less affluent populations* (Martinez & Chavez, 1971) have yielded a pattern of reduction in average flow during the fourth as compared to the third trimester postpartum. There is thus apparently a compensatory mechanism at work in women of poorer nutritional status, whereby decline in milk production occurs at a later date. In the sample of poorly nourished Mexican women, infant birthweight was predictably lower than the birthweight of infants of well-nourished comparisons. However, maternal milk volume was actually greater among the poorly nourished women so that by 1 year of age many of their low-birthweight infants were heavier than the comparison children of well-nourished mothers (Martinez & Chavez, 1971).

The similarity of the curves for volume and trace minerals makes it very tempting to view 9 months as the approximate period postpartum during which breast milk would serve as an exclusive nutrient resource. The corollary is that beyond that 9-month period, supplementation in some form is essential. Jelliffe & Jelliffe (1978) have argued convincingly that the human infant is essentially an extero uterine fetus during the first 9 months postpartum. The above observations support that argument. Figure 4.1, showing calcium concentration in the milk of well-fed human mothers, illustrates another aspect of the changes occurring during that period.

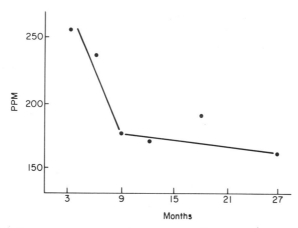

**Figure 4.1.** Calcium concentrations (in parts per million) in human milk during the first 27-months postpartum.

Using a 9-month period of exclusive breast-feeding as the norm for the evolutionarily determined nutritional pattern for human infants, it is possible to compare the growth performance of infants being so nourished with those under different nutritional programs. If this can be accomplished with any precision, we might finally be capable of estimating what is "normal." Conclusions concerning obesity or obese tendencies derived from early nutritional patterns are probably premature until such estimates can be made. However, from the bulk of evidence now available, it appears that in the affluent nations of the world, infant growth tends to be more maximized than optimized. This maximization, if it can be demonstrated to occur, may prove to be of fundamental importance in future efforts to gain an understanding of the patterns of aging and senescence characterizing an increasingly large proportion of the world's population.

Finally, what are the factors that determine whether breast-feeding or bottle-feeding is elected? Some of these factors are of a purely social nature. For instance, it is often difficult for a woman to breast-feed while she must work outside the home. The obstacles raised by outside employment are not insurmountable. But, all too often, concessions such as time off during the working day are not forthcoming. When the income earned by the nursing mother is crucial to economic survival, the choice of breast-feeding versus bottle-feeding comes down to no choice at all. This may be true in both industrialized and in less developed countries. Superimposed against a background of opinion consigning breast-feeding to "backward" or "primitive" segments of the population (an opinion still held in surprisingly numerous societies), economic factors take on added weight. In most parts of the world, it is still difficult for a woman to simultaneously breast-feed and pursue an occupation outside the home. Only in the more affluent segments of the more affluent countries is the practice of breast-feeding for an extended period on the increase. While the trend in these populations is encouraging, the fact is that these are the populations in which the need is least urgent.

That is not to say that important benefits cannot be gained by a return to breast-feeding in more affluent populations. As experience accumulates and as accurate information about the process and its effects becomes widely available, an increasing number of newborns will begin life under a nutritional regime closely paralleling their actual needs. Overfeeding and artificially stimulated growth will be less prevalent. Only in the future will we be able to determine how the combination of breast-feeding and advanced systems of health care will influence future life expectancies and aging patterns.

In less affluent countries, a determined effort is needed to ensure that expectant mothers receive adequate nourishment to sustain both a normal gestation and lactation without detriment to their own health. Habicht, Yarbrough, Lechtig, and Klein (1974) have shown that supplementation of mothers is far less demanding than later efforts to support undersized newborns. However, severe malnutrition of the mother could frustrate attempts to breast-feed with serious consequences for both mother and infant. Thus, supplementation of the newborn in many cases is the only possible course. Once bottle-feeding has been established there is little likelihood of a successful reinstitution of breast-feeding. Unless a wet nurse is available, high-quality supplements will continue to be needed. Although breast-feeding is desirable for the many reasons already enumerated, we must also conclude that for the foreseeable future there will be a need for nutritional supplementation of one type or another.

## REFERENCES

Abdel Kader, M., Abdel Hay, A., El-Safouri, S., Abdel Aziz, M., Saad El-Din, J., Kamal, I., Hefnawi, F., Ghoneim, M., Talaat, M., Younis, N., Tagui, A., & Abdalla, M. Clinical, biochemical and experimental studies on lactation. *American Journal of Obstetrics and Gynecology*, 1969, *105*, 978–985.

Adolph, E. F. Development of physiological regulations. In M. Winick (Ed.), *Nutrition and development*. New York: Wiley, 1972. Pp. 1–25.

Ajans, Z., Sarrif, A., & Husbands, M. Influence of vitamin A on human colostrum and early milk. *American Journal of Clinical Nutrition*, 1965, *17*, 139–142.

Barltrop, D., & Hillier, R. Calcium and phosphorus content of transitional and mature human milk. *Acta Paediatrica Scandinavica*, 1974, *63*, 347–350.

Barsivala, V., & Virkar, K. The effect of oral contraceptives on concentrations of various components of human milk. *Contraception*, 1973, 7, 307–312.

Belavady, B., & Gopalan, C. Chemical composition of human milk in poor Indian women. *Indian Journal of Medical Research*, 1959, 47, 234–245.

Blackburn, M. W., & Calloway, D. H. Basal metabolic rate and work energy expenditure of mature, pregnant women. *Journal of the American Dietetic Association*, 1976, 69, 24–28. (a)

Blackburn, M. W. and Calloway, D. H. Energy expenditure and consumption of mature, pregnant and lactating women. *Journal of the American Dietetic Association*, 1976, 69, 29–37. (b)

Bourges, H., Martinez, C., & Chavez, A. *Effect of dietary supplements on nutrient content of milk from mothers in a rural Mexican town*. Paper presented at the Western Hemisphere Nutrition Congress V, Quebec, Canada, August 1977.

Burman, D. Nutrition in early childhood. In D. S. McLaren & D. Burman (Eds.), *Textbook of paediatric nutrition*. Edinburgh: Churchill-Livingstone, 1976. Pp. 46–75.

Burman, D., Perham, T. G. M., & Ward, M. R. Nutrition and systemic disease. In D. S. McLaren & D. Burman (Eds.), *Textbook of paediatric nutrition*. Edinburgh: Churchill-Livingstone, 1976. Pp. 294–345.

Cavell, P., & Widdowson, E. Intakes and excretions of iron, copper, and zinc in the neonatal period. *Archives of Diseases of Childhood*, 1964, 39, 496.

Fomon, S. *Infant nutrition* (2nd Ed.). Philadelphia: Saunders, 1967.

Frisch, R. Weight at menarche: Similarity for well nourished and undernourished girls at differing ages and evidence for historical constancy. *Pediatrics*, 1972, 50, 445–450.

Frisch, R. A method of prediction of the age of menarche from height and weight at ages 9 through 19 years. *Pediatrics*, 1974, 53, 384–390.

Frisch, R. Population, food intake, and fertility. *Science*, 1978, 199, 22–30.

Gebre-Medhin, M., Vahlquist, A., Hofvander, Y., Uppsall, L., & Vahlquist, B. Breast milk composition in Ethiopian and Swedish mothers. 1. Vitamin A and B-carotene. *American Journal of Clinical Nutrition*, 1976, 29, 441–451.

Guthrie, H., Picciano, M., & Sheehe, D. Fatty acid patterns of human milk. *The Journal of Pediatrics*, 1977, 90, 39–41.

György, P. Biochemical aspects. *American Journal of Clinical Nutrition*, 1971, 240, 970–975.

Habicht, J.-P., Yarbrough, C., Lechtig, A., & Klein, R. E. Relation of maternal supplementary feeding during pregnancy to birth weight and other sociobiological factors. In M. Winick (Ed.), *Nutrition and fetal development*. New York: Wiley. Pp. 127–147.

Hagyard, S. *Constituent analysis of human milk*. M.S. Thesis, University of Arizona, Tucson, 1972.

Hanafy, M., Seddick, Y., & Habib, Y. Maternal nutrition and lactation performance. *Journal of Tropical Pediatrics, Environment and Child Health*, 1972, 18, 187.

Hefnawi, F., Badraoui, M., Younis, N., & Hassib, F. Lactation patterns in Egyptian women. 1. Milk yield during the first year of lactation. *Journal of Biosocial Science*, 1972, 4, 397–401.

Hytten, F. Clinical and chemical studies in human lactation. II. Variation in major constituents during a feeding. *British Medical Journal*, 1954 1, 1976. (a)

Hytten, F. Clinical and chemical studies in human lactation. III. Diurnal variation in major constituents of milk. *British Medical Journal*, 1954, 1, 179. (b)

Insull, W., Hirsch, J., James, T., & Ahrens, E. The fatty acids of human milk. II. Alterations produced by manipulation of caloric balance and exchange of dietary fats. *Journal of Clinical Investigation*, 1959, 28, 443.

Jelliffe, D. B., & Jelliffe, E. F. P. The interrelationships of lactation, conception and nutrition of the nursing couple. In A. Chavez, H. Bourges, & S. Basta (Eds.), *Prognosis for the undernourished surviving child*. Basel: S. Karger, 1975. Pp. 11–15.

Jelliffe, D. B., Jelliffe, E. F. P. The volume and composition of human milk in poorly nourished communities. *American Journal of Clinical Nutrition*, 1978, 31: 492.

Kader, M., Bahgat, R., Aziz, M., Hefnawi, F., Badraoui, M., Younis, N., & Hassib, F. Lactation patterns in Egyptian women. II. Chemical composition of milk during the first year of lactation. *Journal of Biosocial Science*, 1972, 4, 403–409.

Karmarkar, M., Kapur, J., Deodhar, A., & Ramakrishnan, C. Studies on human lactation. Part 1. Diet survey of lactating women in different socioeconomic groups and the effects of socioeconomic status and stage of lactation on the proximate principles and essential amino acids of human milk. *Indian Journal of Medical Research*, 1959, 47, 344–351.

Karmarkar, M., & Ramakrishan, C. Studies on human lactation: Relation between the dietary intake of lactating women and the chemical composition of milk with regard to principal and certain inorganic constituents. *Acta Paediatrica Belgica*, 1960, 49, 599.

Lindblad, B., & Rahimtoola, R. A pilot study of the quality of human milk in a lower socio-economic group in Karachi, Pakistan. *Acta Paediatrica Scandinavica*, 1974, 63, 125.

Lonnerdal, B., Forsum, E., Gebre-Medhin, M., & Hambraeus L. Breast milk composition in Ethiopian and Swedish mothers. II. Protein content and composition. *American Journal of Clinical Nutrition*, 1976, 29, 1134.

Lonnerdal, B., Forsum, E., & Hambraeus, L. A longitudinal study of the protein, nitrogen and lactose contents of human milk from Swedish well-nourished mothers. *American Journal of Clinical Nutrition*, 1976, 29, 1127–1133. (a)

Lonnerdal, B., Forsum, E., & Hambraeus, L. The protein content of human milk. 1. A transversal study of Swedish normal material. *Nutrition Reports International*, 1976, 13, 125–134. (b)

Lonnerdal, B., Forsum, E., & Hambraeus, L. A longitudinal study of the protein content of human milk from well-nourished Swedish mothers. *Nutritional Metabolism*, 1977, 21 (suppl. 1), 106–109.

Lowrey, G. H. *Growth and development of children* (6th ed.). Chicago: Year Book Medical Publishers, 1973. Pp. 335–337.

Macy, I. G. The composition of human colostrum and milk. *American Journal of Diseases of Childhood*, 1949, 78, 589.

Macy, I., Kelly, H., & Sloan, R. *The composition of milks*. National Research Council Publication No. 254. Washington, D.C.: National Academy of Sciences, 1953.

Macy, I., Nims, B., Brown, M., & Hunscher, H. Human milk studies. VII. Chemical analysis of milk representative of the entire first and last halves of the nursing period. *American Journal of Diseases of Childhood*, 1931, 42, 569.

Martinez, C., & Chavez, A. Nutrition and development in infants of poor rural areas. 1. Consumption of mother's milk by infants. *Nutrition Reports International*, 1971, 16, 356–359.

McLeod, B., & Robinson, M. Dietary intake of manganese by New Zealand infants during the first six months of life. *British Journal of Nutrition*, 1972, 27, 299.

Naismith, D. J., & Ritchie, C. D. The effect of breast-feeding and artificial feeding on body weights, skinfold measurements and food intakes of forty-two primaparous women. *Proceedings of the Nutrition Society*, 1975, 34, 116A–118A.

Neumann, C. G., & Alpaugh, A. Birthweight doubling time: A fresh look. *Pediatrics*, 1976, 59, 469–473.

Nims, B., Macy, I., Brown, H., & Hunscher, H. Human milk studies. IX. Variations in the composition of milk at four hour intervals during the day and night. *American Journal of Diseases of Childhood*, 1931, *43*, 828–844.

Potter, J., & Nestel, P. The effects of dietary fatty acids and cholesterol on the milk lipids of lactating women and the plasma cholesterol of breast-fed infants. *American Journal of Clinical Nutrition*, 1976, *29*, 54.

Prinsloo, J., Wittmann, W., Strydom, E., de Villiers, D., Wehmeyer, A., Laubscher, N., & Botha, M. Composition of breast milk from Bantu and white women on the fifth postpartum day. *South African Medical Journal*, 1970, *53*, 738–739.

Puffer, R. R., & Serrano, C. V. (Eds.). *Patterns of mortality in childhood*. Scientific Publication #262 PAHO/WHO. Washington, D.C.: WHO, 1973. Pp. 257–271.

Read, W., Lutz, P., & Tashjian, A. Human milk lipids. II. The influence of dietary carbohydrates and fat on the fatty acids of mature milk. A study in four ethnic groups. *American Journal of Clinical Nutrition*, 1965, *17*, 180–183. (a)

Read, W., Lutz, P., & Tashjian, A. Human milk lipids. III. Short-term effects of dietary carbohydrate and fat. *American Journal of Clinical Nutrition*, 1965, *17*, 184–188.

Read, W., & Sarrif, A. Human milk lipids. I. Changes in fatty acid composition of early colostrum. *American Journal of Clinical Nutrition*, 1965, *17*, 177–179.

Ritchie, C. D., & Naismith, D. J. A comparison of growth in wholly breast-fed infants and in artificially fed infants. *Proceedings of the Nutrition Society*, 1975, *34*, 118A.

Schou, M., & Amdisen, A. Lithium and pregnancy—III: Lithium ingestion by children breast-fed by women on lithium treatment. *British Medical Journal*, 1973, *2*, 138.

Sevy, S. Acute emotional stress and sodium in breast milk. *American Journal of Diseases of Children*, 1971, *122*, 459.

Stichm, E. R. Biology of Immunoglobulins: Humoral and secetory—a review. In R. M. Suskind (Ed.), *Malnutrition and the immune response*. New York: Raven Press, 1977. Pp. 141–154.

Svanberg, U., Gebre-Medhin, M., Ljumgqvist, B., & Olsson, M. Breast milk composition in Ethiopian and Swedish mothers. II. Amino acids and other nitrogenous substances. *American Journal of Clinical Nutrition*, 1977, *30*, 499–507.

Underwood, B., Hepner, R., & Abdullah, H. Protein, Lipid and fatty acids of milk from Pakistani women during prolonged periods of lactation. *American Journal of Clinical Nutrition*, 1970, *23*, 400.

Winberg, J., & Wessner, G. Does breast milk protect against septicemia in the newborn? *Lancet*, 1971, *1*, 1091–1094.

Winick, M. (Ed.). *Malnutrition and brain development*. New York: Oxford University Press, 1976.

Winick, M., Brasel, J. A., & Rosso, R. Nutrition and cell growth. In M. Winick (Ed.), *Nutrition and development*. New York: Wiley, 1972. Pp. 59–67.

Woodruff, C. W., Latham, L. L., & McDavid, S. Iron nutrition in the breast-fed infant. *Journal of Pediatrics*, 1977, *90*, 36–38.

# 5

# Interrelationships between Diet, Infectious Disease, and Nutritional Status

REYNALDO MARTORELL

## INTRODUCTION

Most people in the developing nations of Asia, Africa, and Latin America live in a state of abject poverty, resulting in poor dietary intakes and a high incidence of infectious disease. The mechanisms that produce these effects vary, but generally involve inequalities in the distribution of wealth, lack of educational opportunities, and the absence of public services. For example, the characteristically low income levels of developing nations limit the kinds and the amounts of food available for consumption. Low incomes also lead to increased environmental exposure to pathogens by adversely affecting such variables as the size and quality of the dwelling and the availability of facilities and supplies necessary for personal hygiene. Similarly, misconceptions or ignorance about the nutritional needs of special groups such as infants and women during pregnancy and lactation and about the importance of simple hygienic procedures are examples of the salience of educational factors. Finally, lack of public services such as potable water, waste disposal systems, and preventive and curative medical care is also an important factor in determining disease patterns.

Poor diets and a high incidence of infectious diseases operate in conjunction, as shown in Figure 5.1, to produce malnutrition, so characteristic of

Social and Biological Predictors of
Nutritional Status, Physical Growth,
and Neurological Development

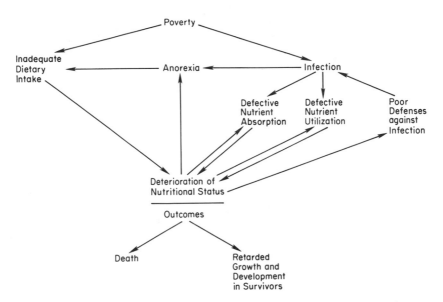

**Figure 5.1.**   The biological mechanisms through which poverty affects nutritional status.

developing nations. In this chapter, evidence documenting this relationship is reviewed and policy implications for health and nutrition planning are discussed.

## EFFECT OF LOW DIETARY INTAKES ON NUTRITIONAL STATUS

The relative importance of deficiencies in energy and in protein intake as causes of malnutrition has been the subject of intense debate in the last few years (Payne, 1975; Scrimshaw, 1977). Much of the literature prior to the 1970s ascribed malnutrition to deficiencies in the quantity and quality of protein rather than to energy, a situation that has been reversed by recent developments. Most researchers now agree that relative to the most recent FAO/WHO protein–energy requirements (FAO/WHO, 1973), energy is often limiting in the diets of most people in developing nations while protein appears to be adequate, even after adjusting for quality (Payne, 1975; Sukhatme, 1974; Valverde, Arroyave, & Flores, 1975). However, when energy needs are not met, portions of the otherwise ample supply of protein will be metabolized as energy fuel and not utilized for tissue repair and synthesis. Therefore, both energy and protein are limiting at the cellular level.

Protein–energy deficits are frequently accompanied by intake deficits in vitamins, notably vitamin A, and in minerals, especially iron. As shown in Figure 5.1, these deficiencies contribute directly to the deterioration of nutritional status, protein–energy malnutrition (PEM) being the most common expression of this deficient state. However, PEM will often occur in conjunction with other nutritional problems.

Bengoa (1973) has classified nutritional problems into three main groups according to their geographical range and prevalence. The first group is made up by those problems common to most of the developing countries: protein–energy malnutrition (PEM), nutritional anemia, endemic goiter, ariboflavinosis, and dental problems. The second group includes xerophthalmia and rickets, which are found in large areas of the world but with less frequency. The third group includes problems such as pellagra, beriberi, and scurvy which are limited to specific geographical areas.

### Preschool Child Malnutrition

Protein–energy malnutrition and other nutritional problems occur with greater frequency among young children, partly because of their greater nutritional needs relative to body mass. Figure 5.2 shows how the energy requirement of males, expressed as kilocalories per kilogram of body weight, falls dramatically with age from a high of 120 kcal/kg at less than 3 months to 47 kcal/kg at 19 years of age. Female requirements are similar. In addition, requirements for protein vary in the same way. A second factor contributing to the high frequency of PEM in young children, and one which will be discussed extensively, is the high incidence of infectious disease during infancy and early childhood.

Protein–energy malnutrition comprises a continuum from the severe syndromes of kwashiorkor and marasmus, which quickly lead to death in the absence of adequate and prompt medical treatment, to moderate and mild forms which can be detected only by poor physical growth (Gopalan, 1968; Keller, Donoso, & DeMaeyer, 1976). Most nutritional surveys of children under 5 years of age find that although less than 10% of children suffer from severe PEM, two-thirds or more will show signs of mild or moderate PEM (Jelliffe, 1966). Thus, PEM has been likened to an iceberg, with kwashiorkor and marasmus representing the small visible portion and the less severe forms representing the greater invisible mass (Jelliffe & Jelliffe, 1969). This pattern can be observed in Figure 5.3 which expresses in graphic form the relative proportions of severe, moderate, and mild malnutrition in Central American children 5 years of age or less. Because studies have demonstrated a mortality risk gradient from mild to severe malnutrition (Puffer & Serrano, 1973; Sommer & Loewenstein, 1975) and because of the large number of

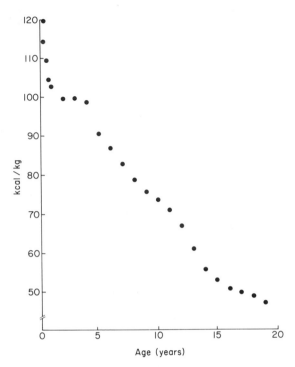

**Figure 5.2.** Energy requirements (kcal/kg of body weight) for males by age. Drawn from data in Tables 6 and 7, FAO/WHO Report, 1973.

children involved, the less severe or "hidden" forms of PEM are considered the more important public health problem.

## Malnutrition and the Outcome of Pregnancy

Because of their increased nutritional requirements, women during pregnancy and lactation are the second group most likely to be malnourished in developing nations. A normal pregnancy should result in a total weight gain of 12.5 kg and lead to a birthweight of 3.3–3.5 kg and to maternal fat stores of 4.0 kg (Hytten & Leitch, 1971). The total energy cost of a normal pregnancy is 80,000 kcal, representing an extra 150 kcal/day in the first trimester and 350 kcal/day in the second and third trimesters (FAO/WHO, 1973). During pregnancy an additional daily intake of 9 gm of quality protein is recommended to achieve safe levels of protein intake (FAO/WHO, 1973). Increments in other nutrients are required as well (FAO/WHO, 1962, 1967, 1970).

These increased nutritional needs are rarely satisfied in poor societies. Numerous dietary surveys indicate that intakes may be several hundred calories below recommended levels and may be deficient in other nutrients (Lechtig, Habicht, Delgado, Klein, Yarbrough, & Martorell, 1975b; PAHO, 1970; WHO, 1965). The consequences are severe: Weight gains average around 5–7 kg, 40–60% of normal; there is little or no fat accumulation during pregnancy; and the prevalence of low-birthweight babies (less than 2.5 kg) is high. For example, the percentage of babies with low birthweight is 7% in the United States but 20–40% in rural Guatemala (Lechtig *et al.*, 1975b; Mata, Urrutia, Albertazzi, Pellecer, & Arellano, 1972). Low weight at birth is an important public health problem because newborns weighing less than 2.5 kg are more likely to die during the first year than heavier babies (Chase, 1969; Lechtig, Delgado, Lasky, Yarbrough, Martorell, Habicht, & Klein, 1975a; Mata *et al.*, 1972).

## Malnutrition and Lactation

Nutritional demands during lactation are greater than those during pregnancy. According to FAO/WHO (1973), milk production in the first 6 months

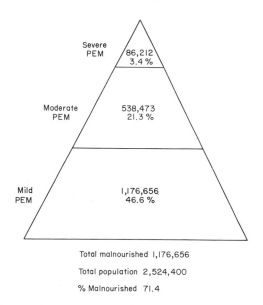

Total malnourished 1,176,656

Total population 2,524,400

% Malnourished 71.4

**Figure 5.3.**    The malnutrition iceberg. Prevalence of severe, moderate, and mild malnutrition (PEM) in Central America in 1965 in children less than 5 years of age. Based on Table 25, INCAP/INCCD, 1972. Severe, moderate, and mild malnutrition refer to the Gómez categories of weight for age (Gómez, Ramos Galván, Frenk, Cravioto, Chávez, & Vásquez, 1956).

of life should be around 850 ml for normal rates of growth during infancy. Since the energy value of 100 ml of breast milk is 70 kcal and the efficiency of production is estimated at 80%, a mother would require 750 kcal per day. This represents 135,000 kcal for the first 6 months of lactation or 100,000 kcal if the energy equivalent of the amount of fat normally accumulated during pregnancy, 4 kg, is subtracted. In other words, an additional 550 kcal/day is needed during the first 6 months of lactation (FAO/WHO, 1973). Similarly, an additional 17 gm of high-quality protein per day is recommended to achieve safe levels of protein intake (FAO/WHO, 1973). Increments in other nutrients are also needed (FAO/WHO, 1962, 1967, 1970).

Dietary data from developing countries show that intakes during lactation, as in pregnancy, are generally several hundred kilocalories below the recommended levels (PAHO, 1970; WHO, 1965). Furthermore, unsatisfactory weight gains during pregnancy often make the fat stores that can be drawn upon during lactation inadequate. As a result, the quantity of breast milk produced is notably reduced, often to levels below 500 ml/day, although nutrient composition is usually not unaffected (Bailey, 1965; Edozien, 1970; Gopalan, 1958; Rao, Swaminatham, Swarup, & Patwardhan, 1959). All things considered, milk yields of malnourished women are remarkable. However, they are achieved at the expense of maternal tissues which become depleted with successive pregnancies and breastfeeding periods.

Children in developing nations generally fare well in the first few months of life primarily because of breastfeeding. However, after 3 months or so, growth rates become increasingly inadequate as the volume of breast milk becomes limiting. Furthermore, the nutrient mixes provided to supplement breast milk are often inadequate nutritionally, and, because of deficient hygienic conditions during their preparation, may serve as carriers of disease agents of the well-known weanling diarrheas (Gordon, Chitkara, & Wyon, 1963).

### Improved Nutrition

Food supplementation experiments carried out in rural Guatemala have shown that the prevalence of low birthweight babies can be reduced by modest energy increments during pregnancy (Lechtig et al., 1975b), and that this in turn leads to reductions in infant mortality (Delgado, Lechtig, Yarbrough, Martorell, Klein, & Irwin, 1977). Improved dietary intakes of children result in better growth rates, energy apparently being responsible for the improvements except where the dietary staples are roots, tubers, and starchy fruits, and the main limiting nutrient is protein (Martorell, Lechtig, Yarbrough, Delgado, & Klein, 1976b).

## EFFECT OF INFECTION ON NUTRITIONAL STATUS

Dietary improvements alone will not eliminate malnutrition (División de Desarrollo Humano, 1975). Infection must be eradicated as well. Indeed, Mata, Kronmal, Urrutia, and Garcia (1977a) state that dietary inadequacy has been overemphasized and suggest that infection is a much more important cause of malnutrition.

### The Infective Load in Developing Countries

The frequency, duration, and severity of infectious illnesses are definitely much greater at all stages of life in poorer societies (Freij & Wall, 1977; Mata, Urrutia, Serrato, Mohs, & Chin, 1977b). Fetal infection and antigenic stimulation are common in developing countries and are important causes of intrauterine malnutrition (Mata *et al.*, 1977a, 1977b). Mothers also experience ordinary illnesses such as respiratory and gastrointestinal infections with greater frequency (Lechtig, Martorell, Delgado, Yarbrough, & Klein, 1976; Mata *et al.*, 1977b), and these lead to intrauterine growth retardation (Lechtig *et al.*, 1976), perhaps by depressing maternal appetite (Lechtig, Habicht, Guzmán, & de León, 1972). Illnesses are also more frequent and severe in children from developing countries (Martorell, Habicht, Yarbrough, Lechtig, Klein, & Western, 1975a).

### Breast Milk and Infection

Breast milk protects the infant against infection in a number of ways (Jelliffe & Jelliffe, 1971). Immunoglobulins present in colostrum confer partial immunity to the young infant against intestinal enteropathogenic bacteria (Stiehm, 1977). Breast milk also promotes the growth of certain types of beneficial bacteria, such as *Lactobacillus bifidus*, which colonize the gut and produce an acidic environment which inhibits the growth of harmful bacteria and parasites. Infants who ingest cow's milk have neutral or alkaline stools. Breast milk also contains leukocytes which can kill and digest bacteria as well as synthesize antimicrobial factors such as lysozyme, complement, and lactoferrin (Pitt, 1976).

In most societies foods to supplement breast milk begin to be offered with increasing frequency after 4–6 months of age. These foods introduce a number of pathogenic organisms which become responsible for the endemic diarrheal diseases and the high mortality rates so characteristic of the time of weaning in poor societies (Gordon *et al.*, 1963; Gordon, Wyon, & Ascoli, 1967). By the time the stormy period of weaning is over, children are more

resistant to infections. This is illustrated in Figure 5.4, which shows how the
percentage of time the child is ill with diarrhea (dotted line) peaks from 6 to
18 months of age (the weaning period in the Guatemalan communities where
these data were gathered), and rapidly falls thereafter. The patterns for
upper and lower respiratory infections, which are several times more common than diarrheal diseases, and of other common ailments are of a similar
nature (Martorell, Habicht, Yarbrough, Lechtig, & Klein, 1976a).

## Epidemiological Associations between Infection and
## Nutritional Status

Pediatricians and other health practitioners in malnourished populations
are well aware that acute infectious episodes can precipitate severe malnutri-

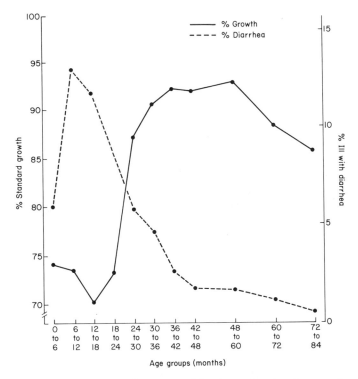

**Figure 5.4.** Age changes in the prevalence of diarrhea and in the adequacy of growth rates
in height in Guatemalan children. Growth adequacy was defined as the mean growth observed
in the study villages expressed as a percentage of the mean growth rate at the same age
exhibited by a well-nourished population (McCammon, 1970). Drawn from data in Martorell,
Yarbrough, Lechtig, Habicht, and Klein (1975b).

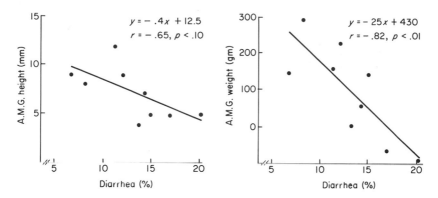

**Figure 5.5.** Relationship between average monthly gains (A.M.G.) in height and weight and mean percentage of time ill with diarrhea in Gambian children. Each observation repre sents a 2-month period of study and includes an average of 134 child measurements. Data are from Table 2, Rowland *et al.* (1977).

tion in a matter of days (Morley, 1969; Salomón, Mata, & Gordon, 1968). It is also widely recognized that children do not grow as well at the ages when illnesses are more frequent. In rural Guatemala, for example, the curve for percentage of time ill with diarrhea from birth to 7 years of age is almost the inverse of that of the adequacy of growth rates in height ($r = .84$, $N = 11$, $p < .01$; see Figure 5.4).

A recent study from the Gambia clearly points out that the seasonality of physical growth is strongly associated with variations in the prevalence of diarrhea (Rowland, Cole, & Whitehead, 1977). The authors studied eleven distinct 2-month periods and recorded, for children averaging 1.6 years of age, mean growth rates in height and weight as well as mean percentage of the time ill with diarrhea for each specific period. Regressions from these values are presented in Figure 5.5. Clearly, when the prevalence of diarrhea is higher, rates of growth in height and in weight are lower.

## Specific Studies of Illness and Growth

Confirmation of the relationship between illness and physical growth is best derived from longitudinal studies in which individual illness and growth histories are gathered. The results of such studies are summarized in Table 5.1 for developed countries and in Table 5.2 for developing countries. The separation according to country of origin reveals contrasting results. While most of the studies from *developed* nations report no associations between illness and physical growth, those from *developing* nations report that common childhood ailments, in particular diarrheal diseases, are clearly associated with poor physical growth.

**TABLE 5.1**

Illness and Physical Growth Indicators of Nutritional Status: Developed Nations

| Source | Illness variables | Growth variables | Conclusion |
|---|---|---|---|
| Evans (1944)<br>Ninety-three 2.5- to 5-year-old children of high socioeconomic status (United States) | Days absent from school; children were divided into five groups according to severity of illnesses | Six-month increments in various measurements including height and weight | The growth of all five groups was similar |
| Hardy (1938)<br>Four hundred and fifteen school children of all socioeconomic classes (United States) | Incidence of ordinary diseases of childhood exclusive of minor colds and rickets as determined from a single interview of mothers (for history prior to age 8) and from yearly interviews of mothers and school records for absences due to illnesses (for history after age 8) | Annual growth rates in height from 8 to 12 years; various measures of body size throughout childhood, middle childhood, and adulthood | No association was found between growth and disease; children in extreme categories of illness did not differ in terms of growth even when they were matched for national and social origins |
| Hewitt, Westropp, and Acheson (1955)<br>Six hundred and fifty children followed from 2 to 5 years of age (England) | Annual sickness records; the sample was divided into five diagnostic groups and into three categories according to severity of illness | Yearly height increments | The growth of all diagnostic groups was similar; however, the "severe" disease group grew less in height |
| Kubát, Kouřim, Nováhová, Moderová, and Stloukalová (1971)<br>Three hundred and thirty-three middle-class children followed from birth to 6 years of age (Czechoslovakia) | The sample was divided into high and low groups according to disease incidence data obtained from pediatric records | Height and weight at 6 years of age as well as increments from birth to 6 years of age | In all comparisons, the growth of frequently ill children was greater than that of the infrequently ill children. Only in the case of girls and with height increments did this reach statistical significance |

| Study | Morbidity measure | Growth measure | Findings |
|---|---|---|---|
| Martens and Meredith (1942) Ninety 5- to 6-year-old children of high socio-economic status (United States) | Days absent from school on account of illness | Six-month increments and attained size of various measurements including height and weight | No association between absence from school on account of illness and physical growth |
| Meredith and Knott (1962) Thirty-five elementary school children followed from 5 to 10 years of age (United States) | Interviews of parents every 6 months. Healthiest 20% compared to least healthy 20%; breakdown based on number of illnesses, severity, and duration | Various measures of body size at 5 years; growth increments in height, weight, as well as in other measures over a 5-year period | The growth of both groups was similar |
| Palmer (1936) Four thousand school children (United States) | Days absent from school on account of illness | Attained height and weight | No associations were found |
| Turner, Longee, Saravia, and Fuller (1965) One hundred and twenty school children 6 to 14 years (United States) | School records and yearly recall interviews of parents and children by the health teacher | Sixty children with poor weight gains were compared to 60 randomly chosen children of the same age and sex with above-average weight gains | Poor growers experienced more communicable, respiratory, and noncommunicable illnesses |
| Valadian, Reed, Stuart, Burke, Pyle, and Cornoni (n.d.) One hundred and thirty-five children followed from 0 to 17 years of age (United States) | Interviews at 3, 6, 9, and 12 months of age, every 6 months thereafter till 10 years, and every year from 10 to 18 years. Complex score system used as the morbidity variable | Height and weight at various ages from birth to 17 years of age | The high-illness groups had the greater proportion of larger children at maturity. Greater illness was associated with rapid growth in preschool children and to some extent also in adolescence |

**TABLE 5.2**

**Illness and Physical Growth Indicators of Nutritional Status: Developing Nations**[a]

| Source[b] | Illness variables | Growth variables | Conclusion |
|---|---|---|---|
| Cole and Parkin (1977) Forty-five children followed from birth to 3 years of age (Uganda) | The children were examined routinely once a month and whenever they attended the clinic on account of illness. Incidence per month were recorded for various symptoms | Monthly weight gains | The incidence of diarrhea, fever, and measles was significantly related to monthly weight gains. Other illnesses, including respiratory infections, were not related to weight gains |
| Condon-Paoloni, Cravioto, Johnston, de Licardie, and Scholl (1977) Two hundred and seventy-six children studied from birth to 3 years of age (Mexico) | Illness histories collected every 2 weeks. The highest and lowest quartiles were identified for each of three variables: percentage of the time ill with diarrhea, percentage with upper respiratory infections, and percentage with lower respiratory infections | Yearly increments in height and weight | Diarrheal diseases were significantly related to height but not to weight increments. Respiratory infections were not related to growth in height or weight |
| Draper and Draper (1960) Eighty-eight infants (Tanzania) | Weekly clinic of irregular daily attendance | Two groups: 37 who lost more than 1 lb in a month and 51 who lost only .5 to 1 lb in a month | The group who lost more weight had more diarrhea but less respiratory infections and fevers |

| | | | |
|---|---|---|---|
| Guzmán, Scrimshaw, Bruch, and Gordon (1968) Indian children studied from birth to 2 years of age (Guatemala) | Illness histories collected every 2 weeks. Information obtained about diarrhea, respiratory problems, and all other causes of disease | Growth rates in height and weight | No association between terciles of growth and frequency or extent of illness. No significant relationship between days of illness and growth |
| Mata, Urrutia, and Lechtig (1971) Forty-three Indian children followed from 0.5 to 3 years (Guatemala) | Weekly interviews of mothers. Incidence of various illnesses were recorded | Weight increments over a 2½ year period | There was no association between number of illnesses and growth rates in weight. The 10 best growers had significantly more dysentery but not more overall diarrhea than the 10 worst growers |
| Mata, Urrutia, Albertazzi, Pellecer, and Arellano (1972) Forty-five Indian children followed from birth to 6 months of age (Guatemala) | Weekly laboratory cultures. The sample was divided into high and low groups according to their enterovirus attack rates | Height and weight at 6 months of age | At 6 months, high and low groups were similar in height but different in weight by 140 gm (low group heavier) |
| Mardsen (1964) Ninety-five children followed from birth to 18 months (The Gambia) | Regular weekly and daily clinic; more reliance on examination than on interview of mother | Faltering in weight (a gain of less than .5 lb in 3 months) | Sixty-three percent of attacks of diarrhea and 14% of lower respiratory infections associated with weight faltering |
| Martorell et al. (1975a, 1975b) Seven hundred and sixteen Ladino children under 7 years of age studied for 23 months (Guatemala) | Illness histories collected every 2 weeks. Data were expressed as percentage of the time ill per semester of per year | Semestral and yearly increments in height and weight | Diarrheal diseases were related to weight and height gains. This finding was independent of potentially confounding factors. No relationship with fever and respiratory illness |

*Continued*

**TABLE 5.2—**Continued

| Source[b] | Illness variables | Growth variables | Conclusion |
|---|---|---|---|
| Morley, Woodland, and Martin (1966) Two hundred and thirty-two children (Nigeria) | Clinical diagnosis of whooping cough from an "under-5" clinic and hospital admissions | Weight gains | Whooping cough resulted in weight loss. Nearly 20% lost between 5 and 10% of their weight while 26% of the children took more than 2 and 15% more than 3 months to recover their weight |
| Morley, Bicknell, and Woodland (1968) One hundred and four children studied from birth to 12 months (Nigeria) | Regular monthly clinic and "under-5" irregular attendance clinic | Two groups: 52 children had weights below 10th percentile at 6, 9, or 12 months (Group A) and 52 children were always above the 50th percentile (Group B) | From 0–6 incidence of diarrhea was greater in Group A. From 6–12, whooping cough and measles greater in Group A. No difference in respiratory tract infections |
| Rowland et al. (1976) One hundred and fifty-two children, .6 to 3 years in age, studied for 19 months (The Gambia) | The children were examined approximately once a month and whenever they attended the clinic on account of illness. Data were expressed as percentage of the time ill with each of nine disease categories | Weight and height gains per month | Diarrhea was negatively related to growth in height and weight. Malaria was related to growth in weight but not in height. All other symptoms, including fever and symptoms, including fever and respiratory infections, were not |

[a] All samples are from the rural areas.
[b] The Guatemalan samples studied by Guzmán et al. (1968), Martorell et al. (1975a, 1975b), and Mata et al. (1971, 1972) were independent studies carried out in separate communities.

Differences in methodology may explain the results. The measurement of illness was more direct in developing countries and greater reliance in the studies done in wealthier nations on school records and on lengthy recall interviews with parents may have obscured existing associations. However, it may be that the findings reflect contrasting ecological settings. The disease load experienced by children in developed countries is light in comparison to that of malnourished populations. Another obvious difference is the superior nutritional status of children from developed nations. Perhaps no associations were evident in the wealthier countries because such children, with ample nutritional resources, quickly made up the losses which the infrequent episodes of illness may have caused.

The magnitude of the impact of illness on physical growth can be estimated from the results of studies carried out in four rural Guatemalan villages (Martorell et al., 1975a, 1975b). Children who were relatively free from diarrhea from birth to 7 years of age grew significantly better than children not so fortunate. The differences in growth at 7 years of age between both groups were 3.5 cm in height and 1.5 kg in weight. These differences are of large magnitude if we consider that 7-year-old children from such communities differ from well-nourished children from the United States by about 13 cm in height and 5 kg in weight.

In conclusion, common childhood illnesses in developing nations, particularly those syndromes involving diarrheal symptoms, have a profound negative impact on nutritional status. The vulnerability of malnourished children to infection is best illustrated by the fact that immunizations with live agents (BCG, smallpox, polio, DPT + polio), which are innocuous experiences to most well-nourished children, can lead to substantial weight loss, particularly in children less than 6 months of age or with a poor initial status (Kielman, 1977).

## Mechanisms for the Effect of Infection on Nutritional Status

Infection influences nutritional status through effects on appetite and on nutrient absorption and utilization as shown in Figure 5.1. This subject has been extensively discussed in the proceedings of a recent symposium published in the *American Journal of Clinical Nutrition* (1977). Perhaps the most significant impact of ordinary illnesses on nutritional status is its effect on appetite, an aspect so obvious that its full public health significance has not yet been recognized. While the effect of minor illnesses on dietary intake has been demonstrated in pregnant women (Lechtig et al., 1972) and in children (Mata et al., 1977a) in developing nations as well as in adult volunteers in the laboratory (Beisel, Sawyer, Ryll, & Crozier, 1967), it is impossible at this time to estimate the extent to which illness-induced anorexia rather than lack of food is responsible for the low dietary intakes in developing nations. For example, what is the full significance of the fact that over half of all children 3 years or less in rural Guatemala will be sick on any given day (Martorell *et al.*, 1976a)? Basic questions such as these await answering.

Another important consideration is the effect of cultural beliefs and practices on feeding of the ill, particularly as they interfere with the provision of liquids to children with severe diarrhea and vomiting. Nutrition education in this and other aspects of child and maternal nutrition is undoubtedly of great importance.

Illnesses also affect nutritional status by limiting the absorption of nutrients, therefore compounding the effects on appetite. Nutrient absorption may be limited by the so-called "intestinal hurry" of enteric disturbances: That is, the food does not remain in the gastro-intestinal tract long enough to be absorbed (Laughlin & Mullin, 1955). Diarrheal diseases are also accompanied by malabsorption of sugars, nitrogen, fats, and micronutrients (Rosenberg, Solomons, & Schneider, 1977).

Illnesses have profound effects on nutrient metabolism and utilization. A variety of infectious agents, including bacteria, ricketsia, and viruses, have been shown to produce similar but marked alterations in virtually all aspects of nutrient metabolism. The nature and sequence of these responses from the moment of exposure through the incubation phase and the febrile period to convalescence have been extensively studied by Beisel (1977). Foremost among the changes are the disturbances in protein metabolism. Infections bring about protein catabolism and, if the illness is severe and prolonged, lead to a depletion of the lean body mass stores. There are also urinary losses of the other major intracellular elements, potassium, magnesium, and phosphorus. Diarrhea and vomiting, if frequent and severe, will, of course, rapidly lead to electrolytic imbalance. Finally, parasitic diseases such as tapeworm and malaria utilize significant amounts of nutrients for their own growth and reproduction and thus compete with the host's needs.

## MALNUTRITION AND THE BODY'S MECHANISMS OF DEFENSE AGAINST INFECTION

The publication in 1968 of the World Health Organization monograph, *Interactions of nutrition and infection*, by Scrimshaw, Taylor, and Gordon motivated a great deal of research on the interrelationship between nutrition and infection. The proceedings of a recent workshop conference entitled "Malnutrition and the Immune Response" (Suskind, 1977) are an impressive testimonial to the progress achieved to date.

There is now enough evidence to demonstrate conclusively that malnutrition impairs the body's defense mechanisms. In fact, malnutrition must be regarded as the world's most prevalent immunodeficiency disease. A brief description of some of the principal defense mechanisms as well as summaries of the effects of malnutrition are provided in Table 5.3. These conclusions are derived from recent overviews of the field (Chandra, 1976; Chandra, 1977; Douglas & Schopfer, 1977; Edelman, 1977; Faulk, Pinto Paes, & Marigo, 1976; Katz & Stiehm, 1977; Neumann, 1977; Sirisinha, Suskind, Edelman, Kulapongs, & Olson, 1977).

One of the most significant findings is that malnutrition markedly depresses the integrity of the cell-mediated immune system while it hardly affects the humoral immune system. Therefore, the malnourished child is at a particular disadvantage against most viruses, mycobacteria, and protozoa, as well as against fungi (Edelman, 1977). This might explain why epidemiological studies have shown that the severity of measles, chicken pox, mumps, and rubella is greater in severely malnourished children (Salomón et al., 1968).

Another salient aspect of the research results is that maternal malnutrition may seriously impair the ability of the infant to respond to infections (Katz & Stiehm, 1977; Chandra, 1976). This may explain the already noted higher infant mortality rates for low-birthweight babies.

It should also be clarified that the term malnutrition, as used in the literature, refers to generalized deficiencies of protein and energy as well as vitamins and minerals. Few of the studies carried out permit the isolation of nutrient-specific effects. However, this is not critical as single nutrient deficiencies are the exception and not the rule in developing nations. More importantly, most of the studies on the interrelationship between nutrition and infection have been carried out in severely malnourished children while they were recuperating in clinics and hospitals (Katz & Stiehm, 1977). These children comprise only 3–5% of the population; little is known about the majority of children who suffer from mild and moderate malnutrition (Figure 5.3). Enough is known, however, to suggest that there is a gradient in immunocompetence from mild and moderate to severe malnutrition (Kielman, Uberoi, Chandra, & Mehra, 1976; Reddy, Jagadeesan, Ragharamulu, Bhaskaram, & Srikantia, 1976).

The results of a pioneering study conducted in India by Kielman et al. (1976) are shown in Table 5.4. Children from rural communities were divided into three groups according to whether body weight was above the fiftieth percentile, between the fiftieth and the tenth percentile, or below the tenth percentile of the weight for age local percentile distribution. A series of measures of immunocompetence were then evaluated including

**TABLE 5.3**

**Effects of Severe Malnutrition on Major Components of the Body's Defense System**

| Component | Nature and function | Summary of effects of malnutrition |
|---|---|---|
| Anatomic barriers | The skin and mucous membranes of the body constitute an important defense against infections. The secretions found in these surfaces contain bactericidal and fungicidal properties. In addition, the ciliated respiratory epithelium remove bacteria and debris. These substances are eventually swallowed and destroyed by gastric secretions | Malnutrition profoundly affects the integrity of body tissues. Deficiencies of vitamins A, B complex, C, protein, and zinc appear to be highly detrimental. Among the many effects that have been reported are (a) cells become keratinized; (b) breaks appear in membranes; (c) secretions are diminished; (d) loss of ciliated epithelium; and (e) poor wound healing |
| Cell-mediated immunity | T cells (thymus dependent) regulate B-cell functions and protect against infectious agents which enter the cells such as viruses and tubercle bacilli. T-cell effects include (a) the liberation of lymphokines after contact with specific antigens and (b) direct attack (by cyotoxic T cells) of antigens on the surface of foreign cells. Lymphokines are responsible for the delayed-type hypersensitivity reactions by attracting, retaining, and activitating uncommitted lymphocytes and phagocytes at the inflamatory site | Cell-mediated immunity is profoundly impaired in severe malnutrition. Among the effects found are (a) atrophy of tissues responsible for T-cell production (thymus gland and the thymic dependent areas of lymphoid tissue); (b) reduction of the number of T lymphocytes; (c) interference with lymphocyte transformation, a process whereby T cells become mature and sensitized to antigens and able to undergo mitosis; (d) reduction or absence of delayed hypersensitivity reaction |
| Serum immune system | B cells (thymus independent) are responsible for antibody production (IgG, IgM, IgA, IgD, IgE). Antibodies perform at least three functions: (a) neutralization of bacterial toxins and viruses; (b) participation with complement in the direct killing of microorganisms; and (c) preparation of microbial cell surfaces to promote efficient phagocytosis | Serum immunity is remarkably resistant to the effects of malnutrition. The major findings are (a) normal number of B lymphocytes; (b) normal or elevated levels of immunoglobulins; and (c) generally adequate antibody responses to immunizations |
| Secretory immune system | Secretory IgA is present in seromucous secretions such as saliva, tears, nasal fluids, and secretions of the lung and gastrointestinal tract. It plays an important role in the local defense system of these surfaces. Secretory IgA is also found in breast milk | Secretory IgA, relative to total protein or albumin content, appears to be reduced in malnutrition |

TABLE 5.3—*Continued*

| Component | Nature and function | Summary of effects of malnutrition |
|---|---|---|
| Complement system | The plasma proteins known as complement interact with certain antibody molecules once these have combined with antigen. The combination of complement to the antigen–antibody complex is lethal, the complement apparently damaging the cell wall and killing the bacterium by catabolic enzyme activity | Most complement component levels are reduced in malnutrition. Function may also be affected as suggested by reduced hemolytic complement activity |
| Phagocytosis | Phagocytosis is the ingestion of a particle or an entire cell (i.e., a microorganism) by a cell. The cells which perform this function are collectively termed phagocytes and include the polymorphonuclear leukocytes (PMN), the monocytes, and the macrophages. In addition, macrophages serve the function of stimulating antibody production by passing on antigens to the lymphoid cells | Phagocyte function appears to be largely unaffected by malnutrition. Some reports suggest delays in the migratory response of PMNs (chemotaxis) and defects in the bactericidal properties of phagocytes |

aspects of cellular immunity, as measured by means of postvaccinal (BCG) tuberculin sensitivity and of humoral immune response, as measured by tetanus antibody production following DPT vaccination and by IgA, IgG, and IgM level determinations. Complement $C_3$ levels were also determined. Both the specific antibody response to tetanus immunization as well as IgG and IgM levels were unrelated to variations in weight for age, confirming the findings that the humoral immune system is less affected by malnutrition. However, a gradient with nutritional status was shown for cellular-mediated immunity, IgA, and $C_3$ levels as shown in Table 5.4. The existence of this gradient in turn provides a mechanism for a similar gradient between malnutrition and mortality (Puffer & Serrano, 1973; Sommer & Loewenstein, 1975).

## POLICY IMPLICATIONS

The interplay between low dietary intakes and infectious disease has been shown to affect nutritional status through the mechanisms outlined in Figure

**TABLE 5.4**

Immune Capacity According to Categories of Nutritional Status[a]

| | Weight for age categories, local percentiles | | | | | | | | | Comparisons between extremes | |
| | ≥50 | | | 10-50 | | | ≤10 | | | | |
| | N | X̄ | SD | N | X̄ | SD | N | X̄ | SD | t | p |
|---|---|---|---|---|---|---|---|---|---|---|---|
| Increment of induration after tuberculin sensitivity test[b,c] | 77 | 5.5 | 5.1 | 74 | 5.1 | 5.1 | 44 | 3.6 | 4.5 | 2.11 | <.05 |
| IgA levels (%)[d] | 19 | 120.9 | 60.9 | 19 | 111.4 | 49.5 | 15 | 102.6 | 59.5 | 0.88 | n.s. |
| Complement (C₃) (%)[d] | 19 | 62.8 | 21.0 | 19 | 67.1 | 20.9 | 15 | 46.0 | 15.5 | 2.68 | <.05 |

[a] Adapted from Kielman, A. A., Uberoi, I. S., Chandra, R. K., and Mehra, V. L. The effect of nutritional status on immune capacity and immune responses in preschool children in a rural community in India. *Bulletin of the World Health Organization*, 1976, *54*, 477–482.

[b] Day 235 minus Day 0. Data derived from Kielman *et al.* (1976), Table 1, p. 479.

[c] Percentage of children demonstrating a positive response (induration greater than 6 mm) was 84, 72, and 61%, respectively, for the three categories of weight for age.

[d] Expressed as a percentage of the levels found in the control population. This was made up of children of the same age from the United States. The data for IgA are derived from Kielman *et al.* (1976), Table 4, p. 480, that for C₃ are from Table 5, p. 481. IgA levels are higher in all three groups studied than in the control population. This reflects a greater exposure to infection in rural India.

5.1. Some of the implications of a deficient nutritional status have already been noted, namely, increased risk of infection and mortality. It has also been pointed out that malnutrition leads to physical growth retardation, in fact the former is often measured by the latter.

Other effects not covered in this chapter but of great importance include the effects on mental development and on work performance (Read, 1977). Berg (1973) has evaluated the economic implications of these effects and concluded that malnutrition must be regarded as a major obstacle to national socioeconomic development.

The nutrition and health problems of the poor nations of the world are not unlike those that existed a century ago in the industrialized nations of Europe and North America (Aykroyd, 1971). These problems gradually disappeared as the standard of living improved and certainly long before vaccines and antibiotics were widely used. There is a simple lesson to be learned from this experience. The magnitude of the health and nutrition problems of the poor nations cannot be substantially decreased in the absence of effective measures for the eradication of poverty. One must not be misled into thinking that the direct application of knowledge or technology in a few key instances is all that is needed for a final solution, such as in the case of smallpox, where effective vaccination programs may finally lead to the eradication of the disease. This is not to say, however, that knowledge of the causes and effects of malnutrition and disease should not be applied directly toward the solution of such problems, only that they are not, by themselves, enough.

There is much in this chapter that has policy implications for health and nutrition planning in developing nations. There are, however, two aspects that appear to be salient. The first has to do with the relative importance of protein and energy as limiting nutrients in the dietary intakes of developing countries. The current assessment of the problem indicates that the lack of food per se rather than the quality of the food is the most important problem. Past strategies which concentrated on quality aspects such as the genetic modification of cereals to alter the amino acid composition or the development and distribution of expensive high-protein foods were probably not the most appropriate. Instead, higher priority should go to policies aiming to increase consumption of the usual foods but not necessarily through food supplementation programs. As the staples in most cultures are cereals, high in bulk and moderately low in energy density, the question arises as to whether young children can possibly satisfy their relatively high needs with the usual diets. Surprisingly little research on this question has been carried out to date. Similarly, the extent to which the bulk problem would be alleviated by moderate amounts of oil is also unknown. It may turn out that the vegetable protein mixes elaborated to combat protein malnutrition, such as Incaparina, which also have high-energy densities, may prove to be the most adequate weaning foods. For rural populations with restricted cash incomes, emphasis on home prepared weaning foods would seem more appropriate.

The second issue with vast policy implications is intimately related to the first. Infectious disease may well be one of the most important causes of low food consumption and a direct cause of malnutrition. Not only environmental sanitation but health and nutritional education should receive high priority. In particular, the customs and practices during weaning should be examined and modified to reduce the risk of infection. In view of the fact that most developing nations face severe resource constraints, higher priority should go to the most cost-effective programs. It is therefore highly unlikely that food supplementation programs, which are generally very expensive and never a long-term solution, should take precedence over investments in environmental sanitation and health and nutritional education.

## REFERENCES

Aykroyd, W. R. Nutrition and mortality in infancy and early childhood: Past and present relationships. *American Journal of Clinical Nutrition*, 1971, *24*, 480–487.

Bailey, K. V. Quantity and composition of breast milk in some New Guinean populations. *Journal of Tropical Pediatrics*, 1965, *11*, 35–49.

Beisel, W. R., Sawyer, W. D., Ryll, E. D., & Crozier, D. Metabolic effects of intracellular infections in man. *Annals of Internal Medicine*, 1967, *67*, 744–779.

Beisel, W. R. Magnitude of the host nutritional responses to infection. *American Journal of Clinical Nutrition*, 1977, *30*, 1236–1247.

Bengoa, J. M. Significance of malnutrition and priorities for its prevention. In A. Berg, N. S. Scrimshaw, & D. L. Call (Eds.), *Nutrition, national development, and planning.* Cambridge, Mass.: MIT Press, 1973. Pp. 103–128.

Berg, A. *The nutrition factor: Its role in national development.* Washington, D.C.: Brookings Institution, 1973.

Chandra, R. K. Nutrition as a critical determinant in susceptibility to infection. *World Review of Nutrition and Dietetics*, 1976, *25*, 166–188.

Chandra, R. K. Immunoglobulins and antibody response in protein–calorie malnutrition: A review. In R. M. Suskind (Ed.), *Malnutrition and the immune response.* New York: Raven Press, 1977. Pp. 155–168.

Chase, H. C. Infant mortality and weight at birth: 1960—United States with cohort. *American Journal of Public Health*, 1969, *59*, 1618–1628.

Cole, T. J., & Parkin, J. M. Infection and its effect on the growth of young children: A comparison of the Gambia and Uganda. *Transactions of the Royal Society of Tropical Medicine and Hygiene*, 1977, *71*, 196–198.

Condon-Paoloni, D., Cravioto, J., Johnston, F. E., de Licardie, E. R., & Scholl, T. O. Morbidity and growth of infants and young children in a rural Mexican village. *American Journal of Public Health*, 1977, *67*, 651–656.

Delgado, H. L., Lechtig, A., Yarbrough, C., Martorell, R., Klein, R. E., & Irwin, M. Maternal nutrition: Its effects on infant growth and development and birthspacing. In K. S.

Moghissi & T. N. Evans (Eds.), *Nutritional impact on women throughout life with emphasis on reproduction*. New York: Harper & Row, 1977. Pp. 133–150.

División de Desarrollo Humano. Nutrición, crecimiento y desarrollo. *Boletín de la Oficina Sanitaria Panamericana*, 1975, *LXXVIII*, 38–51.

Douglas, S. D., & Schopfer, K. The phagocyte in protein-calorie malnutrition: A review. In R. M. Suskind (Ed.), *Malnutrition and the immune response*. New York: Raven Press, 1977. Pp. 231–243.

Draper, K. C., & Draper, C. C. Observations on the growth of African infants: With special reference to the effects of malaria control. *Journal of Tropical Medicine and Hygiene*, 1960, *63*, 165–171.

Edelman, R. Cell-mediated immune response in protein–calorie malnutrition: A review. In R. M. Suskind (Ed.), *Malnutrition and the immune response*. New York: Raven Press, 1977. Pp. 47–75.

Edozien, J. C. Malnutrition in Africa: need and basis for action. In P. György & O. L. Kline (Eds.), *Malnutrition is a problem of ecology*. Basel: Karger, 1970. Pp. 64–71.

Evans, M. E. Illness history and physical growth. II. A comparative study of the rate of growth of preschool children of five health classes. *American Journal of Diseases of Children*, 1944, *68*, 390–394.

Faulk, W. P., Pinto Paes, R., & Marigo, C. The immunological system in health and nutrition. *Proceedings of the Nutrition Society*, 1976, *35*, 253–261.

FAO/WHO Report. *Expert group on calcium requirements*. FAO Nutrition Meetings Report Series No. 30. WHO Technical Report Series No. 230, 1962.

FAO/WHO Report. *Expert group on requirements of vitamin A, thiamine, riboflavine and niacin*. FAO Nutrition Meetings Report Series No. 41. WHO Technical Report Series No. 362, 1967.

FAO/WHO Report. *Expert group on requirements of ascorbic acid, vitamin D, vitamin $B_{12}$, folate and iron*. FAO Nutrition Meetings Report Series No. 47. WHO Technical Report Series No. 452, 1970.

FAO/WHO Report. *Expert group on energy and protein requirements*. FAO Nutrition Meetings Report Series No. 52. WHO Technical Report Series No. 522, 1973.

Freij, L., & Wall, S. Exploring child health and its ecology. The Kirkos study in Addis Ababa. *Acta Paediatrica Scandinavica* 1977 (Suppl.) No. 263.

Gómez, F., Ramos Galván, R., Frenk, S., Cravioto, J., Chávez, R., & Vásquez, J. Mortality in second and third degree malnutrition. *Journal of Tropical Pediatrics*, 1956, *2*, 77–83.

Gopalan, C. Studies in lactation in poor Indian communities. *Journal of Tropical Pediatrics*, 1956, *2*, 77–83.

Gopalan, C. Studies in lactation in poor Indian communities. *Journal of Tropical Pediatrics*, 1958, *4*, 87–97.

Gopalan, C. Kwashiorkor and marasmus: Evolution and distinguishing features. In R. A. McCance & E. M. Widdowson (Eds.), *Calorie deficiencies and protein deficiencies*. Boston: Little, Brown, 1968. Pp. 49–58.

Gordon, J. E., Chitkara, L. D., & Wyon, J. B. Weanling diarrhoea. *American Journal of Medical Sciences*, 1963, *245*, 345–377.

Gordon, J. E., Wyon, J. B., & Ascoli, W. The second year death rate in less developed countries. *American Journal of Medical Sciences*, 1967, *254*, 357–380.

Guzmán, M. A., Scrimshaw, N. S., Bruch, H. A., & Gordon, J. E. Nutrition and infection field study in Guatemalan villages, 1959–1964. IIV. Physical growth and development of preschool children. *Archives of Environmental Health*, 1968, *17*, 107–118.

Hardy, M. C. Frequent illness in childhood, physical growth and final size. *American Journal of Physical Anthropology*, 1938, *23*, 241–246.

Hewitt, D., Westropp, D. K., & Acheson, R. M. Oxford child health survey: Effect of childish ailments on skeletal development. *British Journal of Preventive and Social Medicine*, 1955, *9*, 179–186.

Hytten, F. E., & Leitch, I. *The physiology of human pregnancy* (2nd ed.). Oxford: Blackwell, 1971.

INCAP/ICNND. *Nutritional evaluation of the population of Central America and Panama*. Regional Summary. DHEW Publication No. (HSM) 72–8120. Washington, D. C., 1972.

Jelliffe, D. B. *The assessment of the nutritional status of the community*. 1966, No. 53. World Health Organization Monograph Series.

Jelliffe, D. B., & Jelliffe, E. F. P. (Eds.). The uniqueness of human milk. *American Journal of Clinical Nutrition*, 1971, *24*, 968–969.

Jelliffe, E. F., & Jelliffe, D. B. The arm circumference as a public health index of protein-calorie malnutrition of early childhood. (1) Background. *Journal of Tropical Pediatrics*, 1969, *15*, 179–188.

Katz, M., & Stiehm, E. R. Host defense in malnutrition. *Pediatrics*, 1977, *59*, 490–495.

Keller, W., Donoso, G., & DeMaeyer, E. M. Anthropometry in nutritional surveillance: Review based on results of the WHO collaborative study on nutritional anthropometry. *Nutrition Abstracts and Reviews*, 1976, *46*, 591–609.

Kielman, A. A. Weight fluctuations after immunization in a rural preschool child community. *American Journal of Clinical Nutrition*, 1977, *30*, 592–598.

Kielman, A. A., Uberoi, I. S., Chandra, R. K., & Mehra, V. L. The effect of nutritional status on immune capacity and immune responses in preschool children in a rural community in India. *Bulletin of the World Health Organization*, 1976, *54*, 477–483.

Kubát, K., Kourim, J., Nováhová, M. Moderová, M., & Stloukalová, M. The relation of acute morbidity in preschool age to the weight and height in six years old children. *Ceskoslovenská Pediatrie*, 1971, *26*, 105–106.

Lechtig, A., Delgado, H., Lasky, R. E., Yarbrough, C., Martorell, R., Habicht, J-P., & Klein, R. E. Effect of improved nutrition during pregnancy and lactation on developmental retardation and infant mortality. In P. L. White & N. Selvey (Eds.), *Proceedings of the Western Hemisphere Nutrition Congress IV, 1974*. Acton, Mass.: Publishing Sciences Group Inc., 1975. Pp. 117–125. (a)

Lechtig, A., Habicht, J-P., Delgado, H., Klein, R. E., Yarbrough, C., & Martorell, R. Effect of food supplementation during pregnancy on birth weight. *Pediatrics*, 1975, *56*, 508–520. (b)

Lechtig, A., Habicht, J-P., Guzmán, G. G., & de León, E. Morbilidad materna y crecimiento fetal en poblaciones rurales de Guatemala. *Archivos Latinoamericanos de Nutrición*, 1972, *22*, 243–253.

Lechtig, A., Martorell, R., Delgado, H., Yarbrough, C., & Klein, R. E. Effect of morbidity during pregnancy on birth weight in a rural Guatemalan population. *Ecology of Food and Nutrition*, 1976, *5*, 225–233.

Loughlin, E. H., & Mullin, W. G. Certain aspects of deficiency diseases of the tropics and treatment of some related infections. *Annals of the New York Academy of Sciences*, 1955, *63*, 276.

Mardsen, P. D. The Sukuta project. A longitudinal study of health in Gambian children from birth to 18 months of age. *Transactions of the Royal Society of Tropical Medicine and Hygiene*, 1964, *58*, 455–489.

Martens, E. J., & Meredith, H. V. Illness history and physical growth. I. Correlation in junior primary children followed from fall to spring. *American Journal of Diseases of Children*, 1942, *64*, 618–630.

Martorell, R., Habicht, J-P., Yarbrough, C., Lechtig, A., & Klein, R. E. Underreporting in fortnightly recall morbidity surveys. *Journal of Tropical Pediatrics*, 1976, *22*, 129–134. (a)

Martorell, R., Habicht, J-P., Yarbrough, C., Lechtig, A., Klein, R. E., & Western, K. A. Acute morbidity and physical growth in rural Guatemalan children. *American Journal of Diseases of Children*, 1975, *129*, 1296–1301. (a)

Martorell, R., Lechtig, A., Yarbrough, C., Delgado, H., & Klein, R. E. Protein–calorie supplementation and postnatal physical growth: A review of findings from developing countries. *Archivos Latinoamericanos de Nutrición*, 1976, *26*, 115–128. (b)

Martorell, R., Yarbrough, C., Lechtig, A., Habicht, J-P., & Klein, R. E. Diarrheal diseases and growth retardation in preschool Guatemalan children. *American Journal of Physical Anthropology*, 1975, *43*, 341–346. (b)

Mata, L. J., Kronmal, R. A., Urrutia, J. J., & Garcia, B. Effect of infection on food intake and the nutritional state: Perspectives as viewed from the village. *American Journal of Clinical Nutrition*, 1977, *30*, 1215–1227. (a)

Mata, L. J., Urrutia, J. J., Albertazzi, C., Pellecer, O., & Arellano, E. Influence of recurrent infections on nutrition and growth of children of Guatemala. *American Journal of Clinical Nutrition*, 1972, *25*, 1267–1275.

Mata, L. J., Urrutia, J. J., & Lechtig, A. Infection and nutrition of children of a low socioeconomic rural community. *American Journal of Clinical Nutrition*, 1971, *24*, 249–259.

Mata, L., Urrutia, J. J., Serrato, G., Mohs, E., & Chin, T. D. Y. Viral infections during pregnancy and in early life. *American Journal of Clinical Nutrition*, 1977, *30*, 1834–1842. (b)

McCammon, R. W. *Human growth and development*. Springfield, Ill.: Charles C Thomas, 1970.

Meredith, H. V., & Knott, V. B. Illness history and physical growth. III. Comparative anatomic status and rate of change for schoolchildren in different long-term health categories. *American Journal of Diseases of Children*, 1962, *103*, 146–151.

Morley, D. Severe measles in the tropics. *British Medical Journal*, 1969, *1*, 297–300.

Morley, D., Bicknell, J., & Woodland, M. Factors influencing the growth and nutritional status of infants and young children in a Nigerian village. *Transactions of the Royal Society of Tropical Medicine and Hygiene*, 1968, *62*, 164–195.

Morley, D., Woodland, M., & Martin, W. J. Whooping cough in Nigerian children. *Tropical and Geographical Medicine*, 1966, *18*, 169–182.

Newmann, C. G. Nonspecific host factors and infection in malnutrition: A review. In R. M. Suskind (Ed.), *Malnutrition and the immune response*. New York: Raven Press, 1977. Pp. 355–374.

PAHO *Maternal nutrition and family planning in the Americas*. Report No. 204, 1970.

Palmer, C. E. The relation of body build to sickness in elementary school children. *American Journal of Physical Anthropology* (Supplement), 1936, *21*, 7–8.

Payne, P. R. Safe protein–calorie ratios in diets. The relative importance of protein and energy intake as causal factors in malnutrition. *American Journal of Clinical Nutrition*, 1975, *28*, 281–286.

Pitt, J. Breast milk leukocytes. *Pediatrics*, 1976, *58*, 769–770.

Puffer, R. R., & Serrano, C. V. *Patterns of mortality in childhood*. Report of the Inter-American Investigation of Mortality in Childhood. Scientific Publication Series No. 262. Washington, D. C.: Pan American Health Organization, 1973.

Rao, K. S., Swaminatham, M. C., Swarup, S., & Patwardhan, V. N. Protein malnutrition in South India. *Bulletin of the World Health Organization*, 1959, *20*, 603–639.

Read, M. S. Malnutrition and human performance. In L. S. Greene (Ed.), *Malnutrition, behavior, and social organization*. New York: Academic Press, 1977. Pp. 95–107.

Reddy, V., Jagadeesan, V., Ragharamulu, N., Bhaskaram, C., & Srikantia, S. G. Functional significance of growth retardation in malnutrition. *American Journal of Clinical Malnutrition*, 1976, *29*, 3–7.

Rosenberg, I. H., Solomons, N. W., & Schneider, R. E. Malabsorption associated with diarrhea and intestinal infections. *American Journal of Clinical Nutrition*, 1977, *30*, 1248–1253.

Rowland, M. G. M., Cole, T. J., & Whitehead, R. G. A quantitative study into the role of infection in determining nutritional status in Gambian village children. *British Journal of Nutrition*, 1977, *37*, 441–450.

Salomón, J. B., Mata, L. J., & Gordon, J. E. Malnutrition the common communicable diseases of childhood in rural Guatemala. *American Journal of Health*, 1968, *58*, 505–516.

Scrimshaw, N. S. Through a glass darkly: Discerning the practical implications of human dietary protein–energy interrelationships. *Nutrition Reviews*, 1977, *35*, 321–337.

Scrimshaw, N. S., Taylor, C. E., & Gordon, J. E. *Interactions of nutrition and infection*. World Health Organization Monograph Series, No. 57, 1968.

Sirisinha, S., Suskind, R. M., Edelman, R., Kulapongs, P., & Olson, R. E. The complement system in protein–calorie malnutrition: A review. In R. M. Suskind (Ed.), *Malnutrition and the immune response*. New York: Raven Press, 1977. Pp. 309–320.

Sommer, A., & Loewenstein, M. S. Nutritional status and mortality: A prospective validation of the QUAC stick. *American Journal of Clinical Nutrition*, 1975, *28*, 287–292.

Stiehm, E. R. Biology of immunoglobulins: Humoral and secretory: A review. In R. M. Suskind (Ed.), *Malnutrition and the immune response*. New York: Raven Press, 1977. Pp. 141–154.

Sukhatme, P. V. The protein problem, its size and nature. *Journal of the Royal Statistical Society*, 1974, *137*, 166–191.

Suskind, R. M. (Ed.). *Malnutrition and the immune response*. New York: Raven Press, 1977.

Turner, C. E., Longee, W. W., Saravia, K., & Fuller, R. P. Rate of growth as a health index. *Research Quarterly*, 1935, *6*, 29–40.

Valadian, I., Reed, R. B., Stuart, H. C., Burke, B. S., Pyle, S. I., & Cornoni, J. C. *Interrelationships between protein intake, illness, and growth as manifested by children followed from birth to 18 years*. Unpublished manuscript.

Valverde, V., Arroyave, G., & Flores, M. Revisión del aporte calórico y proteinico de las dietas de poblaciones de bajo nivel socioeconómico en Centroamérica. Existe un problema de proteinas? *Archivos Latinoamericanos de Nutrición*, 1975, *25*, 327–349.

WHO *Nutrition in pregnancy and lactation*. WHO Technical Report Series No. 302, 1965.

# Part III

## BENIGN NEGLECT

# 6

# Benign Neglect and Toddler Malnutrition

## CLAIRE MONOD CASSIDY

## INTRODUCTION

The purpose of this chapter is to introduce the concept of *benign neglect*[1] as a way of gaining perspective on the relationships between weaning customs and the development of malnutrition[2] in toddlers. Many weaning customs of nonindustrialized peoples potentiate malnutrition. Classified by culture change agents as "harmful," these customs are frequently the targets of reeducation projects. The success of such projects is, however, typically no

---

[1]The phrase "benign neglect" was used by Patrick Moynihan in a memo to President Nixon (1970) in an entirely different context, but has fallen into disuse. The present use and Moynihan's use should not be confused. Ideas similar to but not identical with my concept of benign neglect have been expressed by Hegsted (1972), Rosenberg ("attenuated infanticide," 1973), Prugh and Harlow ("masked deprivation," 1966), and Gokulanathan and Verghese ("socio-cultural malnutrition," 1969). For a definition of my use, see pp. 129–130.

[2]The term malnutrition has been used many ways. Properly it includes the states of deficient or excessive energy intake, and the unbalanced intake of nutrients. Both clinical and subclinical states of malnutrition can be distinguished. Although malnourishment traceable to deficiency or excess of single nutrients is known, most cases of naturally occurring malnutrition demonstrate multiple imbalances. In this chapter, because I am attempting to draw generalizations and not describing clinical data, I shall use the term *malnutrition* in its commonest broad sense as deficient intake of energy and/or nutrients.

*Social and Biological Predictors of*
*Nutritional Status, Physical Growth,*
*and Neurological Development*

more than moderate; users of the customs (toddlers' parents and primary caretakers) tend to persist in employing them.

This situation presents a paradox: It seems puzzling as to why parents who otherwise demonstrate signs of concern and affection for children should "insist" on practicing customs which produce a deleterious result. This apparent contradiction can be resolved through the use of the concept of benign neglect. Though practicing "harmful" customs is "neglectful" as interpreted by nutrition workers, it is "benign" from the parental perspective because parents do not intend to cause malnutrition (furthermore, they typically do not conceptualize such a disorder). Instead, they practice the customs because they form part of the traditional ways in which the child becomes a recognizable and "normal" member of the social group, and by which the social group maintains its distinctive character generation after generation. Hence the practice of these customs is actually fundamentally *benevolent*, because parents are showing that they are concerned with the welfare of both the group and the child. Malnutrition is accordingly a secondary, indirect, often accidental *effect* of actions whose actual goal is to delineate and enhance social membership. These customs also act as indirect population control and (probably) physiological adaptive mechanisms.

The concept of benign neglect permits customs considered "harmful" from a conventional biomedical (etic[3]) perspective to be recognized as "not harmful" within other contexts, particularly the cultural (emic[3]). The phrase benign neglect is selected to remind the user of this emic–etic (insider–outsider) discontinuity, and the conflict of interpretation it represents. Through its use the culture change agent is encouraged to achieve a more accurate, sympathetic, and ultimately more effective approach to nutrition intervention.

In this chapter I shall selectively review customs which potentiate malnutrition, detailing (where known) both their emically perceived purposes and their emically and etically observed effects. I shall then briefly review other interpretations of parental motive besides that conceptualized as benign neglect, and will consider the utility of the concept of benign neglect for nutrition intervention.

---

[3]Emic and etic are terms used by anthropologists to signify interpretation, respectively, from the insider's or outsider's position. The terms were coined by Pike (1967) and defined by Harris (1968) as follows: "Emic statements refer to logico-empirical systems whose phenomenal distinctions or 'things' are built up out of contrasts and discriminations significant, meaningful, real, accurate, or in some other fashion regarded as appropriate by the actors themselves [p. 571]." "Etic statements depend upon phenomenal distinctions judged appropriate by the community of scientific observers [p. 575]."

## THE PERIOD OF TODDLERHOOD

I shall consider as the period of *toddlerhood* the months 13–48 or the second–fourth years of life. The relatively brief time during which actual weaning from the breast takes place within this period is the "circum-weaning" period, and children of this age group are "weanlings."

The period of toddlerhood is peculiarly difficult both psychologically and physiologically. Toddlers must master many new tasks in a brief time if they are to be accepted as "normal" by their communities. For example, they must simultaneously learn to walk, talk, switch from an infant to a more adult diet, and respond appropriately to many social requirements not made upon infants. Most important and most difficult, they must break the close infant–maternal bond and separate physically and psychically from their mothers or primary caretakers. These requirements, combined with their immaturity, represent a severe stress. In addition, their rapid rate of growth produces particularly high nutrient and energy needs, while their increased mobility exposes them to many "new" pathogens to which they are vulnerable owing to loss of infantile passive immunity.

That toddlers frequently experience difficulty in adaptation is demonstrated among individuals by high frequencies of psychological malfunction, and in populations by high mortality and morbidity rates characteristic of the age period. For example, in developed areas toddler mortality rates average 15% of the infant rates, and in underdeveloped areas approximate 50% (Gordon, Wyon, & Ascoli, 1967). The second year (13–24 months) is the most difficult. The rates for malnutrition and infection peak (Gordon *et al.*, 1967), and the proportion dying matches or exceeds the total dying in the following 3 years (Puffer & Serrano, 1973). Ethnographic data also suggest that in the second year signs of psychological malfunction are commonest. Many societies recognize how difficult it is for children to make the required adjustments of toddlerhood. Their struggles may be viewed with pity (e.g., Maretski & Maretski, 1963; Nydegger & Nydegger, 1963) or with impatience. Among the Nyansongo (Kenya), "The word for weaning . . . is *ogotacha* which literally means to stamp on or to step on. The painful aspect of the weaning process for the child is thus explicitly conceptualized [LeVine & LeVine, 1963, p. 149]."

A certain amount of stress is imposed by the developing child's physiological needs and the character of its physical environment, and is associated with making the transition from wholly dependent infant to somewhat independent child. Factors such as unsanitary environment and inappropriate weanling diet can raise this stress load significantly above the minimum. Similarly weaning does not take place in a social vacuum, but amid a welter of child-care customs, expectations, habits, and beliefs, the ultimate function of which is to produce culturally normal children and adults. Some of these may ease physically and physiologically imposed stress; others may exacerbate it.

As weaning stress rises, the likelihood that the child will experience some form of sickness, even as slight as anorexia, also rises, and with it the probability that the child will experience malnutrition. Thus the occurrence and severity of toddler malnutrition is closely linked to the severity of stress the child encounters during weaning.[4] In this context any customs which potentiate weaning stress also potentiate malnutrition.


## CUSTOMS THAT POTENTIATE MALNUTRITION

There are many customs that potentiate malnutrition (perhaps particularly among nonindustrialized peoples), although no one society practices all of them. Many are familiar to culture change agents who designate them "harmful" (cf. Jelliffe, 1957; Jelliffe & Jelliffe, 1976). They may frequently be discovered by looking at the rules surrounding the provision of the toddler diet, and at other behavior patterns aimed at modifying toddler activity toward the adult pattern, such as the means used to encourage the severance of the maternal–infant bond. All potentiate malnutrition by limiting toddler access to the food supply, either *indirectly,* by (*a*) permitting or encouraging caretakers and toddlers to engage in interpersonal relationships which exacerbate the already high psychological stress of weaning, or *directly*, by permitting or encouraging (*b*) the imposition of dietary restrictions and (*c*) food competition between age and sex groups (Table 6.1).

The examples which follow are representative selections from the ethnographic and nutrition literature. No attempt is made to review weaning customs worldwide or to summarize all customs which potentiate malnutrition, however, every custom or activity pattern selected for discussion is both "harmful" from a biomedical perspective and "normal," "traditional," or

[4]There are many correlates of toddler malnutrition in addition to the customs discussed herein, all of which can be conceptualized as increasing the stress load the toddler must bear. Briefly summarized, malnutrition is most common in children of malnourished mothers (Petros-Barvazian, 1970); demonstrating diminished reactivity and responsiveness (Pollitt, 1973); with infections (Jelliffe, 1957; Scrimshaw, Taylor, & Gordon, 1968); from impoverished homes or communities (Galle, Gove, & McPherson, 1972; Jelliffe, 1957; Pollitt, 1973; Puffer & Serrano, 1973; Ward, 1975); of late birth order, of older mothers, of large families, or of close age to the next sibling (Christiansen, Mora, & Herrera, 1975; Gordon *et al.*, 1967; Grant, 1964; Petros-Barvazian, 1970; Puffer & Serrano, 1973); whose diet is inappropriate (Okeahuialam, 1975; Pollitt, 1973); whose access to food is limited by certain child-care customs; and who are rejected or unwanted. The last two items are covered in the body of the chapter.

TABLE 6.1

Expressions of Benign Neglect during the Toddler Years

Exacerbation of psychological stress during weaning
    Arrival of new infant when toddler is 24 months of age or less
    Abrupt weaning, with or without enforced maternal separation
    Expectation of mature behavior and punishment for dependent behavior
    Deviation of attention to sibling of culturally preferred sex
Food restriction
    Concept of the "good" diet
    Food taboos
    Dietary adjustments during illness
Food competition
    With elders, siblings, and caretakers
    With persons of culturally preferred sex

"customary" from a sociocultural perspective, hence illustrative of the concept of benign neglect (which will be more fully defined in the following section). For the inevitable somewhat anecdotal effect this approach entails, I apologize. The analysis of the examples is frequently frustrated by the fact that while enthnographic studies describe weaning customs in great detail, they rarely consider their nutritional impact, and while nutrition studies discuss nutritional effects at length, they usually do not consider customs in a cultural context. Some of the more recent studies, aware of these limitations, provide the most integrated information.

## Exacerbation of Psychological Stress during Weaning

Psychological stress is always present in the weaning period because the immature toddler must quickly master a large number of difficult tasks if it is to be accepted as "normal" by its society. Most difficult to accomplish is the severance of the maternal–infant bond, both physically (weaning from the breast) and psychically (weaning from constant attention).

### Maternal Deprivation Syndrome

The infant–maternal bond is that affectionate and nurturant relationship (usually called "loving") between primary caretaker and child which is established early in life. It has been shown to be necessary not only for normal psychosocial development but also for maintainence of life itself (Bowlby, 1951, 1973; Prugh & Harlow, 1966). Even brief severance of this bond in the first 2 years of life causes great distress to the child, who reacts—as if it believed itself rejected ("unloved")—with a series of symptoms which have been termed "maternal deprivation syndrome" (Bowlby, 1951). These symptoms are most likely to develop if separation is sudden, and if it occurs between the sixth and twenty-fourth month of life (when the child is old enough to recognize its special relationship to its primary caretaker, but too immature to do without her or him comfortably). More severe reactions occur when separation is prolonged or when the maternal–infant relationship in the first year of life has been particularly close.

Early symptoms of separation stress are usually weeping and temper tantrums. If separation lasts more than a few hours or days, insomnia, anorexia, weight loss, increased susceptibility to infection, and withdrawal from human contact may ensue in a fairly predictable sequence lasting several weeks or months. This sequence culminates in adaptation of the child to its new position in life, in maladaptation with the development of an abnormal personality, or in death (Bowlby, 1951; Rohner, 1975). Death, usually proximally from malnutrition (specifically marasmus), may occur even when the offered diet is entirely adequate. This syndrome has been described in institutionalized and abandoned children (Bowlby, 1951; Widdowson, 1951 quoted in Harrison, Weiner, Tanner, & Barnicot, 1964), in children who are less preferred among their siblings in intact households (the "masked deprivation" of Prugh & Harlow, 1966), and as part of the normal weaning process in many societies worldwide (Rohner, 1975).

While most children react as if they believe they were rejected, parents may or may not actually feel they have rejected their child. It is important to recognize this distinction, because it affects not only the severity of toddler symptoms and thus the probability that the child will suffer permanent sequelae, but also the proper interpretation of parental motive. Rohner (1975) discusses a continuum from affection to rejection and makes a useful distinction between parental rejection, that is more or less constant and can therefore be expected to have major maladaptive effects on psychological development (seen, for example, among the Alorese, Ik) and rejection that is associated with specific events of child-rearing, is therefore only occasional, and is much less likely to cause long-term psychological damage. The latter form of occasional rejection Rohner terms "molecular." It is apparently extremely common worldwide, especially during the toddler years.

While molecular rejection at weaning may have few psychopathological sequelae, it can have considerable effect on physical development by making malnutrition more likely. In this respect molecular rejection may be very important to the future of the child, and therefore the customs that explain instances of molecular rejection deserve our attention. However, in none of the cases which follow was quantification of the effect of maternal deprivation provided. We are thus forced to depend upon Western biomedical descriptions of rejected children for assurance that these examples of psychological stress at weaning, encouraged by specific parental habits and attitudes, are capable of potentiating toddler malnutrition and indirectly increasing the toddler death rate.

### Customs Potentiating Molecular Rejection

In nonindustrialized societies, infants commonly enjoy an extremely close relationship with their mothers in their first year, in many cases even to the extent of near continuous body contact and demand feeding such that the infant rarely experiences more than brief passing episodes of hunger. Supplementation, when it is practiced, is accomplished slowly and typically with great gentleness. Indeed, the solicitude and indulgence shown infants are so great that by the end of their first year most children of nonindustrialized societies have experienced very little rejection or separation stress.

This situation changes abruptly with the onset of weaning. The frequency of events which can be classified as molecular rejection rises sharply, even in groups which fall high on the affection scale (Rohner, 1975). These events include customs which dictate abrupt weaning, forcible separation of toddler and mother, punishment for the expression of various dependency behaviors, and proportionate neglect of one sex due to preference for the other. All these present major discontinuities to children compared with their former experiences.

The age at which weaning must begin varies (cf. discussion in Cravioto & DeLicardie, 1976) in different societies, depending on tradition, expediency, the occurrence of an event interpreted as signifying adequate maturity (e.g., presence of several teeth; walking), or most often the onset of the mother's next pregnancy. (Indeed, where birth control mechanisms are inefficient, the widespread cross-cultural preference for late weaning—emically recognized as protective of the child—is often nullified by the swift recurrence of pregnancy.) Thus, in practice, in nonindustrialized societies weaning usually begins in the second year of life—coincidentally the very time at which biomedical studies find that children experience most separation stress. It is accompanied by rising frequencies of customs which demonstrate molecular rejection. The stage is set for the development of the maternal separation syndrome and, indirectly, for malnutrition.

### Cross-cultural Examples of Molecular Rejection

In the following examples solicitousness for the infant is the norm and the parents undergo a marked change of attitude at weaning.[5] Ethnographers

[5]The Alorese (Pacific; DuBois, 1941) furnish an additional but atypical example since feeding even during infancy has been unpredictable and the child has experienced repeated privation. The situation worsens with weaning. There is the psychological stress of being left home when its mother goes to the fields, plus nutritional stress. DuBois (1941) states that

frequently report that the robust, laughing infant becomes at weaning a pot-bellied, thin, and petulant toddler.

Among the Sotho (Basutoland; Ashton, 1939) the infant diet is gradually supplemented to the age of weaning and weight gain (not quantified) is reportedly steady until the mother refuses the child her breast near the end of its second year, when weight falls abruptly. Similarly Nyansongo (Kenya; LeVine & LeVine, 1963) children are accustomed to transitional and adult foods before weaning but weaning itself is abrupt, and "There is the general belief that the more severe the mother is with the child she wants to wean, the quicker and more smoothly will the goal be achieved [p. 149]." She may put bitter substances on her nipples, slap the child, burn its arms with caustic plant juice, ignore its cries, or send it to live with its grandmother for several days. Mothers recognize the distress they cause their children, as epitomized by the word for weaning which literally means "to stamp on"; they complain that children cry and are cranky. Nyansongo mothers punish toddlers for two other reasons—for crying or having temper tantrums "for nothing" and for crying when mothers are holding the new infant. In the latter case mothers fear the *okoema* or "murderous jealousy" of the toddler which could harm the infant. In these cases it may be argued that as soon as the child ceases to demand the breast weaning is accomplished. But clearly the psychological severance of the maternal–infant bond takes longer, because children continue to cry, whine, complain, and generally beg for nurturance well into their third year.

Tarongans (Philippines [Nydegger & Nydegger, 1963]) are primarily concerned with the "comfort" of their infants. However, weaning (at approximately 18–30 months) "rudely awakens the younger Tarongan to the harsher realities of childhood by putting an abrupt end to this indulgence, his primary position in the household hierarchy, and the solicitous care hitherto surrounding him [p. 827]." Mothers set a specific date for weaning, and despite the fact that they feel pity for their weanling, they accomplish their task within 2–3 days. No preparation has been provided the child; parents cope with the expected emotional storm by bribing, threatening, and by sending the child to another household to sleep. This treatment "results in intense crying and unhappiness for a number of days, followed by a sullen, miserable, whining period that lasts from a few weeks to a number of months [p. 830]."

---

no one is responsible for feeding the child and no one is greatly incommoded by his crying . . . the child is left from about eight in the morning until five in the afternoon without regular provision of food . . . all he gets during that time may be odd bits an older child cedes more or less willingly and generously to him when he begs for it [p. 275].

According to DuBois these stresses lead to food rejection, anorexia, and weight loss.

The Mixtecans (Mexico [Romney & Romney, 1963]) also typically wean abruptly, separate toddlers from mothers, and punish crying. Romney and Romney comment that crying is frequent for 2 to 6 months following weaning, that children are "given a poor diet" (not quantified), and that the authors came away "with a distinct impression that the frequency of illness during the year of weaning is relatively high compared to the year preceding and the years succeeding this period [p. 651]." Sanjur, Cravioto, Rosales, and van Veen (1970) also comment on the relationship between abrupt weaning and the development of malnutrition and other illness in Latin American children.

Ruth Benedict (1967) describes abrupt weaning, its consequences, and its values for rural Christian Poles:

> It is believed that a child will die if it is nursed beyond two St. John's Days of its life—or the day of some other saint—and therefore, when the child is on the average eighteen months old, the mother chooses a day for weaning. The child is not given an opportunity beforehand to accustom itself to eating solid food; the sudden transition is good because it is "hardening" [p. 346].

The care of weanlings is left to their sibs of 3 or 4 years of age; even if present, adult women will not intervene to appease crying toddlers. Tantrums are common, but parents do not respond by comforting. Food may be denied toddlers. These acts are all carried out with the goal of "hardening" the child, "hardness" or resistance being a characteristic much valued among this group.

Okinawan children (Maretski & Maretski, 1963) are carried until about age 2, even if they can walk, and are accustomed early to supplemented diets. Nevertheless, a period of withdrawal and misery follows weaning. For about 1 month before true weaning the child is required to demand its food, where formerly it had been fed frequently and regularly. Then in a period of 4–5 days it is fully weaned and sent to live with another relative. It is no longer carried. As it tries to accomplish new tasks, it experiences derision for the first time. The child responds with crying, tantrums, whining, obstinacy, and sullenness: "For about three months the child's bleary eyes, tear-streaked face, and woebegone expression are unquestionable evidences of the most unhappy interval of his childhood [p. 477]."

Richards (1948) reports on the temporary adoption of weanlings by maternal relatives among the Kafir, Thonga, and Babemba (West Africa); the severe resulting emotional disturbance in the child is recognized and fully expected by adults, at least among the Kafir. But that it increases the child's chance of death may not be recognized. On the other hand, again among the Kafir, Richards describes how toddlers displaced by newborns are introduced to the latter according to a set procedure, in order to avoid the development of "jealousy" in the older child, which, they realize, can make the child sick. And Gerlach (1969) states that among the Northeast Coastal Bantu, relatives of a toddler displaced too soon by a newborn may accuse the parents of trying to kill the toddler.

In summary, many societies have customs that exacerbate the psychological stress of weaning, provoke the maternal deprivation syndrome, and thus indirectly potentiate malnutrition. Though long-term psychological damage may be slight (i.e., individuals develop "normal" adult personalities), some biomedically disvalued physical sequelae may be permanent. Parents recognize that weaning is stressful, but continue to practice stress-exacerbating customs because they find them customary, traditional, expedient, "necessary" (as when a pregnant mother believes she cannot suckle and nourish a fetus at the same time), and, most importantly, benevolent, because they help socialize the child to its own group.

## Food Restriction

Food is a central component of activity and concern in all societies. Among lay persons food is associated with the satisfaction of hunger, although it is not necessarily conceived of as the conveyor of nutrients or even of health as it is for the scientist. Food also serves important social integrative and symbolic functions. For children, food is a powerful tool of socialization. Through the food eaten and the patterning affecting its access, a child learns something about being a member of a particular society, and it learns more about its relationships with parents, siblings, other people, and often with the spirit world as well. Parents demonstrate some aspects of their comprehension of cultural norms and a considerable degree of their interest in and concern for the welfare of their families through food selection, preparation, and use.

Every society selects from among the foods available a number which they define as edible. These foods are further subdivided by ideas about appropriateness for different occasions, sexes, or ages. With weanlings we are concerned primarily with the aspect of age appropriateness, although sex appropriateness is of equal significance in some societies.

It is probably safe to say that all (normal) parents attempt to provide their toddlers with "good" diets. Of course, the definition of what constitutes "good" differs from group to group and from time to time. In the West it is currently supposed to be defined by principles of scientific nutrition— although practically speaking we must not lose sight of the existence of many old customs recently rationalized in scientific terms, and of the continuing effect of tradition. Many ideas about what constitutes the "good" diet are shared by scientists and lay people, but mechanisms for achievement may differ. Thus preweanlings and weanlings everywhere are given special relatively soft diets which provide the important foods (staples) of the society, and which, in addition (like all diets, presumably), "should" be symbolically appropriate, digestible, and not liable to provoke sickness. Societies differ in how they select the components of the weaning diet, and in how long they will continue to supply it. Some provide a relatively high-protein diet, while others provide a high-carbohydrate pap. It is among the latter that malnutrition most often occurs (and use of pap often causes much concern to culture change agents). The soft weaning diet eventually gives way to use of adult types of foods. Some societies permit a gradual transition to the adult diet, while others expect the child to eat an essentially adult diet within days of weaning. The concept of a "good" diet is itself restrictive, some examples show how in providing a "good" diet parents may also potentiate malnutrition.

A good diet provides the society's staple in generous amounts. This is not only economically efficient, but also has the symbolic virtue of making the child more of a member. Hence, for example, the Malayans give large amounts of rice (Wolff, 1965) and the New Guinea Highlanders give sweet potatoes (Binns, 1976) because these are the best of all possible foods. Ladino families in Guatemala City recognize some "growth promoting foods" which are felt to be especially good for toddlers, (Gonzalez, 1969, p. 220). Among the Nyika (Northeast Coastal Bantu) the word for food (*chakuria*) specifies a

> starchy protein-deficient porridge or gruel made from corn, millet, cassava meal or rice. Only this can properly be termed "food".... Only this is emotionally satisfying; only this "fills the belly" and makes one feel as if he has really eaten well. Meat, fish, eggs, animal milk, and the like are all regarded not as "food" but as "sauce" or "dressing" (*chitoweo*). The Nyika are convinced that, while healthy adults can eat such *chitoweo* with relative impunity, children under about three or four years of age must be protected and should be restricted to a diet of mother's milk and *chakuria* [Gerlach, 1969, p. 392].

Burgess and Dean (1962) report from Thailand another categorization of food as staple (rice) and protein-rich side dish as sauce. Here it is less fear of causing sickness than desire to practice the ethically highly valued *frugality* that explains why children are permitted to take only the smallest quantity of sauce to flavor their rice. Similarly Wolff (1965) states that among Malayans rice and certain "strength"-promoting items (meat, fish, eggs) are necessities (i.e., food) while vegetables, fruits, and spices are merely pleasant additions to the diet. Toddlers are usually not allowed "strength" foods. Thus the "good" diet also does not cause sickness. Sickness of toddlers can be avoided by restricting intake of foods which are too "strong," "indigestible,"[6] or of

---

[6]The concept of "indigestibility," although it may strike Westerners as unfounded, should perhaps not be dismissed too easily. Until the recognition of the prevalence of adult lactase deficiency, the refusal of many non-Westerners to drink milk past infancy was often labeled a "culture block."

the wrong symbolic temperature (cf., e.g., Cassidy, 1976; Flores & Garcia, 1960; Gonzalez, 1969; Huenemann & Collazos, C., 1954; Jelliffe, 1957; Mathur, 1975; Weise, 1976; Wolff, 1965), or which are inbued with ritual qualities which make them unsuitable for the uninitiated (Jelliffe, 1957). Finally, the advent of sickness is widely viewed as a reason to restrict food (especially protein) intake, either to aid a compromised digestion, to purify the sick individual, or to oppose the symbolic temperature of the sickness and bring the body back into "balance" (reported in, e.g., Cassidy, 1976; Gokulanathan & Verghese, 1969; Gonzalez, 1969; Huenemann & Collazos, C., 1954; Jelliffe, 1957; Mathur, 1975).

Though Western nutritionists identify nutritional dangers in these practices, in each case parents are acting in ways that are socially condoned, and parental goals are essentially benevolent, ranging from simply feeding the child, to promoting growth and protecting from illness, or to formalizing its social membership.

## Food Competition

The nutritional "danger" in competition lies in the fact that because toddlers are small and relatively inexperienced, and because they are of comparatively low social value, they may get either too little food or too few nutrients.

### Competition as a Consequence of Age

Food competition takes two forms. In the first the newly weaned toddler is expected to compete on a more or less equal basis with older sibs and adults for the available food supply. The pap of the circum-weaning period is quickly replaced with all or most of the adult dietary items, and often no special care is taken to check that toddlers receive a proportionate share of available food. Parents appear to assume that what the child gets is what it wants and needs, and toddlers are expected to feed themselves or aggressively demand feeding. This idea can perhaps partly be attributed to not viewing the toddler as different from an older child, or of attributing skills to it irrespective of the length of its experience. Toddlers can partially control the effect of this competition by gaining experience; in the interim they experience frustration and hunger, and sometimes develop malnutrition. This form of competition is also a result of feeding family members in terms of their productivity or economic importance; working members get more than nonworking members.

The Malayan toddler begins to eat the adult diet when it starts walking and within a few months it is expected to compete for food equally with siblings (Wolff, 1965). Parents attribute independence and responsibility to toddlers, and explain that the thin child has simply "refused to eat"—the child's prerogative. Wolff attributes the high toddler malnutrition and mortality rates to these attitudes and practices. On Rarotonga (Pacific; Fry, 1957) toddlers of 12–14 months consume an adult diet, "learning quickly" to compete successfully with siblings. Their parents do little to ensure that they get a proportionate share. DuBois (1941) also described sibling competition among the Alorese.

It is also common for toddlers to receive a disproportionately small share of total family food. For example, where a staple "food" and a high-protein "sauce" are differentiated, the sauce typically goes preferentially to adults. Similarly "strong" foods are typically reserved for adult use. Elsewhere established and traditional food flow patterns favor adults, especially those who are male or productive. In Rarotonga, the male head of household is served first, followed in order by the female head of household, the adolescents, and other children in age-descending order (Fry, 1957). Fry believes (but does not provide figures) that while all get adequate quantity, only the older members have access to valued high-protein foods. A similar pattern is said to be common in West Africa (Cuthbertson, 1964). The Highland Sotho (Ashton, 1939) eat meat mainly at ceremonies—from which children are excluded. (On the other hand the Sotho reserve milk for use first to infants, then to children in age-ascending order, a factor which may partly offset the lack of meat in toddler diets.) Sanjur et al. (1970) report that similar patterns are common in Latin America and Mexico, while Sebrell and King (1970) mention them for Haiti. Flores and Garcia (1960) measured the effects of differential food flow in Amatitlan, a village in Guatemala. They found the most marked dietary deficiencies occurred below the age of 3 when the children's diets differed from those of adults, but that after that age children consumed more or less adult diets in disproportionately small amounts. By another measure, the money spent for food was insufficient to purchase an adequate family diet, particularly so for toddlers (a mean of 22¢/individual but only 11¢/toddler). Cassidy (1976) measured dietary intake among Lowland Maya in Belize. She found that while toddlers might be fed before older persons, food restrictions and the expectation that working members required and should receive more food resulted in toddlers receiving approximately one-half and adults approximately two times their recommended daily allowances for calories ($p < .05$). The difference in access to protein was similar in direction but less marked in degree.

### Competition as a Consequence of Sex

The second form of competition is determined by sex and is widespread. In some cases foods are clearly defined as feminine or masculine; in other cases one sex is defined as less desirable and less food overall is provided the less desired sex. Here the child itself has little control over the situation.

The Sotho give milk to children and feeble adults, greens and sprouted maize to women and children, and meat to adults. Men eat their meals from one communal dish, women and children from another. In this case women appear to profit from the arrangement. Ashton (1939) argues that they receive about the same quantity of food as the males, but of higher quality. More often, women suffer nutritionally from such sex-related food categorizations. Many examples are reviewed in Rosenberg (1973).

More to our purpose are cases in which weaning customs favor one sex over another. More societies for which we have data favor males (e.g., Gessain, 1963; Gopalan & Naidu, 1972; Gordon et al., 1967; Greene, 1978; Lang, 1946; Lestrange, 1954; Lindebaum, 1977; Maretski & Maretski, 1963; Minturn & Hitchcock, 1963; Pakrisi, 1970; Rosenberg, 1973; Russell, 1976) than females (Burrows & Spiro, 1957; Falade, 1963; Orent, 1975); in cases in which the question has been investigated, the preference is found to be intimately associated with ideas about preferred population size and density.

The child who receives earlier supplementation (assuming it is relatively sanitary) and the one who is weaned later are less at risk to malnutrition. Jelliffe (1957) states that the Hindu *Mukhe Bhat* ceremony which ritually ushers in supplementation is traditionally planned for the male at 6 months, for the female at 7. Also in India, new pregnancies follow on the birth of a female sooner than on the birth of a male, thus forcing the earlier weaning of female children (Gordon et al., 1967). In Jordan females are traditionally weaned 2 months sooner than males (Pharaon, Darby, Shammout, Bridgeforth, & Wilson, 1965). However, among the Wolof (West Africa [Falade, 1963]), females are breast-fed up to 24 months but males only to 18), while again, among the Sotho, the restriction on greens and certain other nutritious foods for males favors females. Lindebaum (1977) notes the fact that male toddlers receive more food and other forms of care than do female toddlers in Bangladesh; Greene comments on the same phenomenon in rural Ecuador (1978); and Gessain (1963) states that although both sexes receive meat in adulthood among the Coniagui (West Africa), only male toddlers do.

The older toddler (postweanling) is at greater disadvantage in food competition than the younger. Benefit goes to older members of the society and to persons of preferred sex; emphasis is less on the welfare of the toddler than on that of the larger social group.

## PARENTAL NEGLECT—POSSIBLE EXPLANATIONS

I have reviewed examples of child-care customs and caretaker expectations and attitudes which predispose toddlers to malnutrition. The problem now to be addressed is: Why do parents practice customs which potentiate malnutrition? Malnutrition is harmful in conventional biomedical assessment because it is associated with short- and long-term decreased viability and sometimes death in the individual, and with decreased economic efficiency in affected societies. By extension, therefore, any customs that promote malnutrition are "harmful."

Alternative explanations are sometimes seen in both the nutrition and demography literatures. Malnutrition serves as a population control mechanism because it removes individuals from the population directly by causing their deaths (data in Jelliffe, 1957; Puffer & Serrano, 1973; Rosenberg, 1973; Scrimshaw, Taylor, & Gordon, 1968; others), and indirectly by permanently affecting the reproductive efficiency of both sexes (Nag, 1962). Thus, using population control as the yardstick, customs promoting malnutrition can be seen as potentially beneficial to the society although harmful to the individual. The experience of malnutrition in early childhood may also be adaptive in the sense that it biases developmental plasticity toward the hunger-resistant (Newman, 1961; Robson & Wadsworth, 1977). Using adaptation as the yardstick, we can see malnutrition causing short-term damage but providing long-term benefits to both individual and society.

Although these three interpretations of the significance of malnutrition are rational and have theoretical validity, only the first currently has practical significance in biomedical and humanistic perspective. It drives a vast international effort, the goal of which is to alleviate (or even eliminate) malnutrition. Malnutrition in toddlers is a central concern.

The steps taken to alleviate malnutrition are various; most significant to our discussion are those aimed at "educating" (more properly, *re*educating) parents, such that they cease practicing customs that potentiate malnutrition. These efforts have met with only limited success (cf. case histories in Lynch, 1969; Mead, 1955; Paul, 1955; but for a recently reported success see Sebrell & King, 1970).

To the culture change agent—a product of Western scientific training enmeshed in a  humanistic philosophy which emphasizes primacy of children and physical health—the persistence with which parents cling to customs which "obviously hurt their children" is puzzling (not to say frustrating) and requires explanation. Two explanations are current; I shall propose a third. All three are based on the interpretation that by acting to potentiate malnutrition parents are *neglecting* their children. The explanations differ in their understanding of parental motive and thus in their interpretation of the quality of the neglect.

Neglect is a term with a strong negative connotation. Rohner (1975), whose lead I follow, argues that it can be used objectively by "operationalizing" its definition, that is, by defining it in terms that have the characteristics of measurability and replicability. In Rohner's scheme neglect is the main expression of parental indifference, and indifference is one of two cross-cultural expressions of rejection. Rejection is characterized by the absence or withdrawal of warmth and affection; parents may dislike, disapprove, or resent their child or view it as a burden. This attitude may be expressed through hostility or indifference. Indifferent (neglecting) parents are unsympathetic, distant, unresponsive, and lacking in concern for the child's welfare.

## Current Explanations of Parental Neglect—the "Ignorance" and "Lack of Affection" Hypotheses

One explanation attributes behavior causing neglect to simple *ignorance* of appropriate child-care techniques (e.g., Sebrell & King, 1970; summarized in Hegsted, 1972; Pollitt, 1973). Parents lack knowledge of how best to raise their children. They do not mean to hurt or deny them; they simply do not know how to avoid doing so. In fact, malnutrition does occur more frequently in the offspring of parents who show lack of knowledge of Western child-care techniques, a status which has been measured by, for example, the occurrence of low literacy rates (Puffer & Serrano, 1973) or low rates of radio listening (Cravioto & DeLicardie, 1976).

A second explanation suggests (more or less directly) that parental persistence in clinging to "harmful" customs may be explained by the fact that traditional parents feel an underlying *lack of affection* for their children.

Care of infants and toddlers shows many cross-cultural similarities among nonindustrialized peoples, a point Sanjur *et al.* (1970) consider at some length in their excellent paper. This care does not necessarily follow patterns predictable from a Western perspective, something the authors emphasize by reminding Western readers that people choose food, not nutrients. A partial result of this bias is the selection of food on bases which are often irrelevant or erroneous when judged from the nutritionist's perspective. Speaking of these facts, Sanjur *et al.* conclude that prescientific conceptions are more important than economic factors in determining food access of the child in nonindustrialized societies, and that as parents become "more educated," the use of "traditional" methods decreases, as does the frequency of toddler malnutrition.

As discussed, psychosocial stimulation has a significant effect on a child's resistance to malnutrition. Cravioto and DeLicardie (1976) found that mothers who accepted the "traditional" role were passive, less affectionate, less stimulating, took their child for granted, and engaged in much less interaction with the child than did mothers who kept more contact with the outside world (as through radio listening). Malnutrition was commoner among the children of these "traditional" mothers. Indeed, the relationship was so strong that these authors felt they could predict the appearance of malnutrition among offspring simply by knowing how "traditional" the mothers were.

Both these studies employ the concept of a "traditional" (also called "agrarian"; cf. Gokulanathan & Verghese, 1969) personality type which is supposed to occur among nonindustrialized peoples. This personality type supposedly believes in a set of "traditional" ("agrarian") values, and demonstrates a constellation of behaviors which, using Rohner's terminology, may best be characterized as rejecting, and specifically as neglecting. Shorter (1977) takes this position directly in an historical paper in which he argues that the expression of affection for infants depends upon the existence in the society of a philosophy of "maternal sentiment." He suggests that this idea appeared in the late nineteenth century in Europe among the upper classes, and has only gradually and incompletely spread elsewhere. Shorter (1977) concludes that traditional parents, both historically and cross-culturally, demonstrate *and feel* a true lack of affection for their children: "They had not internalized rules of the social game which commanded: 'preserve infant life about [sic] all else,' and so went about their days guided by different priorities, prepared to accept the mortality risks they knew their actions entitled [sic] [p. 69]." To the extent that this lack of affection is conscious, and parents recognize that they neglect their children, parental persistance in clinging to customs which potentiate malnutrition must, I suppose, be interpreted as malign.

Something of this idea is contained in Cravioto and DeLicardie's (1976) definition of protein–calorie malnutrition (PCM):

> a disease complex occurring primarily among the poor in preindustrialized societies where the *social system, consciously or unconsciously, creates malnourished children*, generation after generation, through a series of social misfortunes, among which are limited access to goods and services, limited social mobility and restricted opportunities for social stimuli at crucial points in life [p. 25, italics added].

It would appear that a social system, which *consciously* creates *malnourished* children practices abuse, demonstrates an attitude of malignancy toward its offspring.

Both explanations noted start from a wholly biomedical (etic) position. They assume that malnutrition is a disease entity which is or should be recognized by all, and they measure the quality of parental behavior in terms of the Western-feared outcome, malnutrition. Malnutrition is, however, a recent discovery/construct of Western scientific medicine, and it reflects the limitations of the model from which it came (discussion in Hedlund, 1972). Some of its symptoms *are* recognized elsewhere, although often given other interpretations. For example, Sebrell and King (1970, p. 35) state that apathy, listlessness, and edema are "in many places" considered merely normal phases in childhood development. Gerlach (1969) notes that the

Northeast Coastal Bantu view a set of symptoms (*chirwa*)—which Westerners would associate with malnutrition—as evidence that the parents have
broken the taboo on sexual intercourse during lactation. Perhaps the commonest interpretation is that the child is suffering from "jealousy." Jealousy,
recognized in biomedicine as contributing to malnutrition, is often viewed
elsewhere as a specific psychological entity of toddlers which follows on the
birth of a sibling. In none of these cases is food or diet viewed as having any
relationship to the perceived illness.

One point to be taken from these examples is that malnutrition cannot be
feared—or avoided—where it is not conceived. A second point is that, lacking a good idea of why Westerners want them to change their child-care
customs, non-Western parents resist changing them. The biomedical response to these widely recognized facts has been to initiate education efforts,
to introduce the concept of malnutrition, and to explain why certain customs
are "harmful." This response derives from a series of Western cultural attitudes which not only provoke interest in and concern for the experience of
the non-Western toddler, but also permit the idea of intervention to be
entertained (Arensberg & Niehoff, 1975). The response is also based in the
linearity of philosophy which permits Westerners to view cultural systems as
if they were organized in nonoverlapping categories (cf. discussion in Jelliffe
& Jelliffe, 1976), hence capable of changing in limited and specified directions. However, *a culture is a system*; child-care customs are embedded in a
matrix and function at many more levels than the overt or mechanical.

## A Further Critique of the "Ignorance" and "Lack of Affection" Hypotheses

Thus the "ignorance explanation" is inadequate because while etically
accurate (i.e., non-Western parents *are* ignorant of Western ways), it is
emically irrelevant (i.e., it is not surprising non-Westerners are ignorant of
or resistant to Western ideas). The "lack of affection" explanation is also
limited, but is more complex and warrants further discussion.

First, there may be some truth to the idea of a "traditional personality
type," although alternative explanations may be more useful in understanding the pattern of Maternal–Infant interaction under conditions of nutritional
stress. Pollitt (1973) considered the *child's* influence on maternal behavior,
arguing that children of malnourished mothers are from birth at a disadvantage. They are of lower weight and size, and demonstrate lower resistance to
infection and lower reactivity and responsiveness to maternal stimulation.
Early on they have a weak cry and show a decreased sucking response. Not
only does this have potentially serious effects by inadequately stimulating
breast milk production, but also, argues Pollitt, fails to signal the mother to

respond to her child's needs. Such unresponsive children are often weaned early, and show higher rates of severe PCM and higher mortality in the late infant and early toddler period than do more active children. If we now combine this data with that of Cravioto and DeLicardie (1976), we can see how a cycle of unresponsiveness may develop, in which both mother and child are malnourished and, reinforcing each other, express progressively deteriorating behavior patterns. This could lead to the expression of unresponsiveness and neglect by mothers even if these were *not* among the culturally preferred attitudes toward toddlers. Such a situation would, more likely, develop in "traditional" societies in which hunger is commonplace, hence the deteriorated behavior may be common among "traditional" mothers *without being necessarily characteristic of them or preferred by their societies*.

Second, although "traditional" values appear to be rejecting of children's needs, at least as conceived by Westerners, to accept the presence of these values as the source of malnutrition, we must be convinced that the potentiation of malnutrition is (at least sometimes) the *goal* of parents or social systems. This is the implication of Cravioto and DeLicardie's phrase "social system consciously . . . creates [1976, p. 25; previously quoted]." This idea is difficult to accept for several reasons. First, the concept of malnutrition is not universal; second, consciously potentiating malnutrition while recognizing its deleterious effects is counterproductive for any society, and, as Rohner (1975) points out, probably not compatible with long-term survival of the social group; third, the vast majority of ethnographic works report that parents (with some exceptions in all societies) typically demonstrate and report considerable affection for their offspring.

Sanjur *et al.* (1970) warn against confusing food choice with nutrition; we must also avoid confusing hunger with malnutrition. If parents who know about malnutrition create it in their children, they practice abuse and demonstrate a malign attitude. But if parents create *hunger* in their children, the interpretation of motive is more difficult. To permit children to experience hunger where hunger if a fact of adult life is probably utilitarian, hence benign, to the extent that it trains the child and sharpens its social identity, but to do the same where hunger is a rarity is once more malign. Furthermore, a social system (except in the most abstract of terms) cannot create malnutrition consciously unless it has the concept in its philosophical repertoire; it can only consciously create hunger.

Finally, the majority of the ethnographic literature reports that parents in most nonindustrialized societies are nurturant and affectionate with their children, expressing much concern with their welfare. They can rarely be accused of indifference. To take two examples: Robert Coles' (1967–1977) studies of American minority groups (Amerindian, Mexican–American, Eskimo, Afro-American)—though perhaps not strictly comparable with nonindustrialized societies—indicate that affection is high among these people, even when they practice customs that nutritionists decry, even when malnutrition is a fact of life. Indeed he finds the levels of affection shown infants and toddlers to be *higher* among these minority groups than those shown by upper middle-class Euro-American parents, ostensibly the inheritors of the philosophy of "maternal sentiment." Rohner (1975) also takes up this question in a study of 101 societies reported upon in the Human Relations Area Files. He finds that both affection and rejection occur in all societies; he speaks of a continuum. At one extreme are groups with child-care customs which primarily emphasize affection (e.g., Papago) and at the other those that are very rejecting (e.g., Ik). The majority express *both* affection and rejection in an intricate societally specific probably adaptive balance, the effect of which is finally reflected in the character of the adult personality.

Rohner also distinguishes (see p. 114) between rejection that is relatively constant and generalized and rejection that is sporadic, short-term, and activated only by certain phases of childrearing. The latter, molecular, is common and occurs in settings that otherwise emphasize affection. Part of the socialization process, it acts to train children nonacceptingly about some specific aspect of life, e.g., about the unacceptability or "danger" associated with body waste, certain acts or certain foods, or the scarcity hence preciousness of food. It is quite commonly associated with weaning or toilet training. The concept of molecular neglect is important because it shows that neglect can simply be a technique for child training rather than a global parental attitude. Thus it helps resolve the conflict between the argument that non-Western parents lack affection for their children and the mass of ethnographic data that report the reverse, by explaining that neglect affecting but one aspect of life can occur in an otherwise supportive environment and that parents can be simultaneously neglecting *and* affectionate.

### The Benign Neglect Hypothesis

The third explanation starts from the premise, suggested by the ethnographic literature, that (most) parents (usually) attempt to do well by their children, that in fact they do have the welfare of the child at heart. Accepting this possibility, we are led to consider whether there may be some unrecognized utilitarian aspect(s) to the practice of customs which potentiate malnutrition which could explain what otherwise appears to be contradictory behavior.

I have already mentioned two examples of the potential utility of malnutrition—population control and adaptation to recurrent food scarcity. But both of these are still biomedical in focus, and cannot be expected to reflect societal goals (with some exceptions to be discussed). What we really need to know is *what parents think* they are doing, and what functions these "harmful" customs play which are important enough to explain their persistence. The preceding analysis indicated the parents commonly reported that the customs *help* the child or its social group in some way. For example, they function to protect children from sickness, or to promote their growth or social membership. They also function to funnel food toward the members of the society perceived to be most important, indirectly and simultaneously teaching the toddler details of its social status.

In fact, the customs that potentiate toddler malnutrition represent a subset of all customs, beliefs, and activities associated with the weaning process. All of these, in a broad sense, have the ultimate function of socializing the child. All (healthy) societies attempt to socialize the child to their own ways, measuring its normalcy and its need—thus its welfare—in these terms. Under these circumstances appropriate parental behavior is any behavior that promotes the development of the child in directions the society recognizes as acceptable, and which maximizes the social normalcy of the child.

Since socialization is central to the maintenance of cultural congruity, success in socialization benefits the *entire* social group (hence customs which promote social normalcy may be expected to be resistant to change). Although individuals appear to be the focus of socialization efforts, it is, in fact, the group that derives the ultimate benefit, one measurable in terms of the "goodness of fit" of individuals. Indeed, what benefits the social group may *not* benefit the individual, especially in the short run.

Socialization is accomplished through the use of culturally specific accepting and rejecting training techniques. Both may potentiate malnutrition and thus be interpreted as "neglectful" by outsiders. In addition, the rejecting techniques may be recognized as potentiators of psychological stress by users, but nevertheless be utilized for their long-term socialization benefits. Since persons who do not act or do not appear in culturally acceptable ways are often denied equal regard by their peers, normal (customary) child-rearing acts of normal (socially accepted) parents are *benevolent* and *not* neglectful if they serve to enhance the social membership of their offspring, *even* if some aspect of this care appears, to outsiders, to damage the child.

Thus, toddlers suffer excessive stress because their parents (social group) practice customs which promote this stress. Westerners see a source of neglect in these practices. However, since users do not see their acts as neglectful, but rather as useful or benevolent, the neglect is secondary and accidental, an untoward side-effect of progress toward another goal. It is *benign* neglect.

Benign neglect refers to actions permitted or encouraged by customs and beliefs which potentiate physical dysfunction although their goal is to achieve a positively valued social effect. Since our subject is toddler malnutrition, I shall specify this definition and classify as benign neglect parental–caretaker actions supported by customs and beliefs which limit toddler access to the food supply and thereby indirectly potentiate weaning stress and malnutrition, but do so with the benevolent goal(s) of promoting social congruity and normal socialization of the child.

The distinction between neglect which is benign and neglect which is not rests on whether the people involved have the welfare of the child or society at heart. If they do, even if damage occurs at some level, the goal is benevolent and the neglect may be categorized as "benign."[7]

## EFFECTS OF BENIGN NEGLECT

Benign neglect of toddlers has four effects. It helps socialize children and maintain cultural congruity; it raises the likelihood of individuals experiencing suffering, sickness, and death in toddlerhood; it acts as a population control factor; and it enhances physiological adaptation of individuals and probably genetic adaptations of populations to food scarcity. The first two effects have already been discussed, so this discussion will be confined to the latter two issues.

### Benign Neglect and Toddler Malnutrition

A moderate amount of information actually links the customs of benign neglect (under other titles or categorizations) and toddler malnutrition.

[7]Dr. Lawrence Greene (personal communication, 1978) relates the story of a female toddler in a rural area of Ecuador who died of malnutrition and dehydration. The indigenous parents of this child lived some 50 m from the home of an Ecuadorian physician who had the wherewithall to treat her. The child's father told Greene that the child's death was not important because she was only a girl, a comment which reflected the lower economic valuation put on women in this society. This case seems superficially to be a simple one of neglect. Further investigation indicates, however, that it is better interpreted as a case of benign neglect. The father did not merely ignore his sick baby girl. He attemped to feed her properly (i.e., according to the usual food restrictions imposed on the ill) and he consulted a Franciscan nun who had some hospital training and who was the only source of Western medicine prior to the arrival of the physician. In fact, the father acted entirely within the normal expectation patterns of his society, and did all he felt was normal to protect his child. After she died he aired a sentiment which could probably have been echoed by any other village member. While it is likely that had the child been male the father would have consulted the physician, this act would have had to have been interpreted correctly—as *emically extreme*. In the case of the girl child we cannot fault the father for not visiting the physician. She had a normal type of sickness for which his society provided what appeared to be adequate care. The father "did his best"—even taking on the cost of the medicine from the Franciscan nun. The little girl died of benign neglect, not simple neglect, for her father had no malign motives, although he expressed a view of women disapproved of in Western society.

Examples are given in Jelliffe (1957), Puffer and Serrano (1973), Scrimshaw *et al.* (1968), and others. Wolff (1965) states that the Malayan habits of eating when hungry instead of at specified times, of letting weanlings compete with siblings, and of attributing independence and responsibility to them account for the fact that mortality between ages 1 and 5 is twice that of their Chinese neighbors who do not have these beliefs and habits. Fry (1957) attributes high observed rates of sickness and mortality among Rarotongan toddlers to food distribution patterns which deny protein but not energy to children of 12–30 months. Several researchers (Cassidy, 1976; Flores & Garcia, 1960; Sebrell & King, 1970) believe the disproportionately lesser distribution of total family food to toddlers explains the high observed frequencies of malnutrition in this age group. Newman (1961) attributes the high rates of beri-beri in Upper Burmese toddlers to food rules which restrict thiamine intake of lactating women and weanlings. Binns (1976) associates feeding of New Guinea Highlander toddlers with large amounts of sweet potatoes with high observed incidences of growth retardation, with diarrheal and respiratory disease, and with high toddler death rates. In Jordan, Pharaon *et al.* (1965) find malnutrition in 5.9% of boys and 11.7% of girls; they explain that females are traditionally weaned 2 months earlier than males. Gopalan and Naidu (1972) show that in India four females suffer kwashiorkor for every three males, yet males are more often admitted to hospitals for treatment. They attribute these differences to higher valuation of boys. Listing sex ratios (number of females:number of males) for several countries, they show that where girls are less preferred, sex ratios are depressed. The sex ratio in India has fallen progressively during the twentieth century, despite the fact that female infanticide has long been illegal. For Bangladesh, Lindenbaum (1977) reports that mortality rates for females under 5 are in some years 50% higher than those for males.

## Utilitarian Aspects of Benign Neglect for Populations

The nonutilitarian aspects of malnutrition for individuals are widely understood, and do not bear repeating. However, the utilitarian aspects for populations have been less discussed.

### Population Control

Benign neglect functions in population control by causing the deaths of toddlers, thus removing them from the reproductive pool, and by decreasing the reproductive capacities of survivors. Presumably the survivors are not a random sample of all toddlers, but represent those more resistant to weaning stress.

The reproductive capacities of survivors are decreased in several ways. Food access in nonindustrialized societies often remains limited for children into the adolescent years, when, for the first time, they begin "eating like adults" and gaining weight (Ashton, 1939; Cassidy, 1976; Richards, 1948; Rosenberg, 1973). The planned fattening of females at adolescence in many African groups has been extensively described (Leith-Ross, 1939; Meek, 1925; Paulme, 1952; Talbot, 1915); in most cases the express purpose is to make the girl fertile and to prepare her for marriage. That fattening may in fact be pivotal in bringing about reproductive maturity is suggested by the research of Frisch and McArthur who found menarche did not occur and ovulation was not maintained in females who had too little body fat (Frisch, 1978). Nag (1962) reviews the literature on nutrition and fertility and shows that menarche is delayed in malnourished girls. Also, when menarche occurs late, menopause commonly occurs early (for a dissenting opinion see Janzmann, Dvanlith, & Zaat, 1969), so that the total available reproductive period of malnourished women may be shortened. Angel (1976) and others have shown that even very minor degrees of malnutrition in childhood can negatively alter the shape of the birth canal, decreasing the ease with which females can bear children. Gopalan and Naidu (1972) quantify the considerable decrease in fertility in the Indian population due to increased pregnancy wastage, difficult labor, and raised maternal and perinatal mortality rates.

The population control effects of customs that potentiate toddler malnutrition fall into B. Benedict's (1972) category of indirect social factors affecting fertility. This category also includes age of marriage, incidence of separation and divorce, widowhood and widow remarriage, polygamy, postpartum sexual abstinence or abstinence during some ceremonies or seasons, and temporary or permanent voluntary celibacy. These customs are categorized as indirect factors because users usually do not recognize that they affect fertility. Benign neglect is indirect for this reason and also because it does not independently cause toddler death or poor growth, but rather increases the likelihood of these results by potentiating malnutrition.

A population control effect is obvious where toddlers die in excessive numbers. However, at least in some groups, women may "make-up" toddler losses by having more live births than women who do not lose toddlers (Frischano, Klayman, & Matos, 1976). Therefore it is more relevant to consider *which* children die as toddlers. The answer is that two groups do— those who are physiologically and psychologically less resistant to weaning stress, and those who are socially less desirable. Into the latter category fall cases of sex preference. Loss of female children decreases the reproductive potential of a population more than does loss of an equivalent number of mixed sex.[8]

---

[8]If users are peripherally or actively aware of the population benefit provided by infanticide (especially female) or toddler neglect ("attenuated infanticide," Rosenberg, 1973), their activities are better classified with Benedict's *direct* social factors affecting fertility. Pakrisi (1970)

The advantages that accrue to a population that maintains stable size include decreased pressure on the food supply, less competition for social goods in adulthood, and greater social stability. Indeed, Wagley (1969) argues that "the social structure of each society is closely interrelated with a specific population level. . . . Each culture has a population policy—an implicit or explicit set of cultural values related to population size [p. 269]."

## Biological Adaptation of Populations to Food Scarcity

Another utilitarian function of toddler malnutrition, and the customs which promote it, lies in forcing adaptation of the population to food scarcity. There is some uncertainty as to whether these adjustments should be viewed as expressions of developmental plasticity or as evidence for on-going evolution. Stini (1971), beginning from the position that hunting–gathering selected for humans with large physiques, suggests that the practice of agriculture requires a different kind of physique for maximum efficiency, and that currently "the limits of developmental plasticity are being tested, with an accompanying high cost in infant and child mortalities [p. 1028]." Lisowski (1966) believes selection for shorter stature has already occurred in response to nutritional stress in the tropics. Newman (1961) connects benign neglect and selection when he says: "Where deaths due to food deprivation are culture or class-limited there is of course differential survival, the *sine qua non* of biological evolution [p. 629]."

Individuals from societies in which malnutrition is common grow more slowly, are shorter, and require less food for maintenance. Newman (1961) thinks they have made physiological adaptations which explain why they live on diets "that would send many others to mass graves [p. 627]," while Robson and Wadsworth (1977) suggest what some of these might be. Both these authors consider that although malnutrition lowers reproductive capacity, the population growth rates for nonindustrialized countries suggest that the effect is not serious, indeed, that their effective adaptation is demonstrated in their high birth rates.

---

analyzed the sex ratio effect of female infanticide for nineteenth-century India. He found that early in the century the female proportion of the population was reduced in some areas to as low as 20–24% of the total. Orent (1975) relates that the Kafa (Ethiopia) inhibit population growth by restricting opportunities for sexual intercourse, and by performing surgery on children under 6 months including circumcision, sometimes clitoridectomy, removal of the uvula, or removal of the tooth buds. This surgery causes massive blood loss and often is followed by infection and death. The uvula is removed "if the child is not taking its food properly." Boys experience toothbud (and other) surgery more than girls, and die in larger numbers because "Kafa men believe that if a male child shows its teeth too early it will steal its patrimony prior to what is considered to be the proper time [p. 84]." It may easily be imagined that even if he survives toothbud surgery in infancy, the small boy would be at a marked disadvantage without deciduous teeth, certainly prey for malnutrition. However, it is uncertain how aware the Kafa themselves are of the population control effects of these practices.

## APPLICATION OF THE CONCEPT OF BENIGN NEGLECT

The material presented makes two important points—(1) customs which potentiate malnutrition may actually have other, benevolent, goals ("benign neglect"); and (2) malnutrition, although harmful to individuals, can be beneficial if considered in terms of the entire population. These points suggest that before culture change agents can reasonably assess the need for change in customs that potentiate malnutrition, they must weigh the suffering associated with malnutrition against the positive effects in socialization, population control, and physiological adaptation to food scarcity. Otherwise they risk waste—waste when parents refuse to accept reeducation, and waste if they cause as much damage as they alleviate, by, for example, damaging cultural congruity, potentiating the population explosion, or producing poorly adapted, less productive adults.

I have alluded to some philosophical conflicts facing the Western-trained culture change agent. Western humanitarian philosophy (Arensberg & Niehoff, 1975) focuses on the individual, views the child as of prime importance, decries suffering, and uses activism to solve problems. These "problems" represent segments of experience that have been sectioned off according to widely accepted categorizations so that, for example, "nutrition" is separate from "medicine" which is separate from "population control." Each problem is usually believed to be separately solvable. In Jelliffe and Jelliffe's terms (1976) this is an expression of *linear* thinking. In contrast, many nonindustrialized peoples focus on the importance of the group, and view the productive adult as of prime importance. They do not enjoy suffering, but may interpret it differently, and do utilize a number of *curvilinear* methods to solve problems in ways which are typically not speed or specificity-oriented. These philosophical differences mean that customs Westerners interpret as damaging, are to many non-Westerners normal, plausible, reasonable, acceptable, or even benevolent.

What does this mean to the culture change agent? Does this conflict imply that they should engage in a "hands-off" policy as regards toddler malnutrition and the customs that potentiate it? Should culture change agents refuse to intervene, withdraw, or "let children suffer"? These are interpretations put on the concept of benign neglect by some persons with whom I have spoken. But I see these as misapprehensions. My aim is, rather, to show that the concept of benign neglect can help the culture change agent (specifically the nutrition interventionist) make more accurate interpretations of cultural context, hence design more effective intervention programs.

Culture change agents must begin by recognizing their own philosophical biases. They should attempt to *adapt program design to the philosophical biases of the receivers*, which requires an emic investigation before programs are designed. In the case of toddler malnutrition they must discover parental views of the functions of local child-care customs. Then if they decide they will (try to) replace customs that potentiate malnutrition, culture change agents can recognize the important social aspects of benign neglect, and can search for alternative but *emically valid* ways to feed the child without either alienating the parents or divorcing the child from its society. It is of course often difficult to fulfill this requirement. Cuthbertson (1967) reports that in Africa adults will take food provided by outsiders for toddlers, if they find it palatable. This is an expression of the value in nonindustrialized groups of feeding the productive members preferentially. Cuthbertson suggests presenting food that in local cultural terms is palatable only to toddlers. Flores, Manchu, Lara, and Guzman (1969) tested to see if the disproportionately low provision of food to toddlers in Guatemala could be altered by providing the whole family with more food. They found that regardless of availability, children received foods high in calories, protein, and thiamine *only upon demand*.

Western concern with suffering caused by malnutrition in the short-term should not cause the culture change agent to ignore the possibility of causing more damage in the long-term by ill-designed intervention. I am thinking here of the sociopsychological and physical damage inflicted by population excess and by insufficient physiological adaptation to food scarcity when food once more becomes scarce—as frequently happens when interventionists leave the locale or child-care centers close up shop. We may also recall the disastrous results of encouraging bottle feeding in impoverished areas (Chen, Ahmed, Gesche, & Mosley, 1974; Knodel, 1977).

Other aspects of Western philosophy may also slow progress. The tendency toward categorization is one of these. Gopalan and Naidu (1972) plead that population control and nutrition intervention programs be carried out simultaneously, since individually neither works. Jelliffe and Jelliffe (1976) make a similar plea. Clearly, intervention utilizing recognition of the emic–etic discontinuity in program design requires more self-awareness in the researcher(s) and more field research time than does the simpler etic approach to intervention. But because it promises better results, both physically and socially, this approach is well worth pursuing.

## SUMMARY

In this chapter I have proposed that customs common in nonindustrialized areas that potentiate toddler malnutrition usually do so accidentally; the potentiation of malnutrition is not a goal of users. On the contrary users see in the customs means to enhance the social membership of their toddlers and to protect the future of the social group. Customs with this dual character are classified as examples of *benign neglect*. Benign neglect also serves some functions in population control and in enhancing adaptation to food scarcity. The concept helps explain parental persistence in clinging to customs which in conventional biomedical (etic) perspective are damaging.

By recognizing this emic–etic discontinuity, and by building recognition into program design, the nutrition interventionist can take important steps toward providing alternatives to benign neglect and alleviating toddler malnutrition. That it is singularly important for the culture change agent to understand the duality expressed in the concept of benign neglect is nicely encapsulated in this comment made in 1900 by a Kentucky mountain woman: "Hit's a lot worse to be soul-hungry than to be body-hungry [Bartlett's, 1955]."

## REFERENCES

Angel, J. L. Colonial to modern skeletal changes in the U.S.A. *American Journal of Physical Anthropology*, 1976, *45*, 723–735.

Arensberg, C. M., & Niehoff, A. N. American cultural values. In J. P. Spradley & M. A. Rynkiewich (Ed.), *The Nacirema, readings on American culture*. Boston: Little Brown, 1975. Pp. 363–378.

Ashton, E. H. A sociological study of Sotho diet. *Transactions of the Royal Society of South Africa*, 1939, *27*, Part 2, 147–214.

*Bartlett's Familiar Quotations* (13th ed.). Boston: Little Brown, 1955.

Benedict, B. Social regulation of fertility. In G. A. Harrison & A. J. Boyce (Ed.), *The structure of human populations*. Oxford: Clarendon Press, 1972. Pp. 73–89.

Benedict, R. Child rearing in Eastern European countries. In R. C. Hurt (Ed.), *Personalties and cultures, readings in psychological anthropology*. Garden City, N.Y.: Natural History Press, 1967. Pp. 340–353.

Binns, C. W. Food, sickness and death in children of the highlands of Papua, New Guinea. *Journal of Tropical Pediatrics and Environmental Child Health*, 1976, *22*, 9–11.

Bowlby, J. Maternal care and mental health. *World Health Organization Bulletin*, 1951, *3*, 355–534.

Bowlby, J. *Separation, anxiety and anger*. Vol. 2. *Attachment and loss*. New York: Basic Books, 1973.

Burgess, A., & Dean, R. F. A. *Malnutrition and food habits*. New York: Macmillan, 1962.

Burrows, E. G., & Spiro, M. E. *An atoll culture, ethnography of Ifaluk in the Central Carolines*. New Haven: Human Relations Area Files, 1957.

Cassidy, C. M. *Food strategies and nutrition in Belize*. Paper presentation to the American Association of Physical Anthropologists. St. Louis, 1976.

Chen, L. C., Ahmed, S., Gesche, M., & Mosley, W. H. A prospective study of birth interval dynamics in rural Bangladesh. *Population Studies*, 1974, *28*, 277–297.

Christiansen, N., Mora, J. O., & Herrera, M. G. Family social characteristics related to physical growth of young children. *British Journal of Preventive Social Medicine*, 1975, *29*, 121–130.

Coles, R. *Children of crisis* (5 vols.) Boston: Little Brown, 1967-1977.

Cravioto J., & E. R. DeLicardie. Microenvironmental factors in severe protein–calorie malnutrition. In N. S. Scrimshaw & M. Behar (Eds.), *Nutrition and agricultural development, significance and potential for the tropics*. New York: Plenum Press, 1976. Pp. 25-35.

Cuthbertson, D. P. Feeding patterns and nutrient utilization: Chairman's remarks. *Proceedings of the Nutrition Society*, 1967, *26*, 143-144.

DuBois, C. Attitudes toward food and hunger in Alor. In L. Spier, A. I. Hallowell, & S. S. Newman (Eds.), *Language, culture and personality, essays in memory of Edward Sapir*. Menasha, Wisc.: Sapir Memorial Publishing Fund, 1941. Pp. 272-281.

Falade, S. Women of Dakar and the surrounding urban area. In D. Paulme (Ed.), *Women of tropical Africa*. London: Routledge & Kegan Paul, 1963. Pp. 17 46.

Flores, M., & Garcia, B. The nutritional status of children of pre-school age in the Guatemalan community of Amatitlan. *British Journal of Nutrition*, 1960, *14*, 207-215.

Flores, M., Menchu, M. T., Lara, M. Y., & Guzman, M. Child intake related to family nutrient availability. *VIIIth International Congress of Nutrition, Abstracts of Papers*, 1969.

Frisch, R. Response to Trussell on menarche and fatness: Reexamination of the critical body composition hypothesis. *Science*, 1978, *200*, 1509-1513.

Frischano, A. R., J. E. Klayman, & Matos, J. Symbiotic relationship of high fertility, high childhood mortality and socioeconomic status in an urgan Peruvian population. *Human Biology*, 1976, *48*, 101-111.

Fry, P. C. Dietary survey on Rarotonga, Cook Islands. III. Feeding practices and growth of Rarotongan children from birth through six years. *American Journal of Clinical Nutrition*, 1957, *5*, 634-643.

Galle, O. R., Gove, W. R., & McPherson, J. M. Population density and pathology: What are the relations for Man? *Science*, 1972, *176*, 23-30.

Gerlach, L. Socio-cultural factors affecting the diet of the Northeast Coastal Bantu. In L. R. Lynch (Ed.), *The cross-cultural approach to health behavior*. Rutherford, N.J.: Farleigh-Dickenson University Press, 1969. Pp. 383-395.

Gessain, M. Coniagui women, Guinea. In D. Paulme (Ed.), *Women of tropical Africa*. London: Routledge & Kegan Paul, 1963. Pp. 17-46.

Gonzalez, N. L. S. de. Beliefs and practices concerning medicine and nutrition among lower-class urban Guatemalans. In L. R. Lynch (Ed.), *The cross-cultural approach to health behavior*. Rutherford, N.J.: Farleigh Dickenson University Press, 1969. Pp. 213-227.

Gokulanathan, K. S., & Verghese, K. P. Socio-cultural malnutrition (growth failure in children due to socio-cultural factors). *Journal of Tropical Pediatrics* 1969, *15*, 118-124.

Gopalan, C., & Naidu, A. N. Nutrition and fertility. *Lancet* November 18, 1972, 1077-1079.

Gordon, J. E., Wyon, J. B., & Ascoli, W. The second year death rate in less developed countries. *American Journal of Medical Sciences*, 1967, *254*, 357-380.

Grant, M. W. Rate of growth in relation to birth rank and family size. *British Journal of Preventive and Social Medicine*, 1964, *18*, 35-42.

Greene, L. Personal communication, 1978.

Harris, M. *The rise of anthropological theory*. New York: Crowell, 1968.

Harrison, G. A., Weiner, J. S., Tanner, J. M., & Barnicot, N. A. *Human biology*. London: Oxford University Press, 1964.

Hegsted, D. M. Deprivation syndrome or protein–calorie malnutrition. *Nutrition Reviews*, 1972, *30*, 51-54.

Huenemann, R. L., & Collazos-C. C. Nutrition and care of young children in Peru. *Journal of the American Dietetic Association*, 1954, *30*, 559-569.

Janzmann, L., Dvanlith, N., & Zaat, J. C. A. The age at menopause in the Netherlands. *International Journal of Fertility*, 1969, *14*, 106-117.

Jelliffe, D. B. Social culture and nutrition cultural blocks and protein malnutrition in early childhood in rural West Bengal. *Pediatrics*, 1957, *20*, 128–138.

Jelliffe, D. B., & Jelliffe, E. F. P. Cultural interaction and child nutrition (toward a curvilinear compromise?). In N. S. Scrimshaw & M. Behar (Eds.), *Nutrition and agricultural development*. New York: Plenum Press, 1976. Pp. 263–273.

Knodel, J. Breast-feeding and population growth. *Science*, 1977, *198*, 1111–1115.

Lang, O. *Chinese family and society*. New Haven: Yale University Press, 1946.

Leith-Ross, J. *African women, a study of the Ibo of Nigeria*. London: Routledge & Kegan Paul, 1939.

Lestrange, M. de Meres et enfants en Afrique Noire. *Concours Medical (Paris)*, 1954, *76*, 4367–4370.

LeVine, R. A., & LeVine, B. B. Nyansongo: A Gusii community in Kenya. In B. B. Whiting (Ed.), *Six cultures, studies of child rearing*. New York: Wiley, 1963. Pp. 19–202.

Lindenbaum, S. The "last course": Nutrition and anthropology in Asia. In T. K. Fitzgerald (Ed.), *Nutrition and anthropology in action*. Amsterdam: van Gorcum, 1977. Pp. 141–155.

Lisowski, F. P. The varieties of man. *Journal of Medicine of Ethiopia*, 1966, *4*, 71–89.

Lynch, L. R. (Ed.). *The cross-cultural approach to health behavior*. Rutherford, N.J.: Farleigh Dickenson University Press, 1969.

Maretski, T. W., & Maretski, H. Taira: An Okinawan village. In B. B. Whiting (Ed.), *Six cultures, studies in child rearing*. New York: Wiley, 1963. Pp. 367–539.

Mathur, Y. C. Feeding habits and beliefs with practical significance in villages: Impact of urbanization on feeding habits and beliefs. *Indian Pediatrics*, 1975, *12*, 70–71.

Mead, M. (Ed.) *Cultural patterns and technical change*. New York: Mentor, 1955.

Meek, C. K. *The northern tribes of Nigeria* (Vol. 1). London: Oxford University Press, 1925.

Minturn, L., & Hitchcock, J. T. The Rajputs of Khalapur, India. In B. B. Whiting (Ed.), *Six cultures, studies in child rearing*. New York: Wiley, 1963. Pp. 207–361.

Moynihan, P. Text of Moynahan memo on the status of Negroes. *New York Times*, March 1, 1970.

Nag, M. Factors affecting human fertility in nonindustrialized society. A cross-cultural study. *Yale University Publications in Anthropology*, 1962, No. 66.

Newman, M. T. Biological adaptation of man to his environment: Heat, cold, altitude and nutrition. *Annals of the New York Academy of Sciences*, 1961, *91*, 617–633.

Nydegger W. F., & Nydegger, C. Tarong: An Ilocos barrio in the Philippines. In B. B. Whiting (Ed.), *Six cultures, studies in child rearing*. New York: Wiley, 1963. Pp. 697–867.

Okeahialam, T. C. Non-nutritional aetiological factors of protein–calorie malnutrition (PCM) in Africa. *Journal of Tropical Pediatrics and Environmental Child Health*, 1975, *21*, 20–25.

Orent, A. Cultural factors inhibiting population growth among the Kafa of Southwest Ethiopa. In M. Nag (Ed.), *Population and social organization*. The Hague: Mouton, 1975. Pp. 75–91.

Pakrisi, K. B. *Female infanticide in India*. Calcutta: Editions Indian, 1970.

Paul, B. (Ed.). *Health, culture and community, case studies of public reactions to health programs*. New York: Russell Sage Foundation, 1955.

Paulme, D. L'Initiation des filles en pays Kissi (Haute-Guinee). *Conferencia internacional dos Africanistas Ocidentais*, 1952, 303–331.

Petros-Barvazian, A. The role of maternal and child health programs in the control of malnutrition. *Bibliotheca Nutritio et Dieta*, 1970, *14*, 165–179.

Pharaon, H. M., Darby, W. J., Shammout, H. A., Bridgeforth, E. B., & Wilson, C. S. A year-long study of the nutriture of infants and pre-school children in Jordan. *Journal of Tropical Pediatrics and African Child Health*, 1965, *2*.

Pike, K. L. Language in relation to a unified theory of the structures of human behavior (2nd ed.). The Hague: Mouton, 1967.

Pollitt, E. Behavior of infant in causation of nutritional marasmus. American Journal of Clinical Nutrition, 1973, 26, 264–270.

Prugh, D. G., & Harlow, R. G. "Masked deprivation" in infants and young children. In M. D. Ainsworth (Ed.), Deprivation of maternal care. New York: Schocken Books, 1966. Pp. 205–225.

Puffer, R. R., & Serrano, C. V. Patterns of mortality in childhood. Pan-American Health Organization Scientific Publications, 1973, 262.

Richards, A. I. Hunger and work in a savage tribe. New York: Free Press, 1948.

Robson, J. R. K., & Wadsworth, G. R., The health and nutritional status of primitive populations. Ecology of Food and Nutrition, 1977, 6, 187–202.

Rohner, R. P. They love me, they love me not. New Haven: Human Relations Area Files Press, 1975.

Romney, K., & Romney, R. The Mixtecans of Juxtlahuaca, Mexico. In B. B. Whiting (Ed.), Six cultures, studies of child rearing. New York: Wiley, 1963.

Rosenberg, E. M. Ecological effects of sex-differential nutrition. Paper presentation to the American Anthropological Association, New Orleans, 1973.

Russell, M. Parent–child and sibling–sibling correlations of height and weight in a rural Guatemala population of pre-school children. Human Biology, 1976, 48, 501–515.

Sanjur, D. M., Cravioto, J., Rosales, L., & van Veen, A. Infant feeding and weaning practices in a rural preindustrial setting, a sociocultural approach. Acta Paediatrica Scandinavica, 1970, suppl. 200.

Scrimshaw, N. S., Taylor, C. E., & Gordon, J. E. Interactions of nutrition and infection. World Health Organization Monograph Series, 1968, 57.

Sebrell, W. H., Jr., & King, K. W. The role of community mothercraft centers in combatting malnutrition. Bibliotheca Nutritio et Dieta, 1970, 14, 34–42.

Shorter, E. Maternal sentiment and death in childbirth: A new agenda for psychomedical history. In P. Branca (Ed.), The medicine show, patients, physicians and the perplexities of the health revolution in modern society. New York: Science History Press, 1977. Pp. 67–88.

Stini, W. A. Evolutionary implications of changing nutritional patterns in human populations. American Anthropologist, 1971, 73, 1019–1030.

Talbot, D. A. Women's mysteries of a primitive people, the Ibibios of Southern Nigeria. London: Cassell, 1915.

Wagley, C. Cultural influence on population: A comparison of two Tupi tribes. In A. P. Vayda (Ed.), Environment and cultural behavior. New York: American Museum of Natural History Press, 1969. Pp. 268–280.

Ward, S. K. Methodological considerations in the study of population density and social pathology. Human Ecology, 1975, 3, 275–286.

Weise, H. J. C. Maternal nutrition and traditional food behavior in Haiti. Human Organization, 1976, 35, 193–200.

Wolff, R. J. Meanings of food. Tropical and Geographical Medicine, 1965, 17, 45–51.

# Part IV

## EMPIRICAL STUDIES

# 7

# Biosocial Correlates of Motor Development during Infancy and Early Childhood

ROBERT M. MALINA

The development and refinement of skillful performance in motor activities is one of the major developmental tasks of childhood. All children, barring significant developmental retardation, have the potential to develop and learn a variety of fundamental and special motor activities. Such motor acts comprise an integral part of the developing child's behavioral repertoire. Furthermore, it is through the medium of movement activities that many of the child's experiences with his environments, especially early experiences, are largely mediated.

Many factors influence the motor development and activity of children during infancy and childhood. Factors such as genotype, size, physique, rate of maturation, child-rearing atmosphere, socioeconomic status, ethnicity, nutritional status, and sibling status, though not mutually exclusive, may affect the course of motor development. This discussion considers several factors which have been related to motor development during infancy and early childhood (preschool years). These factors can be viewed as correlates of motor development in the sense that they might be related to and/or might condition or modify the expression of the underlying neuromotor processes.

Motor development is a gradual process of continuing modification of movement patterns based upon the individual's genetic potential, the re-

*Social and Biological Predictors of
Nutritional Status, Physical Growth,
and Neurological Development*

sidual effects of prior experiences, and the new movement experience per se. The developing infant and young child must also adapt to the demands and stresses imposed by his environments, and, in turn, these environments will have an impact on the child's progress in the motor sphere. Hence, motor development is a product of an Organism–Environment interaction and perhaps covariation. The kinds of interactions can vary in different cultures, for example, kinds of stimulation and expected responses. In this vast array of actual and potential Organism–Environment interactions and covariations, variable effects on the development of motor abilities may become apparent.

## OVERVIEW OF MOTOR DEVELOPMENT DURING INFANCY AND EARLY CHILDHOOD

The motor responses of the neonate are extensions of motor patterns established during fetal development. The newborn is essentially at a functional level and reacts to stimulation in a total way. Within this matrix of generalized motor activity, however, there are certain noticeable reflexes that are either present at birth or appear during infancy.

### Reflexes of Infancy

The newborn is endowed with many established reflex patterns that enable it to adapt to the extrauterine environment. Some of the reflexes are mediated at the spinal cord level, whereas others require the integration of brain stem centers, the labyrinths, and other immature nervous centers. Several of the more commonly described reflexes characteristic of the infant early in life will be described (see Caputo, Accardo, Vining, Rubenstein, & Harryman, 1978; Dekaban, 1959; Illingworth, 1967).

Reflexes associated with feeding are well developed in the newborn. These include the sucking, rooting, and tongue retrusion reflexes. Pupillary, corneal, and blinking responses are also well established, while others are present but are more difficult to elicit, for example, the deep tendon and abdominal reflexes.

Although the newborn infant possesses no effective means of locomotion, certain of his responses resemble later voluntary locomotor movement. Included among the locomotor reflexes are reactions similar to creeping, standing, stepping, and even swimming if the infant is placed in water.

The Moro reflex is one of the most consistent reflex patterns in the newborn infant from birth to 3 months of age. It is an extensor response, elicited by striking the surface upon which the infant is lying or by a loud noise.

Upon such stimulation, the neonate reacts with an extension and abduction of the extremities and a noticeable tremor in the hands and feet.

The palmar grasp reflex is a flexor response elicited by placing an object in contact with the infant's palm. It is characterized by a relatively strong flexion of the palm and fingers without thumb opposition.

The plantar reflex consists of an extension or flexion of the toes in response to gentle stroking of the sole of the foot. The extension response is generally most frequent, but the plantar reflex shows more variable responses.

The tonic neck reflex is present in some form, probably incomplete, in the normal newborn infant. When the head is turned to one side, the infant responds reflexly with an increase in muscle tone and extension of both extremities of the side to which the face is turned and by a flexion of the arm and leg of the opposite side.

There is a group of reflexes, collectively called the righting reflexes, that is not completely developed in the newborn infant, but appears later in infancy. The righting reflexes function to help the child regain his balance when, for some reason or other, it is lost. These reflexes play an important role in the development of motor control leading to erect posture, walking, and other activities. According to Bobath (1954):

> The righting reflexes, primitive as they are, enable the child to turn on his side, to roll over to prone lying, to lift his head, to get on hands and knees, and to sit. Though the child's early motor behavior is thus governed by a group of reflexes integrated at a sub-cortical level, the child soon learns to use these basic patterns of co-ordination for his voluntary activities [p. 19].

Variation is the rule rather than the exception in the infant's reflex behavior. There is a wide range of variation in reflex responses among different infants as well as within the same infants. They also may vary depending on the behavioral states investigated (Lenard, von Bernuth, & Prechtl, 1968).

The reflexes of infancy are thus expressions of the immaturity of the infant's nervous system. They provide an important means of assessing the integrity of the developing neuromuscular system early in life. The absence, delayed appearance or disappearance, persistence, or reappearance of certain reflexes may be indicative of neurological disorders (Dekaban, 1959; Johnson, 1958).

The motor activity of the neonate is characterized by an absence of volitional activity and a lack of inhibition of the segmental apparatus, indicating a lack of cerebral control. However, as the central nervous system gradually matures, cortical inhibitory functions begin to operate, reflex movements gradually diminish, and voluntary motor control commences. Evidence suggests that the reflexes are not lost; rather, they are inhibited by the higher brain centers. This becomes apparent in cases of central nervous system pathology, during the administration of drugs, under conditions of stress, and in the aged, when these reflexes can be demonstrated again (Dekaban, 1959; Hellebrant, Houtz, Partridge, & Walters, 1956; Paulson & Gottlieb, 1968). The tonic neck reflex can also be elicited in normal adult subjects by manipulating postural states (Hellebrandt, Schade, & Carns, 1962).

## General Motor Development during Infancy

Motor development during infancy and early childhood has been approached in a variety of ways by researchers in a variety of disciplines,

TABLE 7.1

Selected Motor Items from the Bayley Scales of Infant Development[a]

| Test item | Age placement (months) | Age range (months) |
|---|---|---|
| Head erect vertical | 0.8 | .3–3 |
| Head erect and steady | 1.6 | .7–4 |
| Turns from side to back | 1.8 | .7–5 |
| Sits with support | 2.3 | 1–5 |
| Holds head steady | 2.5 | 1–5 |
| Cube: Ulnar palmar prehension | 3.7 | 2–7 |
| Sits with slight support | 3.8 | 2–6 |
| Turns from back to side | 4.4 | 2–7 |
| Cube: Partial thumb opposition | 4.9 | 4–8 |
| Sits alone momentarily | 5.3 | 4–8 |
| Pulls to sitting position | 5.3 | 4–8 |
| Rolls from back to stomach | 6.4 | 4–10 |
| Cube: Complete thumb opposition | 6.9 | 5–9 |
| Sits alone, good coordination | 6.9 | 5–10 |
| Pellet: Partial finger prehension | 7.4 | 6–10 |
| Raises self to sitting position | 8.3 | 6–11 |
| Pulls to standing position | 8.1 | 5–12 |
| Stands up by furniture | 8.6 | 6–12 |
| Stepping movements | 8.8 | 6–12 |
| Pellet: Fine prehension | 8.9 | 7–12 |
| Walks with help | 9.6 | 7–12 |
| Sits down | 9.6 | 7–14 |
| Stands alone | 11.0 | 9–16 |
| Walks alone | 11.7 | 9–17 |
| Walks up stairs with help | 16.1 | 12–23 |
| Walks down stairs with help | 16.4 | 13–23 |
| Walks up stairs alone; both feet on each step | 25.1 | 18–30+ |
| Walks down stairs alone; both feet on each step | 25.8 | 19–30+ |
| Jumps off floor; both feet | 23.4 | 17–30+ |

[a] Adapted from Bayley (1969).

especially psychologists, pediatricians, and physical educators. The approaches generally take two forms. The first is concerned with the motor "unfolding" of the child as a part of overall behavioral development during infancy and early childhood. The second approach is concerned with the development of specific postural states and movement patterns, for example, the progression from prone to upright posture and then to walking, the sequence of development leading to mature patterns of jumping, throwing, and running, and so on. There is, of course, considerable overlap between the approaches, as is illustrated in the observation that many of the items used in general development scales are concerned with the attainment of the milestones leading to independent walking (see following).

The literature on motor development contains many descriptions and timetables for the attainment of postural, locomotor, and prehensile control during the first 2 years of life, and then of various motor achievements during the immediate preschool years (up through 5 years of age). The data are largely descriptive and are primarily "stage and age" oriented, that is, children are expected to demonstrate certain levels of motor competence at certain chronological ages. Although variation is considered in early motor development, the traditional and most frequently cited studies have the inherent, sequential motor unfolding of the child as the central theme, either implicitly or explicitly. This sequential development is viewed as representing the gradual pattern of neuromuscular maturation in the child. There is a need for further study of individual differences in motor abilities and their interrelationships during infancy and early childhood.

General motor development during infancy and early childhood is well exemplified in the widely used developmental scales of Bayley (1935, 1969) and Gesell and Amatruda (1947; see also Knobloch & Pasamanick, 1974), as well as in modifications of these scales (Knobloch, Pasamanick, & Sherard, 1966). Table 7.1 illustrates selected motor items from the revised Bayley scales of infant development (Bayley, 1969), while Table 7.2 illustrates the gross motor items from the Denver Developmental Screening Test (Frankenburg & Dodds, 1967).[1] The tables indicate age placement and normal variation in the attainment of selected motor tasks. The Bayley scales consist of 81 motor items (29 of which are indicated in Table 7.1), which were standardized on 1262 children divided among 14 age groups, 2–30 months of age. The sample was stratified according to the 1960 United States population census. The Denver Developmental Screening Test norms are based upon 1036 Denver children, 1 month to 6 years of age. The scales are

[1]The Bayley Scales of Infant Development also include mental development test items, while the Denver Developmental Screening Test also includes fine motor-adaptive, language, and personal social functions.

**TABLE 7.2**

**Age at Which 50% of Children Pass Selected Gross Motor Items in the Denver Developmental Screening Test**[a]

| Test item | Age |
|---|---|
| Prone, head up 90° | 2.2 months |
| Prone, chest up, arm support | 3.0 |
| Sits, head steady | 2.9 |
| Rolls over | 2.8 |
| Pulls to sit, no head lag | 4.2 |
| Sits without support | 5.5 |
| Stands holding on | 5.8 |
| Pulls self to stand | 7.6 |
| Walks holding on furniture | 9.2 |
| Stands alone well | 11.5 |
| Stoops and recovers | 11.6 |
| Walks well | 12.1 |
| Walks backwards | 14.3 |
| Walks up steps | 17.0 |
| Kicks ball forward | 20.0 |
| Throws ball overhand | 19.8 |
| Balances on one foot for 1 sec | 2.5 years |
| Jumps in place | 22.3 months |
| Pedals trike | 23.9 months |
| Broad jump | 2.8 years |
| Balances on one foot for 5 sec | 3.2 |
| Balances on one foot 10 sec | 4.5 years |
| Hops on one foot | 3.4 |
| Catches bounced ball | 3.9 |
| Heel-to-toe walk | 3.6 |
| Backward heel-toe | 4.7 |

[a] Adapted from Frankenburg and Dodds (1967).

presented for both sexes combined. Differences between boys and girls, however, are apparent for specific skill items during early childhood and will be considered later.

Developmental scales such as the Bayley Scales of Infant Development and the Denver Developmental Screening Test are essentially schedules of sensory and motor achievements during the first 2 years of life. As the child gets older, test items become more specific. One of the principal purposes of such developmental tests is as a screening device to identify children with developmental problems, which might be indicative of neurological deficits (Illingworth, 1967) or potential learning difficulties in school (Frankenburg, Dick, & Carland, 1975; Frankenburg & Dodds, 1967; Sandler, van Campen, Ratner, Stafford, & Weismar, 1970; Thorpe & Werner, 1974). Emphasis is on early identification and diagnosis so that therapy and/or other forms of intervention can be initiated as early as necessary. The range of variation in normal motor development, however, is considerable. The sequence of development, though rather uniform, also shows occasional omissions and reversals. Such occurrences are not necessarily related to developmental retardation, but are an aspect of developmental individuality and of rearing environments.

## Development of Walking

Independent walking is the major motor development task during infancy. The developmental changes leading to walking behavior are essentially a series of postural changes through which the infant gains the control necessary to maintain upright posture and then locomotion. The general sequence of developmental adjustments leading to walking behavior have been described in detail (see, for example, Gesell, 1954; McGraw, 1945; Pikler, 1968; Shirley, 1931), and can be summarized in general terms as follows. The infant gradually attains control of the head, upper trunk, and upper extremities. Control of the entire trunk follows, first in the development of sitting posture with support and then alone. This is followed by active efforts at locomotion by means of prone progression. Active efforts at upright posture follow, the child standing first with support and then without support. Finally, independent walking develops, the initial efforts at locomotion being rather stiff-legged and generally flat-footed, with a wide base of support and the arms outstretched for balance.

Median ages of walking for several samples are presented in Table 7.3. The data are for boys and girls combined, since evidence of sex differences in age of walking is not consistent. With several exceptions, the range between reported medians is approximately 2–3 months, a relatively narrow range. This is especially noteworthy, for comparisons of age at walking studies are confounded by problems of definition as well as by errors of mothers' recall. Walking is variously defined as first steps alone, taking a step unassisted, first steps, walking a few steps without support, walking well, and taking at least three steps without support.

The significance of upright posture and independent locomotion cannot be overemphasized. It is the distinctly human trait, which requires the ability to support and balance the upright body and to execute stepping movements. The walking pattern is the foundation upon which many motor skills develop or are learned. The ability to walk affords the developing child a new and more rapid means of locomotion, with many possible variations. It likewise frees the hands from their role as supports, so that a variety of manipulative experiences and skills are now possible.

TABLE 7.3

Median and/or Mean Age (Months) of Walking for a Variety of Samples (Sexes Combined)

| Sample | Median or mean | Reference |
| --- | --- | --- |
| United States | | |
| Iowa, white | 13.54 | Smith et al. (1930) |
| California | 13.00[a] | Bayley (1935) |
| New York | 13.30 | Peatman and Higgons (1940) |
| Philadelphia, white | 13.30 | Rhoads et al. (1945) |
| Philadelphia, negro | 13.30 | Rhoads et al. (1945) |
| Heterogeneous United States, white | 12.40[b] | Bayley (1965) |
| Heterogeneous United States, negro | 11.40[b] | Bayley (1965) |
| Denver | 12.10 | Frankenburg and Dodds (1967) |
| Stratified United States sample | 11.70[a] | Bayley (1969) |
| American Indians | | |
|    Hopi, cradleboard used | 14.30[c] | Dennis (1940) |
|    Hopi, cradleboard not used | 14.50[c] | Dennis (1940) |
|    Tewa, cradled for daytime naps | 13.70[c] | Dennis (1940) |
| Peru | | |
|    Quechua (altitude residents, 4050 m) | 16.20 | Baker et al. (n.d.) |
| Europe | | |
| Brussels | 12.48 | Hindley et al. (1966) |
| London | 13.23 | Hindley et al. (1966) |
| Paris | 13.58 | Hindley et al. (1966) |
| Stockholm | 12.44 | Hindley et al. (1966) |
| Zurich | 13.63 | Hindley et al. (1966) |
| Newcastle | 12.80 | Neligan and Prudham (1969) |
| London, English | 12.80 | Pollak and Mitchell (1974) |
| London, West Indian | 12.70 | Pollak and Mitchell (1974) |
| London, Cypriot | 12.90 | Pollak and Mitchell (1974) |
| Africa | | |
|    Uganda, Baganda, rural | 11.70 | Kilbride et al. (1970) |
| Hawaii | | |
| Chinese | 12.72 | Smith et al. (1930) |
| Filipino | 12.50 | Smith et al. (1930) |
| Haole | 12.06 | Smith et al. (1930) |
| Hawaiian | 12.63 | Smith et al. (1930) |
| Japanese | 12.82 | Smith et al. (1930) |
| Korean | 12.50 | Smith et al. (1930) |
| Portuguese | 13.00 | Smith et al. (1930) |

[a] Age placement on Bayley Scales of Infant Development.
[b] Estimates from graphs of percentage passing at each age.
[c] Estimated from grouped data.

The attainment of independent walking does not indicate achievement of the mature walking pattern. The latter develops gradually. Stride length, walking speed, and cadence increase, the width of the stepping base decreases, and movement patterns show greater reproducibility (see Burnett & Johnson, 1971; Scrutton, 1969; Statham & Murray, 1971).

## General Motor Development during Early Childhood

With the development and refinement of the walking pattern, the child's control of his locomotor abilities improves so that independent action is considerable. This is a period of increasing experimentation with a variety of motor tasks; thus it is a period of gradual and progressive motor development and learning. The development of fundamental motor skills is one of the basic tasks of the preschool years. These skills are the elementary forms of movement which can be classified as locomotor (walk, run, jump, gallop, hop, skip, and so on), nonlocomotor (push, pull, bend, swing, and so on), and manipulative (throw, catch, strike, kick, and so on) (Malina, 1980). Fundamental motor skills ordinarily develop by 6 or 7 years of age, and it is generally agreed that after these ages, no new basic skills appear in the child's movement repertoire (Espenschade & Eckert, 1974). Rather, the quality of performance continues to improve as the fundamental patterns are refined and integrated into more complex movement sequences. There are, however, a number of children 5 through 8 years of age who do not have sufficient coordination and control to accomplish specified fundamental motor tasks successfully (see, for example, Gutteridge, 1939; Keogh, 1965; Kiphard & Schilling, 1970).

The achievements of 3-, 4-, and 5-year-old children in fundamental motor skills have been discussed in detail by Rarick (1961) and more recently summarized by De Oreo (1974) and Malina (1980). Motor performance improves with age during the preschool years, although not necessarily in a smooth progression. Variation in performance within an age group, from age to age, and within individual children is considerable during early childhood. Preschool children commonly show a tendency to perform well at one occasion only to perform poorly at the next. This tendency is suggestive of Gesell's (1954) concept of "reciprocal interweaving," that is, development is characterized by alternating from mature stages to less mature stages, and then back to mature stages. Such seemingly irregular developmental trends may be related to the fact that preschool children are learning many new activities, so that when a mature pattern is attained in one task, the child might attempt other movement pursuits that detract from the mature pattern originally demonstrated, resulting in a reversion to a less mature movement pattern.

## CORRELATES OF MOTOR DEVELOPMENT DURING INFANCY
## AND EARLY CHILDHOOD

The preceding discussion would seem to indicate a considerable body of literature on motor development during infancy and childhood. The data, however, are largely descriptive and normative. They focus on the sequence (stages) and timing (ages) of motor development. Correlates of motor development must also be considered. These can take the form of the underlying neuromotor processes (e.g., neural maturation and myelination, error detection and correction, feedback control, integration of sensory, perceptual, and cognitive factors, and so on), or the form of the conditioning factors (e.g., physique, child rearing, cultural aspects, and so on). The two suggested forms of correlates are not mutually exclusive; the degree of sensory and perceptual input, for example, will be mediated by culturally determined behavior patterns of the group of which the child is a member.

Although the present discussion will consider several correlates of motor development, studies of the developmental sequences and stages should not be overlooked. The fundamental motor skills of infancy and childhood develop sequentially, and the sequence is generally uniform although the rate of development varies. There are, however, possible exceptions to the sequence of early motor development that deserve consideration, as do factors related to variation in rate. Variation in the sequence of motor development might be related to a number of factors in the environments of the developing child, such as different rearing conditions, opportunity for practice, availability of toys and equipment, extent of infantile stimulation, and so on. A commonly cited example of a sequential exception in early motor development is that noted by Mead and Macgregor (1951) in a small sample of Balinese children:

> Where the American children go from frogging to creeping on all fours, then to standing and walking, with squatting coming after standing, the Balinese children, who do much less creeping... combine frogging, creeping, and all-fours behavior simultaneously in a flexible, interchangeable state, from which they go from sitting to squatting to standing [p. 181].

Mead and Macgregor relate this sequential variation to the manner in which Balinese adults carry and handle their children (passively, involving minimal interaction).

The motor programming of an Eskimo youth to hunt (Laughlin, 1968) also provides possibilities for sequential variation in motor development. The programming includes a series of general and specific activities beginning very early in childhood, at the age of walking. Activities include special tendon-lengthening exercises and throwing exercises from a seated position designed for hunting from a kayak. The special exercises are reinforced in turn by a series of games.

The range of normal variation in motor development during infancy and early childhood, though rather substantial, is perhaps extended by various cultural practices, demands, and sanctions. There is thus a need for further descriptive developmental data which incorporate significant correlates as critical variables.

The descriptions of ages and stages of motor development might also be reconsidered in terms of the timing of entry into a specific stage of motor behavior, the rate of attaining the stage, and the duration of the stage of motor behavior. For example, are certain stages in a developmental sequence passed through more rapidly than others? How long might a stage last? Can the length of a particular stage be modified by environmental circumstances? If so, when and to what extent? What might be the ideal age to introduce attempts to enhance motor competence? What stages are more discriminating in terms of predicting subsequent motor behavior? Note, however, that motor development, like development in general, is a continuous process, upon which researchers superimpose stages or levels, which themselves may vary between investigators.

## Genetic

Twin studies have been used to estimate genetic influences on motor development and performance. Studies of twins during infancy indicate greater similarity among monozygotic than among dizygotic twin pairs, that is, greater within pair differences for fraternal twins (Freedman & Keller, 1963; Gifford, Murawski, Brazelton, & Young, 1966; Wilson & Harpring, 1972). Two early studies of sitting-up and walking in infant twins (Bossik, 1934; Verschuer, 1927) indicate greater concordance among monozygotic twins (67% and 69%) than among dizygotic twins (35 and 30%) for first efforts at walking. The timing of sitting-up behavior, however, was almost equally concordant among both identical and fraternal twins (82 and 76%, respectively). Although twin data on other aspects and subsequent motor development during infancy and early childhood are not extensive, they do indicate a close correspondence in the development of motor activities among monozygotic twins early in life (see Gesell, 1954).

Studies at older ages indicate a high degree of heritability in such fine motor tasks as pursuit rotor tracking, hand steadiness, card sorting, tapping speed, and two-hand coordination (McNemar, 1933; Vandenberg, 1962, 1966). However, results of twin studies are discordant and equivocal for nerve conduction velocity, reaction time, and reflex time (Komi, Klissouras,

& Karvinen, 1973; Vandenberg, 1962). In the study by Komi *et al.* (1973), female dizygotic twins showed as much variability in the neuromuscular tasks as did monozygotic twins, leading the authors to conclude that such measures might be more susceptible to environmental influences in girls than in boys.

Using gross motor skills in monozygotic and dizygotic twins 11 to 25 years of age, Kovar (1974, 1975) noted that speed (running) and explosive power (jumping, throwing) are more influenced by genetic factors than other motor tasks (e.g., errors in a coordination task, bent arm hang). Analyzing the running pattern of monozygotic and dizygotic twins 9–12 years of age, Skład (1972) observed greater similarity in the kinetic structure of running performance in the monozygotic twins.

Observations derived from studies of motor development and performance of twins, though important, leave several unanswered questions. For example, are monozygotic twins more similar in motor tasks because of genetic similarity or because of environmental pressures for similarity? Or, how important is the role of mutual imitation in the motor development of twins? Similar questions can be extended to the genetic basis of the rate of learning motor skills. Skład (1975) compared the learning curves and rate of improvement in monozygotic and dizygotic twins during the course of learning three motor tasks: ball throwing, tapping, and precision movements. Monozygotic twins were more similar in motor learning than were dizygotic twins. Furthermore, performance levels and rate of learning appeared to be more influenced by genetic factors in boys than in girls. More recently, Marisi (1977) noted a high degree of genetic determination of initial levels of performance on a pursuit rotor apparatus. However, with practice, the strength of genetic determination diminished systematically.

The preceding indicates that genetic factors are important correlates of motor development and performance. This genetic basis can perhaps be viewed in terms of either a predisposition toward motor skills or the capacity to acquire them. The genetic basis can also be viewed as representing potential; whether the potential is attained or developed depends upon the environments in which the child is reared. Genes need a substrate upon which to act, and the nature of the substrate can influence the course of development.

## Status at Birth

Since birth marks the transition from a uterine to an extrauterine existence, it is of interest to view the relationship between status at birth or shortly thereafter, and subsequent motor development. Rosenblith (1966), for example, reported a highly significant prognostic relationship between neonatal assessment of motor status and fine and gross motor development as assessed by the Bayley scales at 8 months of age. Edwards (1968) reported significant relationships between Apgar scores taken at 1 and 5 min after birth and both fine and gross motor performance at 4 years of age.

The significance of such observations is puzzling and, needless to say, rather complex. An infant's status at birth is strongly related to maternal factors, especially in terms of birthweight and length (Penrose, 1961; Tanner, 1974). Birthweight, excluding low-birthweight infants, is in general not consistently related to motor development status at 4 months of age (Solomons & Solomons, 1964), to the age at walking alone (Pineau, 1961), and to gross motor coordination at 4 years of age (Edwards, 1968). On the other hand, fetal movements during the last trimester are significantly related to postnatal motor development during the first year (Richards & Newbery, 1938; Walters, 1965). It is apparent that a number of factors are already operating at this early stage of life, and perhaps bear a significant relationship to motor development. Specific operations of these influences and undoubtedly others in mediating and modifying motor development are unclear.

## Size, Physique, and Composition

Although the preceding data suggest an independence of early motor development and birthweight, the relationship of motor development and other physical characteristics needs to be examined. Studies including measures of size, build, and composition indicate some relationship between these indices and motor development in infancy (Bayley, 1935; Norval, 1947; Peatman & Higgons, 1942; Shirley, 1931). The relationship, as expected, is not simple, and is most apparent at the extremes of the physique continuum, the very linear and the very heavy and the long-legged and the short-legged. Muscular and small-boned infants (Shirley, 1931) and those of linear frame (Norval, 1947), for example, tend to walk at an earlier age. Garn (1966) noted that infants with a greater lean body mass attain superior scores on early developmental tasks and that leg muscle mass at 6 months of age is predictive of walking unaided at 1 year.

Analyses of physique and body composition relative to motor development during the preschool years are lacking (see Malina & Rarick, 1973; Malina, 1975). This lack and the limited observations on infants emphasize the need to extend studies of size, physique, and body composition relative to motor development to infancy and the preschool ages. Subcutaneous fat, for example, decreases from about 1 year of age through the preschool years, the years when basic motor skills are developing at a very rapid rate. Unfortunately, we know very little about the impact of the body's changing composition on the development of motor skills early in life. Behavioral correlates of size, physique, and composition also need to be investigated. Do parents expect and/or encourage certain forms of behavior from children differing in physique, for example, the fat infant as opposed to the thin, muscular infant? Conversely, how does the motor progress of the child influence parental rearing attitudes and expectations?

## Environmental Correlates

The environments in which a child is reared represent a substrate. The term environment is used in the plural, for an individual's environments are many. Environments are likewise cumulative, exerting their influences early in life, in many instances prenatally, and throughout life. The cumulative as well as complex nature of an individual's environments thus renders extremely difficult the partitioning of effects due to specific factors, for example, maternal care, nutrition, and the physical development of the child.

A child must adapt to the stresses imposed by his environments, and, as such, these environments in turn will undoubtedly have an impact on the child's developmental progress, including, of course, motor development. The accurate delineation, definition, and assessment of such correlates in the motor development of the child are thus difficult tasks.

## Nutrition

Interest in nutrition as a critical correlate of psychomotor development is considerable. An adequate nutritional intake is essential to support the needs of normal growth and development, including of course motor development. Severely undernourished infants and young children are retarded in motor development and show neuromuscular involvement (e.g., reduced nerve conduction velocities) (Ashem & Janes, 1978; Cravioto, 1968; Geber & Dean, 1956; Kumar, Ghai, & Singh, 1977a, 1977b; Monckeberg, 1968; Rendon, Hurtado, & Arathoon, 1969). It must be recognized that there are a variety of environmental factors that may negatively influence early development. Severe undernutrition is accompanied by stunted physical growth and skeletal maturation, muscle wasting, general psychomotor change, and reduced levels of physical activity. Furthermore, retarded motor development is indicated as one of the "constant" signs of kwashiorkor (Jelliffe, 1966).

When nutritional stress is considered, the role of organic changes in the central nervous system as underlying retarded development is usually emphasized. However, disturbances in social experiences also accompany malnutrition, and may interact with organic changes. In other words, there is more to the relationship of malnutrition and retarded development than food alone. As summarized by Birch (1968): "Children who are ill-nourished are reduced in their responsiveness to the environment, distracted by their visceral state, and reduced in their ability to progress and endure in learning conditions [p. 596]."

The persistence of detrimental changes associated with severe undernutrition may be dependent upon the timing, severity, and duration of the nutritional stress. Children put on nutritionally adequate diets show some catch-up in growth and development. Nevertheless, it is difficult to assess how much of the child's potential is affected by the nutritional stress. In a 3- to 6-year follow-up of 14 severely malnourished children after nutritional recovery, Monckeberg (1968) noted that motor development was still retarded. Two long-term follow-up studies of infants hospitalized for severe protein–energy malnutrition (PEM) during the first 2 or 3 years of life indicate persistent effects on perceptual motor development into adolescence. Stoch and Smythe (1976) noted deficits in visual–motor perception, which reflected deficits at the central neurosensory integration level, in 13- to 18-year-old Cape Town youths ($N = 20$) followed since hospitalization for marasmus during infancy. Hoorweg and Stanfield (1976) reported lower Lincoln–Oseretsky motor development scores in 11- to 17-year-old Kampala children ($N = 60$), who were hospitalized for PEM between 8 and 27 months of age. Interestingly, there was no relationship between subsequent motor performance and the age at hospital admission, and both "acute malnutrition" and "chronic undernutrition" had similar relationships to motor development.

The preceding has considered severe nutritional inadequacy early in life, primarily due to the widespread prevalence of PEM, associated mortality, and physical and behavioral consequences. Such observations also have implications for motor development in general. What level of development might we expect from children reared at marginally adequate nutritional levels (as compared to those who have been hospitalized for severe nutritional inadequacy)? The question can also be extended to children of school age in those areas in which undernutrition is a chronic problem. School age children in these areas are somewhat special, in the sense that they have survived an infancy and early childhood characterized by undernutrition and infectious disease. Functional implications of the growth retardation (i.e., smaller body size and reduced muscle mass) characteristic of these children warrant concern. There is a need to consider the implications of a childhood characterized by undernutrition on the development and refinement of motor skills, the acquisition of new skills, the development and expression of muscular strength, and so on.

The influence of nutritional inadequacy early in life on motor development may be related to the brain growth spurt described by Dobbing and Sands (1973). The spurt is a period of rapid brain growth which begins at about mid-pregnancy and continues through 3 or 4 years of age. The early part of the spurt, from mid-pregnancy to about 18 months, is characterized by rapid multiplication of glial cells, while the latter part, which lasts to 3 or 4 years, is characterized by myelinization. The extent of the spurt, however, varies with region of the brain, and the unique pattern characteristic of the cerebellum is relevant to motor development. The cerebellum starts its growth spurt later than the other parts (forebrain and stem), but completes the spurt earlier, that is, it is getting its growth faster and over a shorter period of time.

Functions of the cerebellum include the development and maintenance of neuromuscular coordination, balance, and muscle tone. Hence, potential interference with the growth spurt of the cerebellum through nutritional inadequacy prenatally and early postnatally might possibly interfere with normal motor development. Studies of adult rats undernourished during most of gestation and all of lactation indicate poor motor performance, which was attributable to impaired motor coordination. The undernourished rats also had smaller cerebella (Lynch, Smart, & Dobbing, 1975). These data thus suggest a differential vulnerability of the cerebellum to early nutritional stress, with resulting impairments in motor coordination. Implications for motor development in infants and young children are obvious.

### Rearing and Social Class

Studies of child-rearing practices across social class, ethnic groups, and different cultures have primarily concerned socialization and personality development. Emphasis is generally placed upon feeding practices, toilet training, age at weaning, independence and aggression training, mother–infant attachment, and so on. More recently, attention has been given to cognitive development and academic motivation relative to the child-rearing environment, especially in minority, lower class, and/or disadvantaged children. Rearing studies are also limited to a large extent to infancy and early childhood, and have generally not been concerned with motor development and behavior as the central focus of study, save for the age of walking alone.

One can thus inquire as to the effects of child care practices on motor development and motor activity during infancy and childhood. More specifically, how are child-rearing practices translated into different motor development levels or performance styles? Do children reared in overprotective or restrictive atmospheres develop and behave differently in motor activities than children reared in permissive, less protective atmospheres?

Child-rearing practices vary across social class and ethnic group (see, for example, Bronfenbrenner, 1958; Chamberlin, 1974, 1978; Hess, 1970; Jackson, 1973; Waters & Crandall, 1964). Several studies have examined social class criteria relative to early motor development. Bayley and Jones (1937), for example, reported no relationship between socioeconomic variables and age of first walking independently. There was, however, a tendency for an increased number of negative correlations between motor scores and socioeconomic variables, implying somewhat more rapid motor development in children from the lower social strata. Neligan and Prudham (1969) also reported a social class difference in the age of independent walking among a sample of Newcastle (England) children, the social class difference favoring the lower class children. Neligan and Prudham (1969) interpreted the observations as possibly reflecting "deprivation of the opportunity to learn resulting from overprotection [p. 417]" in the upper social class. Hindley, Filliozat, Klackenberg, Nicolet-Meister, and Sand (1966), on the other hand, did not find any social class difference in the age of walking among five European longitudinal samples. There were, however, significant differences between the five samples in the mean age of walking alone.

During early childhood, socioeconomic background is often implicated as an important factor affecting the activity pursuits of children and presumably their development in motor spheres (see Malina, 1973). In general, data suggest greater freedom to move about the neighborhood among lower socioeconomic background children. Such an atmosphere might be conducive to greater freedom of motor activity and opportunity for practice. It should be noted that many of these studies consider ethnic variation in rearing, life style, patterns of socialization, and so on, with little, if any, consideration for motor development and activity (considerations of ethnic aspects of motor development follow).

## Rearing and Sex Differences

It is well known that cultural conditioning for specific sex-associated roles begins early in life. Mothers, for example, treat sons differently than daughters, and this sex difference begins early in infancy (Goldberg & Lewis, 1969; Moss, 1967). Behavioral differences are also apparent early in life. One-year-old boys, for example, already spend more time in gross motor activity, while girls of the same age spend more time in fine motor activity (Goldberg & Lewis, 1969). Boys are also more vigorous in their play and show more exploratory behavior than girls, who are more dependent and prefer a more quiet style of play (Goldberg & Lewis, 1969). Observations on nursery school children 2 to 5 years of age offer similar evidence. Boys spend more time in "rough and tumble" gross motor activities, while girls spend more time in activities requiring fine motor manipulation (Blurton Jones, 1967; Clark, Wyon, & Richards, 1969). In a related study, Walker (1962) compared behavior of mesomorphic boys and girls. Although similar in physique, mesomorphic girls tend to channel their energies into social activities, while mesomorphic boys channel their energies into gross motor activities. Walker suggests that variations in physical energy and in body sensitivity to energy needs may thus be important mediating links between physique and behavior. It would appear, however, that at these early ages, the expectations of our culture already have an impact on what children sense is appropriate behavior for each sex.

The translation of such descriptive data into specific correlates of motor development of preschool boys and girls is difficult and needs a finer approach relating generalized observations to the development of specific motor patterns. Sex differences in motor development during infancy are not systematically apparent (Bayley, 1935, 1965; Frankenburg & Dodds, 1967), although sex differences in rearing practices and play behavior are apparent. Sex differences in motor development and performance, however, are evident during early childhood. From about 2 to 5 years of age, girls, on the average, excel in tasks requiring jumping, hopping, rhythmic locomotion, and balance, while boys generally perform better in tasks requiring strength and speed (Espenschade & Eckert, 1974; Frankenburg & Dodds, 1967; Sinclair, 1971; Welon & Sekita, 1975). From the age of 5 or 6 years on, boys generally perform better in running, jumping, and throwing activities, while girls excel in hopping (Espenschade & Eckert, 1974; Keogh, 1965). Balancing activities show no consistent pattern of sex difference, although girls show better performances at some ages (Keogh, 1965).

The preceding observations are based on group averages and mask the considerable overlap that does exist. The observations, however, need to be related to sex differences in activity interests, opportunity for practice, opportunity and frequency of participation, requirements of specific activities, and so on. Furthermore, the cultural socialization or exclusion of the young girl from activities requiring physical strength and skill is perhaps an important underlying correlate. The significance of western cultural influences on the differential acquisition of motor skills by boys and girls during early childhood needs consideration. These observations suggest, perhaps, differences in cultural expectations and opportunities for boys and girls. These may be viewed in terms of available models to mimic (e.g., father, athletes, etc.), the models that are encouraged, opportunities for practice, parental motivation, sibling relationships, and so on. Motor skill development and acquisition are an integral part of the child's socialization process and they have not received detailed study.

## Rearing and Birth Order

A child's position in the family and sibling-sex status are also factors that influence early motor development. Some data suggest that first born children perform slightly better on motor tasks early in life (Bayley, 1965; Solomons & Solomons, 1964), an observation generally related to greater maternal indulgence and therefore stimulation of the first born compared to later born children. Descriptions of play behavior in nursery school children indicate that first born children spend more time alone, engage in more nonspecific activity, and are generally more dependent upon adults (Clark *et al.*, 1969). Rearing studies of single-child families suggest overprotection, greater restriction on physical mobility, and a strong tendency to keep close track of the child on the part of mothers (Sears, Maccoby, & Levin, 1957). In contrast to an only child, studies of siblings indicate that children with opposite sex siblings have more of the characteristics of the opposite sex than children with siblings of the same sex (Rosenberg & Sutton-Smith, 1964, 1968; see also Sutton-Smith, Roberts, & Rosenberg, 1964). It would be interesting to relate such observations to the motor development and performance of children. For example, does a girl with an older brother develop differently in motor activities or have different activity interests than a girl who has an older sister as a sibling? The same question can be raised for boys with female and male siblings, respectively. On the other hand, the role of a younger sibling in possibly influencing the motor behavior of an older child also warrants study.

### Ethnic Considerations

Available data comparing the early motor development of American Black and White children indicate advanced motor development in Black children during the first 2 or 3 years of life. The differences are more apparent at the younger ages, and superiority in any one class of motor behavior is not responsible for the Black motor precocity (Bayley, 1965; Malina, 1973). These generalizations are not without exception as several studies indicate minor or inconsistent differences in early motor development of Black and White children (Knobloch & Pasamanick, 1958; Walters, 1967). Explanations offered for the observations vary. Some implicate genetic factors, while others indicate socioeconomic variables as affecting the results (Bayley, 1965; Malina, 1973). Note that social class and ethnicity are closely related in the United States. The socioeconomic hypothesis suggests that a more permissive rearing atmosphere characterizes lower socioeconomic classes and enhances motor development (Scott, Ferguson, Jenkins, & Cutter, 1955; Williams & Scott, 1953). Results concerning a socioeconomic interpretation, however, are conflicting. Social class differences in motor development have been reported among American Black (Knobloch & Pasamanick, 1958; Walters 1967) and White infants (Willerman, Broman, & Fiedler, 1970). In these studies, contrary to the suggestions of Scott *et al.* (1955) and Williams and Scott (1953), infants from higher socioeconomic backgrounds had significantly higher motor development scores than those from lower socioeconomic strata. More detailed considerations of the motor development and performance of American Black and White children have been reported elsewhere (Malina, 1969, 1973).

Comparisons of motor development and performance of children with Spanish surnames (Mexican–American, Puerto Rican) are quite limited. Using the Denver Developmental Screening Test, Frankenburg et al. (1975) noted few differences in fine and gross motor items between Anglo (White) and Spanish-surnamed children when controlling for social class (all fathers were unskilled workers). Anglo children were significantly advanced in four motor tasks (all in the first year of life), while the Spanish-surnamed children did not show advancement in any motor tasks. Comparisons of Spanish-surnamed and Black children showed the Black children significantly advanced in 10 fine and gross motor test items. All items were tasks measured during the first year of life. However, after about 3 years of age, the Spanish-surnamed children excelled in two fine motor and one gross motor task. Interpretation of the results is difficult, and may be related to ethnic differences in rearing style. The authors did not consider specific motor items, but only considered components of the Denver Developmental Screening Test as a whole.

## Cross-Cultural Considerations

Cross-cultural observations of early motor development are available for a number of cultural groups. These generally include data for developmental tests (e.g., Bayley, Gesell, Andre-Thomas). However, after the age of 2, the cross-cultural motor development data are scanty at best, with little formally collected motor ability information. This probably reflects the orientation of the researchers, which commonly focuses on cognitive development, mother–infant attachment, Infant–Caretaker interactions, and so on. Since the focus of many studies is cognitive development, motor items on the infant scales are less emphasized as they show reduced correlations with mental items with increasing age (see, for example, Bayley, 1951). The early motor skills are perhaps developing functional specificity as they become more unrelated to cognitive development.

Examples of early motor development data are considered subsequently for samples of children within several cultural groups. Most data are available for sub-Saharan African populations, while less extensive data are available for Jamaica, Mexico, Guatemala, and Japan (see Malina, 1977). Samples of African children are generally precocious in motor development compared with infants of the United States. Precocity against the norms, however, commonly declines with age. Whether this precocity is evident at birth is not entirely clear; however, it is apparent during the first month of life and continues during the first year (Ainsworth, 1967, 1977; Geber, 1956; Geber & Dean, 1957, 1958; Kilbride, Robbins, & Kilbride, 1970; Konner, 1972, 1977; Leiderman & Leiderman, 1977; Leiderman, Bahu, Kagia, Kraemer, & Leiderman, 1973; Super, 1976). There are methodological weaknesses in the African studies (see Warren, 1972), but critical evaluation does not exclude the phenomenon of precocity of African infants in motor development.

The rapid motor development of the African infant in several cultural groups has been attributed to environmental influences, especially to the kinds of mothering and caretaking received, and lack of physical restriction. Early rearing is characterized by physical closeness between mother and child, a constant supply of kinesthetic and tactile stimulation (Ainsworth, 1967, 1977; Goldberg, 1972; Konner, 1972, 1977; Lusk & Lewis, 1972). Observations of 5- and 6-month-old American Black infants show a low to moderate relationship between kinesthetic stimulation and the Bayley psychomotor development index, and fine and gross motor scores (Yarrow, Pedersen, & Rubenstein, 1977). Based upon observations in a Kenyan community, Super (1976) relates African infant motor precocity only to those tasks specifically taught by caretakers and/or incidental effects of daily caretaking practices. Furthermore, among Kenyan communities, encouragement of motor development is a widespread practice. The observations of Leiderman et al. (1973) on Kikuyu infants suggests significant relationships between motor development during infancy and the number of individuals in the household past 40 years of age and the economic status of the father.

These positive correlations are interesting (1) in that they suggest an effect for kinesthetic stimulation and for additional caretaking of the infant by an older woman and/or grandmother in contributing to early motor development, (2) in that they indicate a role for specific teaching, and (3) in that they indicate a small, positive economic effect. The latter is contrary to the observations of Geber and Dean (1958), who suggested that motor precocity was inversely related to social class in Uganda. Interestingly, the Kikuyu data (Leiderman et al., 1973) also indicate a low, negative relationship between motor scores of infants and the number of household members less than 3 years of age.

Three studies of Mayan infants from Mexico and Guatemala provide somewhat different results. Solomons and Solomons (1975) observed consistently accelerated Bayley motor scores during most of the first year of life in Mayan infants in Yucatan. The infants were especially precocious in fine motor items, and slightly delayed in locomotor skills and gross coordination toward the end of the first year. Interestingly, there was no difference in the early motor behavior among three sociocultural groups comprising the Yucatecan infant samples—working- and middle-class Mestizos and rural

Mayan. On the other hand, Brazelton (1972, 1977; see also Brazelton, Robey, & Collier, 1969) reported well-organized neonatal motor responses at birth and shortly after among rural Zinacanteco Indians (Mayan), which were followed by a level of motor development that lagged consistently behind United States standards by about 1 month throughout the first year of life. De Leon, de Licardie, and Cravioto (1964) noted a similar delay in the motor development of rural Guatemalan Mayan (Cakchiquel) infants. The development of independent sitting as well as the development of prehension during the first year showed a progressive delay of 1 or 2 months relative to the Gesell standards. Development of locomotor abilities showed a similar delay relative to the standards. The children progressed in reasonable accord (1 to 2 months) with the standard through 15 months, but became progressively delayed through 48 months. Performance on items of the Gesell adaptive scale also showed a pattern of progressive delay relative to the norms.

Mayan infants are held constantly and are commonly carried on the back during most of their first year of life (Brazelton, 1977; Brazelton *et al.,* 1969; Solomons & Solomons, 1975). Infants, especially lower class and rural, are tightly wrapped in a shawl with head and eyes covered most of the time to protect them from the "evil eye." Brazelton *et al.* (1969) relate the Mother-Child interaction to the imitation and conformity emphasized by the local culture. Such early care, tightly swaddled and covered most of the time, apparently fosters "quiet alertness conducive to imitation and conformity [p. 288]." It should be noted that imitation among rural Zinacantecos is the chief mode of learning in older children, such that children are not confronted with the choice of roles as are children in our cultural complex.

The developmental lag toward the end of the first year and during the second and third years in African and Mayan infants is likely related to the break in continuity of rearing at weaning and to the effects of undernutrition. After weaning, children do not get the adult treatment and attention they had before, while delayed motor development and reduced levels of physical activity accompany PEM. It is also at these ages that stunting in physical growth becomes especially apparent.

The preceding cross-cultural comparisons suggest culturally distinct environmental and child-rearing practices that are related to early motor behavior. Note that the infants are generally compared to western standards, which raises the possibility that some of the observed differences in motor behavior might relate to test items per se. For example, if an infant is never placed in the prone position, it is difficult to elicit a response for test items requiring this position. Placing an infant in this position generally elicits a stress response, which masks the motor performance being tested. In addition, some test items require objects that are not familiar to the particular cultural group, for example, cubes, rattles, spoons, cups, etc. These can perhaps be substituted with culturally appropriate items. Superimposed upon the preceding are problems of stranger-anxiety in older infants and young children, which may make testing or observing motor behavior quite difficult.

Discussion of observed differences in motor development have been generally related to societal variation in mothering and caretaking practices. Relationships, however, do not imply a cause–effect sequence in motor development.

## OVERVIEW

The pattern of motor development during infancy and early childhood has been considered. Motor development is obviously a plastic process. There is variation in the timing and rate of development that can be related to a variety of biocultural correlates. The significance of variation in early motor development for later motor proficiency, however, is not known with certainty, nor is the significance of the effects of both biological and cultural correlates.

The motor activity of the infant and young child presumably represents the foundation upon which subsequent motor proficiency is built. However, the predictive significance of early motor assessments for later, more mature motor patterns is not clear, and not ordinarily investigated. One may ask whether differences in timing and sequence during the first year or two of life lead to parallel differences at later ages. Such data are not available. In other words, it is difficult to extend observations from infancy and early childhood to older ages.

## REFERENCES

Ainsworth, M. D. S. *Infancy in Uganda*. Baltimore: Johns Hopkins University Press, 1967.

Ainsworth, M. D. S. Infant development and mother–infant interaction among Ganda and American families. In P. H. Leiderman, S. R. Tulkin, & A. Rosenfeld (Eds.), *Culture and infancy*. New York: Academic Press, 1977. Pp. 119–149.

Ashem, B., & Janes, M. D. Deleterious effects of chronic undernutrition on cognitive abilities. *Journal of Child Psychology and Psychiatry*, 1978, *19*, 23–31.

Baker, T. S., Little, A. V., & Baker, P. T. *First report on early human development at high altitudes*. Unpublished manuscript, Department of Sociology and Anthropology, Pennsylvania State University, University Park, Pennsylvania, no date.

Bayley, N. The development of motor abilities during the first three years. *Monographs of the Society for Research in Child Development*, 1935, No. 1.

Bayley, N. Development and maturation. In H. Helson (Ed.), *Theoretical foundations of psychology*. New York: Van Nostrand, 1951. Pp. 160–165.

Bayley, N. Comparisons of mental and motor test scores for ages 1–15 months by sex, birth order, race, geographical location, and education of parents. *Child Development*, 1965, *36*, 379–411.

Bayley, N. *Manual for the Bayley scales of infant development*. Berkeley: Psychological Corporation, 1969.

Bayley, N., & Jones, H. E. Environmental correlates of mental and motor development: A cumulative study from infancy to six years. *Child Development*, 1937, *8*, 329–341.

Birch, H. G. Health and the education of socially disadvantaged children. *Developmental Medicine and Child Neurology*, 1968, *10*, 580–599.

Blurton Jones, N. G. An ethological study of some aspects of social behaviour of children in nursery school. In D. Morris (Ed.), *Primate ethology*. Chicago: Aldine, 1967. Pp. 347–368.

Bobath, B. A study of abnormal postural reflex activity in patients with lesions of the central nervous system. *Physiotherapy*, 1954, p. 30 (reprint).

Bossik, L. J. K voprosu o roli nasledstvennosti i sredi v fiziologii i patologii detskovo vovrasta. *Trudi Medytsinsko-Biologicheskovo*, 1934, nr. 3 (as cited by Skład, 1972).

Brazelton, T. B. Implications of infant development among the Mayan Indians of Mexico. *Human Development*, 1972, *15*, 90–111.

Brazelton, T. B. Implications of infant development among the Mayan Indians of Mexico. In P. H. Leiderman, S. R. Tulkin, & A. Rosenfeld (Eds.), *Culture and infancy*. New York: Academic Press, 1977. Pp. 151–187.

Brazelton, T. B., Robey, J. S., & Collier, G. A. Infant development in the Zinacanteco Indians of southern Mexico. *Pediatrics*, 1969, *44*, 274–290.

Bronfenbrenner, U. Socialization and social class through time and space. In E. E. Maccoby, T. M. Newcomb, & E. L. Hartley (Eds.), *Readings in social psychology* (3rd ed.). New York: Holt and Company, 1958. Pp. 400–425.

Burnett, C. N., & Johnson, E. Development of gait in childhood, I and II. *Developmental Medicine and Child Neurology*, 1971, *13*, 196–206, 207–215.

Caputo, A. J., Accardo, P. J., Vining, E. P. G., Rubenstein, J. E., & Harryman, S. *Primitive reflex profile*. Baltimore: University Park Press, 1978.

Chamberlin, R. W. Authoritarian and accommodative child-rearing styles: Their relationships with behavior patterns of 2-year-old children and with other variables. *Journal of Pediatrics*, 1974, *84*, 287–293.

Chamberlin, R. W. Relationships between child-rearing styles and child behavior over time. *American Journal of Diseases of Children*, 1978, *132*, 155–160.

Clark, A. H., Wyon, S. M., & Richards, M. P. M. Free-play in nursery school children. *Journal of Child Psychology and Psychiatry*, 1969, *10*, 205–216.

Cravioto, J. Nutritional deficiencies and mental performance in childhood. In D. C. Glass (Ed.), *Environmental influences*. New York: The Rockefeller University Press and Russell Sage Foundation, 1968. Pp. 3–51.

De Leon, W., de Licardie, E., & Cravioto, J. Operacion Nimiquipalg: VI. Desarrollo psicomotor del niño en una poblacion rural de Guatemala, perteneciente al grupo Cakchiquel. *Guatemala Pediatrica*, 1964, *4*, 92–106.

De Oreo, K. L. The performance and development of fundamental motor skills in preschool children. In M. G. Wade & R. Martens (Eds.), *Psychology of motor behavior and sport*. Urbana, Ill: Human Kinetics Publishers, 1974. Pp. 327–343.

Dekaban, A. *Neurology of infancy*. Baltimore: Williams & Wilkins, 1959.

Dennis, W. *The Hopi child*. New York: Wiley, 1940.

Dobbing, J., & Sands, J. Quantitative growth and development of human brain. *Archives of Disease in Childhood*, 1973, *48*, 757–767.

Edwards, N. The relationship between physical condition immediately after birth and mental performance at age four. *Genetic Psychology Monographs*, 1968, *78*, 257–289.

Espenschade, A., & Eckert, H. Motor development. In W. R. Johnson & E. R. Buskirk (Eds.), *Science and medicine of exercise and sport* (2nd ed.). New York: Harper and Row, 1974. Pp. 322–333.

Frankenburg, W. K., Dick, N. P., & Carland, J. Development of preschool-aged children of different social and ethnic groups: Implications for developmental screening. *Journal of Pediatrics*, 1975, *87*, 125–132.

Frankenburg, W. K., & Dodds, J. B. The Denver Developmental Screening Test. *Journal of Pediatrics*, 1967, *71*, 181–191.

Freedman, D. G., & Keller, B. Inheritance of behavior in infants. *Science*, 1963, *140*, 196–198.

Garn, S. M. Body size and its implications. In L. W. Hoffman & M. L. Hoffman (Eds.), *Review of child development research*, New York: Russel Sage Foundation, 1966. Pp. 529–561.

Geber, M. Développement psycho-moteur de l'enfant Africain. *Courrier*, 1956, *6*, 17–29.

Geber, M., & Dean, R. F. A. The psychological changes accompanying kwashiorkor. *Courrier*, 1956, *6*, 3–15.

Geber, M., & Dean, R. F. A. Gesell tests on African children. *Pediatrics*, 1957, *20*, 1055–1065.

Geber, M., & Dean, R. F. A. Psychomotor development in African children: The effects of social class and the need for improved tests. *Bulletin of the World Health Organization*, 1958, *18*, 471–476.

Gesell, A. The ontogenesis of infant behavior. In L. Carmichael (Ed.), *Manual of child psychology* (2nd ed.). New York: Wiley, 1954. Pp. 335–373.

Gesell, A., & Amatruda, C. S. *Developmental diagnosis* (2nd ed.). New York: Harper and Row, 1947.

Gifford, S., Murawski, B. J., Brazelton, T. B., & Young, G. C. Differences in individual development within a pair of identical twins. *International Journal of Psychoanalysis*, 1966, *47*, 261–286.

Goldberg, S. Infant care and growth in urban Zambia. *Human Development*, 1972, *15*, 77–89.

Goldberg, S., & Lewis, M. Play behavior in the year-old infant: Early sex differences. *Child Development*, 1969, *40*, 21–31.

Gutteridge, M. V. A study of motor achievements of young children. *Archives of Psychology*, number 244, 1939.

Hellebrandt, F. A., Houtz, S. J., Partridge, M. J., & Walters, E. Tonic neck reflexes in exercises of stress in man. *American Journal of Physical Medicine*, 1956, *35*, 144–159.

Hellebrandt, F. A., Schade, M., & Carns, M. L., Methods of evoking the tonic neck reflexes in normal human subjects. *American Journal of Physical Medicine*, 1962, *41*, 90–139.

Hess, R. D. Social class and ethnic influences upon socialization. In P. H. Mussen (Ed.), *Carmichael's manual of child psychology* (Vol. 2, 3rd ed.). New York: Wiley, 1970. Pp. 457–557.

Hindley, C. B., Filliozat, A. M., Klackenberg, G., Nicolet-Meister, D., & Sand, E. A. Differences in age of walking in five European longitudinal samples. *Human Biology*, 1966, *38*, 363–379.

Hoorweg, J. & Stanfield, J. P. The effects of protein energy malnutrition in early childhood on intellectual and motor abilities in later childhood and adolescence. *Developmental Medicine and Child Neurology*, 1976, *18*, 330–350.

Illingworth, R. S. *The development of the infant and young child normal and abnormal* (3rd ed.). London: E. & S. Livingstone, 1967.

Jackson, J. J. Family organization and technology. In K. S. Miller & R. M. Dreger (Eds.),

*Comparative studies of blacks and whites in the United States.* New York: Seminar Press, 1973. Pp. 405–445.

Jelliffe, D. B. *The assessment of the nutritional status of the community.* Geneva: World Health Organization, 1966.

Johnson, E. W. Examination for muscle weakness in infants and small children. *Journal of the American Medical Association,* 1958, *168,* 1306–1313.

Keogh, J. *Motor performance of elementary school children.* Los Angeles, California: University of California, Los Angeles, Department of Physical Education, 1965.

Kilbride, J. E., Robbins, M. C., & Kilbride, P. L. The comparative motor development of Baganda, American white, and American black infants. *American Anthropologist,* 1970, *72,* 1422–1428.

Kiphard, E. J., & Schilling, F. Der Hamm-Marburger körperkoordinationtest für kinder. *Monatsschrift für Kinderheilkunde,* 1970, *118,* 473–479.

Knobloch, H., & Pasamanick, B. The relationship of race and socioeconomic status to the development of motor behavior patterns in infancy. *Psychiatric Research Reports,* 1958, (No. 10), 123–133.

Knobloch, H., & Pasamanick, B. (Eds.). *Gesell and Amatruda's developmental diagnosis* (3rd ed.). New York: Harper and Row, 1974.

Knobloch, H., Pasamanick, B., & Sherard, E. S. A developmental screening inventory for infants. *Pediatrics,* 1966, Suppl. 38, 1095–1109.

Komi, P. V., Klissouras, V., & Karvinen, E. Genetic variation in neuromuscular performance. *Internationale Zeitschrift fur Angewandte Physiologie Einschliesslich Arbeitsphysiologie,* 1973, *31,* 289–304.

Konner, M. J. Aspects of the developmental ethology of a foraging people. In N. B. Jones (Ed.), *Ethological studies of child behaviour.* Cambridge: Cambridge University Press, 1972. Pp. 285–304.

Konner, M. Infancy among the Kalahari desert San. In P. H. Leiderman, S. R. Tulkin, & A. Rosenfeld (Eds.), *Culture and infancy.* New York: Academic Press, 1977. Pp. 287–328.

Kovar, R. *Prispevek ke studiu geneticke podminenosti lidske motoriky.* Autoreferat disertace k zizkani vedecke hodnosti kandidata biologickych ved, Praha, Czechoslovakia, 1974.

Kovar, R. Motor performance in twins. *Acta Geneticae Medicae et Gemellologiae,* 1975, *24,* 174.

Kumar, A., Ghai, O. P., & Singh, N. Delayed nerve conduction velocities in children with protein–calorie malnutrition. *Journal of Pediatrics,* 1977, *90,* 149–154. (a)

Kumar, A., Ghai, O. P., & Singh, N. Failure of marasmus and kwashiorkor to affect distal latencies in infancy and childhood. *Developmental Medicine and Child Neurology,* 1977, *19,* 790–796. (b)

Laughlin, W. S. Hunting: An integrating biobehavior system and its evolutionary importance. In R. B. Lee & I. Devore (Eds.), *Man the hunter.* Chicago: Aldine, 1968. Pp. 304–320.

Leiderman, P. H., Babu, B., Kagia, J., Kraemer, H. C., & Leiderman, G. F. African infant precocity and some social influences during the first year. *Nature (London),* 1973, *242,* 247–249.

Leiderman, P. H., & Leiderman, G. F. Economic change and infant care in an East African agricultural community. In P. H. Leiderman, S. R. Tulkin, & A. Rosenfeld (Eds.), *Culture and infancy.* New York: Academic Press, 1977. Pp. 405–438.

Lenard, H. G., von Bernuth, H., & Prechtl, F. R. Reflexes and their relationship to behavioral state in the newborn. *Acta Paediatrica Scandinavica,* 1968, *57,* 177–185.

Lusk, D. & Lewis, M. Mother–infant interaction and infant development among the Wolof of Senegal. *Human Development,* 1972, *15,* 58–69.

Lynch, A., Smart, J. L., & Dobbing, J. Motor co-ordination and cerebellar size in adult rats undernourished in early life. *Brain Research,* 1975, *83,* 249–259.

Malina, R. M. Growth and physical performance of American Negro and White children. *Clinical Pediatrics,* 1969, *8,* 476–483.

Malina, R. M. Ethnic and cultural factors in the development of motor abilities and strength in American children. In G. L. Rarick (Ed.), *Physical activity: Human growth and develop-ment.* New York: Academic Press, 1973. Pp. 333–363.

Malina, R. M. Anthropometric correlates of strength and motor performance. *Exercise and Sport Sciences Reviews,* 1975, *3,* 249–274.

Malina, R. M. Motor development in a cross-cultural perspective. In R. W. Christina & D. M. Landers (Eds.), *Psychology of motor behavior and sport* (Vol. II). Champaign, Ill.: Human Kinetics Publishers, 1977. Pp. 191–208.

Malina, R. M. The measurement of physical performance. In A. F. Roche & J. H. Himes (Eds.), *Human growth and development: Biological and behavioral perspectives.* Unpublished ms.

Malina, R. M., & Rarick, G. L. Growth, physique, and motor performance. In G. L. Rarick (Ed.), *Physical activity: Human growth and development.* New York: Academic Press, 1973. Pp. 125–153.

Marisi, D. Q. Genetic and extragenetic variance in motor performance. *Acta Geneticae Medicae et Gemellologiae,* 1977, *26,* 197–204.

McGraw, M. B. *The neuromuscular maturation of the human infant.* New York: Hafner, 1945. Reprinted by Columbia University Press, 1963.

McNemar, Q. Twin resemblances in motor skills and the effects of practice thereon. *Pedagogi-cal Seminary and Journal of Genetic Psychology,* 1933, *42,* 70–99.

Mead, M., & Macgregor, F. C. *Growth and culture: A photographic study on Balinese child-hood.* New York: Putnam, 1951.

Monckeberg, F. Effect of early marasmic malnutrition on subsequent physical and psychologi-cal development. In N. S. Scrimshaw & J. E. Gordon (Eds.), *Malnutrition, learning, and behavior.* Cambridge, Mass.: MIT Press, 1968. Pp. 269–278.

Moss, H. Sex, age and state as determinants of mother–infant interaction. *Merrill-Palmer Quarterly,* 1967, *13,* 19–36.

Neligan, G., & Prudham, D. Norms for four standard developmental milestones by sex, social class and place in family. *Developmental Medicine and Child Neurology,* 1969, *11,* 413–422.

Norval, M. A. Relationship of weight and length of infants at birth to the age at which they begin to walk alone. *Journal of Pediatrics,* 1947, *30,* 676–678.

Paulson, G., & Gottlieb, G. Developmental reflexes: The reappearance of foetal and neonatal reflexes in aged patients. *Brain,* 1968, *91,* 37–52.

Peatman, J. G., & Higgons, R. A. Development of sitting, standing and walking of children reared with optimal pediatric care. *American Journal of Orthopsychiatry,* 1940, *10,* 88–110.

Peatman, J. G., & Higgons, R. A. Relation of infants' weight and body build to locomotor development. *American Journal of Orthopsychiatry,* 1942, *12,* 234–240.

Penrose, L. S. Genetics of growth and development of the fetus. In L. S. Penrose (Ed.), *Recent advances in human genetics,* London: J. & A. Churchill, 1961. Pp. 56–75.

Pikler, E. Some contributions to the study of the gross motor development of children. *Journal of Genetic Psychology,* 1968, *113,* 27–39.

Pikler, E. Learning of motor skills on the basis of self-induced movements. In J. Helmuth (Ed.), *Exceptional infant* (Vol. 2): *Studies in abnormalities.* New York: Bruner/Mazel, 1971. Pp. 54–89.

Pineau, M. Developpement de l'enfant et dimension de la famille. *Biotypologie,* 1961, *22,* 25–53.

Pollak, M., & Mitchell, S. Early development of Negro and White babies. *Archives of Disease in Childhood,* 1974, *49,* 40–45.

Rarick, G. L. *Motor development during infancy and childhood* (rev. ed.). Madison: College Printing and Typing Co., 1961.

Rendon, R., Hurtado, J. J., & Arathoon, M. C. The effect of malnutrition on the physical and mental development of children. In G. Farrell (Ed.), *Congenital mental retardation.* Austin: University of Texas Press, 1969. Pp. 262–288.

Rhoads, T. F., Rapoport, l., Kennedy, R., & Stokes, J. Studies on the growth and development of male children receiving evaporated milk. II. Physical growth, dentition, and intelligence of white and Negro children through the first four years as influenced by vitamin supplements. *Journal of Pediatrics,* 1945, *26,* 415–454.

Richards, T. W., & Newbery, H. Studies in fetal behavior. III. Can performance in test items at six months postnatally be predicted on the basis of fetal activity? *Child Development,* 1938, *9,* 79–86.

Rosenberg, B. G., & Sutton-Smith, B. Ordinal position and sex-role identification. *Genetic Psychology Monographs,* 1964, *70,* 297–328.

Rosenberg, B. G., & Sutton-Smith, B. Family interaction effects on masculinity–feminity. *Journal of Personality and Social Psychology,* 1968, *8,* 117–120.

Rosenblith, J. F. Prognostic values of neonatal assessment. *Child Development,* 1966, *37,* 623–631.

Sandler, L., van Campen, J., Ratner, G., Stafford, C., & Weismar, R. Responses of urban preschool children to a developmental screening test. *Journal of Pediatrics,* 1970, *77,* 775–781.

Scott, R. B., Ferguson, A. D., Jenkins, M. E., & Cutter, F. F. Growth and development of Negro infants. V. Neuromuscular patterns of behavior during the first year of life. *Pediatrics,* 1955, *16,* 24–30.

Scrutton, D. R. Footprint sequences of normal children under five years old. *Developmental Medicine and Child Neurology,* 1969, *11,* 44–53.

Sears, R. R., Maccoby, E. E., & Levin, H. *Patterns of child rearing.* New York: Harper and Row, 1957.

Shirley, M. M. *The first two years. A study of twenty-five babies* (Vol. 1): *postural and locomotor development.* Minneapolis: University of Minnesota Press, 1931.

Sinclair, C. B. *Movement and movement patterns of early childhood.* Richmond, Va: State Department of Education, 1971.

Skład, M. Similarity of movements in twins. *Wychowanie Fizyczne i Sport,* 1972, nr. 3, 119–141.

Skład, M. The genetic determination of the rate of learning motor skills. *Studies in Physical Anthropology* (Wrocław, Poland), 1975, *1,* 3–19.

Smith, M. E., Lecker, G., Dunlap, J. W., & Cureton, E. E. The effects of race, sex, and environment on the age at which children walk. *Journal of Genetic Psychology,* 1930, *38,* 489–498.

Solomons, G., & Solomons, H. C. Factors affecting motor performance in four-month-old infants. *Child Development,* 1964, *35,* 1283–1295.

Solomons, G., & Solomons, H. C. Motor development in Yucatecan infants. *Developmental Medicine and Child Neurology,* 1975, *17,* 41–46.

Statham, L., & Murray, M. Early walking patterns of normal children. *Clinical Orthopaedics,* 1971, *79,* 8–24.

Stoch, M. B., & Smythe, P. M. Fifteen year developmental study on effects of severe undernutrition during infancy on subsequent physical growth and intellectual functioning. *Archives of Disease in Childhood*, 1976, *51*, 327–336.

Super, C. M. Environmental effects on motor development: The case of "African infant precocity." *Developmental Medicine and Child Neurology*, 1976, *18*, 561–567.

Sutton-Smith, B., Roberts, J. M., & Rosenberg, B. G. Sibling associations and role involvement. *Merrrill-Palmer Quarterly*, 1964, *10*, 25–38.

Tanner, J. M. Variability of growth and maturity in newborn infants. In M. Lewis & L. A. Rosenblum (Eds.), *The effect of the infant on its caregiver*. New York: Wiley, 1974. Pp. 77–103.

Thorpe, H. S., & Werner, E. E. Developmental screening of preschool children: A critical review of inventories used in health and educational programs. *Pediatrics*, 1974, *53*, 362–370.

Vandenberg, S. G. The hereditary abilities study: Hereditary components in a psychological test battery. *American Journal of Human Genetics*, 1962, *14*, 220–237.

Vandenberg, S. G. Contributions of twin research to psychology. *Psychological Bulletin*, 1966, *66*, 327–352.

Verschuer, O. Studien an 102 eineiigen und 45 gleichgeschlechtlichten zweieiigen zwillings- und an 2 drillingspaaren. *Ergebnisse Innere Medizin und Kinderheilkunde*, 1927, *31* (as cited by Skład, 1972).

Walker, R. N. Body build and behavior in young children: I. Body build and nursery school teacher's ratings. *Monographs of the Society for Research in Child Development*, 1962, No. 84.

Walters, C. E. Prediction of postnatal development from fetal activity. *Child Development*, 1965, *36*, 801–808.

Walters, C. E. Comparative development of Negro and White infants. *Journal of Genetic Psychology*, 1967, *110*, 243–251.

Warren, N. African infant precocity. *Psychological Bulletin*, 1972, *78*, 353–367.

Waters, E., & Crandall, V. J. Social class and observed maternal behavior from 1940 to 1960. *Child Development*, 1964, *35*, 1021–1032.

Welon, Z. & Sekita, B. Physical fitness, body size, and body build in pre-school children. *Studies in Physical Anthropology* (Wrocław, Poland), 1975, *2*, 25–32.

Willerman, L., Broman, S. H., & Fiedler, M. Infant development, preschool IQ, and social class. *Child Development*, 1970, *41*, 69–77.

Williams, J. R., & Scott, R. B. Growth and development of Negro infants. IV. Motor development and its relationship to child rearing practices in two groups of Negro infants. *Child Development*, 1953, *24*, 103–121.

Wilson, R. S., & Harpring, E. B. Mental and motor development in infant twins. *Developmental Psychology*, 1972, *7*, 277–287.

Yarrow, L. J., Pedersen, F. A., & Rubenstein, J. Mother–infant interaction and development in infancy. In P. H. Leiderman, S. R. Tulkin, & A. Rosenfeld (Eds.), *Culture and infancy*. New York: Academic Press, 1977. Pp. 539–564.

# 8

# Biological and Social Correlates of Failure to Thrive[1]

ERNESTO POLLITT AND RUDOLPH LEIBEL

## INTRODUCTION

This chapter reports on the results of a psychosocial study carried out over a 2-year period on nineteen 2- to 5-year-old children with failure to thrive without apparent organic basis. The objective was to gain a better understanding of the characteristics of the social environment that may adversely affect the growth and development of young children. The research design was retrospective and correlational, yet the information collected has heuristic value and provides insight into the dynamic relationship between growth failure and the environment. To some extent, the research strategy of this study conducted in 1972 has characteristics of the ecological approach advocated by Bronfenbrenner (1977) and elaborated by Garbarino (1976, 1977) in connection with child maltreatment. The emphasis in the present study was on the immediate antecedents of growth failure (i.e., deficient dietary intake). However, considerable attention was given to, and large amounts of data were collected on, child care and family conditions that may be precursors of such immediate factors.

[1]This work was supported in part by Contract NIH-71-2417 from the National Institutes of Health, Grant 1R22HD09228 from the National Institutes of Child Health and Human Development, the Carnegie Corporation of New York, and the Grant Foundation.

*Social and Biological Predictors of
Nutritional Status, Physical Growth,
and Neurological Development*

Criteria for the selection of subjects in the study were anthropometric-medical in nature and did not include psychopathology among the children or a pathologic social ambience in their homes. However, as the study unfolded, it became apparent that many children in the sample were psychologically disturbed (Pollitt & Eichler, 1976), and that their relationships with their caretakers were inadequate at best (Pollitt, Eichler, & Chan, 1975). Accordingly, for the purposes of this chapter, some of the literature on failure to thrive secondary to environmental deprivation is discussed before the data on the subjects sampled are presented. Emphasis is placed on the issue of causality.

### Review of the Literature

Failure to thrive secondary to so-called environmental deprivation is a broad term often used to describe a distortion of the physical, socioemotional, or other aspects of somatic and psychic growth in poorly mothered children (Department of Health, Education and Welfare, 1970). Mothers of environmentally deprived, failure-to-thrive children are described as rejecting and aggressive (McCarthy & Booth, 1970; Silver & Finkelstein, 1967), anxious and inadequate (Apley, Davies, Davis, & Silk, 1971), and failing to thrive themselves (Evans, Reinhart, & Succop, 1972). They are also reported to be isolated from the community, with little or no support from friends or neighbors (Apley et al., 1971; Evans et al., 1972; Leonard, Rhymes, & Solnit, 1966). In many cases the fathers are frequently or permanently absent from the home (Brasel, 1973; Elmer, 1960; Hollowell & Gardner, 1965; Leonard et al., 1966; Powel, Brasel, & Blizzard, 1967), or, if present, are often unemployed (Barbero & Shaheen, 1967; Shaheen, Alexander, Truskowsky, & Barbero, 1968). Thus, the families of failure-to-thrive children are often characterized by marital strife and severe financial instability. Public welfare assistance is common, as is overcrowded, substandard housing (Hollowell & Gardner, 1965; Leonard et al., 1966; Shaheen et al., 1968). These socioeconomic stress factors, in conjunction with the emotional instability and caretaker inadequacy of the mother, result in a harsh, nonnurturing environment for the child.

Maternally deprived children who are failing to thrive are often temperamental and difficult to care for. Leonard et al. (1966), for example, have described two very different personality-types commonly seen in such children: One type is described as irritable, hypertonic, and difficult to comfort; the second as placid, passive, and quiet. Barbero and Shaheen (1967), as well as Kreiger (1974), also identify the children in their samples as either intensely irritable or immobile and unresponsive. These behavioral traits may be related to temperament, or they may be the result of a distorted interaction between the child and its immediate environment. At any rate, it is reasonable to postulate that such behavior on the part of the child must affect the mother's caretaking behavior.

There are two different, but not necessarily mutually exclusive, hypotheses regarding the nature of the mechanisms behind growth retardation of the child in a pathologic social ambience (for a review of these hypotheses, see Brown, 1976; Gardner, 1977; McCarthy, 1974). One hypothesis proposes that the nutritional intake of the child is insufficient to meet requirements for growth (Kreiger, 1973; Whitten, Pettit, & Fischhoff, 1969). Kreiger (1973) and Whitten et al. (1969) have argued that the etiology of failure to thrive in the maternal deprivation syndrome is hypocaloric intake. Whitten et al. (1969) attempted to separate the effects of mothering from those of calorie intake in the treatment of failure to thrive secondary to maternal deprivation. Eleven of 13 infants studied gained weight rapidly when they received adequate caloric intake while hospitalized for 2 weeks in an environment simulating conditions in their homes. Moreover, 7 infants who were given high-calorie diets in their homes by their mothers in the presence of an observer also showed high weight gain. The authors concluded that undereating is the major factor in the retardation of somatic growth.

The alternative hypothesis suggests a neuroendocrine derangement secondary to emotional deprivation (Gardner, 1972; Powell et al., 1967). A basis for this hypothesis is found in data published in 1967 by Powell et al on 13 subjects and expanded by Brasel (1973) to include 22 cases (6 females and 16 males with severe growth failure, ranging in age from 21 months to 15 years). In all 22 cases, social and family histories reveal strong evidence of a pathologic psychosocial ambience. Divorce, separation, excessive drinking, and neglect in caretaking were frequently observed among the families. Of the 22 subjects, 18 had evidence of low adrenocorticotrophic hormone release. However, in all cases, stimulation with exogenous adrenocorticotrophic hormone resulted in a rise in cortisol, indicating normal adrenal responsiveness. Deficient growth hormone release after induced hypoglycemia was found in 50–60% of the sample, but the deficit was not as severe as that typically found in idiopathic hypopituitarism or isolated growth hormone deficiency. When the children were placed in convalescent care, they became less withdrawn, showed greater spontaneity, and grew rapidly. However, in most cases growth slowed upon the subjects' return home.

A study by Kreiger and Mellinger (1971; see also Kreiger, 1973) reports data discrepant with the results just described. They studied two groups of children of different ages: One group included nine cases of maternal deprivation, ranging in age from 6 months to 2 years, 8 months (2:8). A "psycho-social dwarfism" group included seven children ranging in age from 3:5 to 10:2. Evidence of maternal rejection or neglect or psychosocial disruption was available in all cases. Laboratory results showed that five of the seven psychosocial dwarfs had inadequate growth hormone release after insulin-induced hypoglycemia. However, the growth hormone release was considered adequate in the two remaining cases of psychosocial dwarfism and in all nine maternal deprivation cases. Three of the five growth hormone-deficient children were retested after significant catch-up growth in a supportive environment. Retesting showed normal growth hormone release after induced hypoglycemia. Five cases in the maternal deprivation group and four cases in the psychosocial dwarfism group had serum growth hormone levels in the elevated or upper normal range on admission to the hospital or before unrestricted feeding began. It is likely, therefore, that children labeled psychosocial dwarfs or maternally deprived have somewhat elevated rather than deficient growth hormone values before treatment.

Apley *et al.* (1971), in a study of "dwarfism without apparent cause" of 12 British children, found no abnormality in serum growth hormone levels in 11 of the subjects. In one case, the growth hormone level was doubtfully low. However, their data are scanty and provide no strong substantiation to warrant including these children in the category of deprivation dwarfism.

The release of growth hormone, an anterior pituitary peptide, is under the control of a number of hypothalamic releasing factors that are, in turn, apparently regulated by higher brain centers. The portion of statural growth under the influence of growth hormone is mediated by somatomedins, which are produced in the liver and kidneys under the trophic influence of growth hormone (Daughaday, 1977). Thus, although growth hormone directly influences carbohydrate, fat, and protein homeostasis, its effect on growth is indirect in that it is mediated by a second agent. It is possible to have elevated growth hormone levels and not grow; conversely, individuals with low growth hormone levels but adequate statural growth have been described. Underfed individuals characteristically show elevated, resting growth hormone levels, presumably due to the hormone's role in fuel homeostasis. These same individuals have low somatomedin levels and therefore fail to show statural growth appropriate to their age (Hintz, Suskind, Amatayakul, Thanangkul, & Olson, 1978). Thus, children with psychosocial dwarfism may have different growth hormone profiles (D'Ercole, Underwood, & Van Wyk, 1977). In one profile, where hypocaloric intake is the major proximate cause of the failure to thrive, one finds elevated growth hormone levels and low somatomedin values. In the other, where hypothalamic and higher centers are directly influencing the anterior pituitary, one finds lowered growth hormone levels and a secondary reduction in somatomedin values. Both types of children fail to grow, but the "lesions" are at different points in the pathway to growth.

This selective review of the literature indicates that substantially different factors have been implicated in the causality of failure to thrive. Yet no study that we know of has attempted to establish the differential contributions of such different factors (see Garbarino, 1977). Evidently, the developmental and multidisciplinary nature of the problem makes it a most difficult research endeavor. A study using a retrospective design would not identify a chain of events or, possibly, relationships among the variables involved, yet an ex post facto approach to research, besides having heuristic value, may establish whether putative causal factors are indeed implicated, and may speak to the robustness of a selective hypothesis.


### Purpose of the Study

The purpose of the present study was

1. To identify socioeconomic, familial, maternal, developmental, and nutritional variables that differentiate children on or below the third percentile curve for height and weight of the Boston growth norms (Nelson, Vaughn, & McKay, 1968) from children on or above the twenty-fifth percentile curve.
2. To construct a linear combination of these variables that would maximally differentiate between the two groups.
3. To identify the weight of contribution of each variable to such discrimination.

The sets of variables included in the study were selected because they have been causally associated in the literature with the failure-to-thrive syndrome in question. Here, they may be identified as links in a hypothetical chain of causality. Socioeconomic status and family organization (i.e., changes in structure) are placed at the distant end of the chain. Their effects on the child must be mediated by other, more specific intrafamily conditions. Caretaker competence (i.e., mental health of the mother, and care practices) is an intermediary link, and dietary intake the final link.

Recognizing that prenatal growth and morbidity as well as genetic endowment influence postnatal growth, we also included these variables in the set of developmental factors. Finally, it should be noted that no variables related to emotional deprivation as such were included. Such a state could be inferred only from analysis of the relationship between caretaker and child.

## METHODS OF PROCEDURE

### Subjects

The subjects were 19 index and 19 contrast children selected from the population attending the Outpatient Pediatric Clinic at Cambridge Hospital, Cambridge, Massachusetts. The criteria for selection of the index cases and the reasons for them are presented in Table 8.1. These criteria also applied to the control cases, with the exception of anthropometry: Height and weight of index children was on or below the third percentile curve of the Boston growth standards (Nelson *et al.*, 1968), that of the contrast children on or above the twenty-fifth percentile curve. Both groups of children were matched for sex, age (±3 months), and color of skin.

All children were selected during a 12-month period. The children had been brought to the hospital usually because of gastrointestinal, ear, or upper respiratory infections. A few of the index cases complained of growth retardation.

The parents of children meeting the anthropometric criteria for the index group were informed of the study and invited to return for a free physical examination of the child. If the results of the examination met the remaining criteria, they were then asked to enroll their child in the study. The contrast cases followed the same procedure, except that they had to be matched with an index child.

Table 8.2 presents the mean age and anthropometric data of the 9 males and 10 females in each group.

With regard to appropriateness of weight or height, most previous studies have relied on a determination of the ratio of actual weight to weight of the fiftieth percentile for height–age. This technique, however, tends to generate artifactual reductions in the ratio for short children, due to the differing geometries of the height and weight curves (Reed & Stuart, 1959). To compensate for this phenomenon, we calculated expected weight for height ($Wt_E$) as follows:

$$Wt_E = Wt_A - R(Ht_{50} - Ht_A)$$

$$R = \frac{Ht_{97} - Ht_3}{Wt_{97} - Wt_3}$$

where

| | |
|---|---|
| $Wt_E$ | = weight expected for actual height |
| $Wt_A$ | = actual weight |
| $Ht_A$ | = actual height |
| $Ht_{50}$ | = height at fiftieth percentile isobar for age |
| $Wt_{97}, Ht_{97}$ | = ninety-seventh percentile values for age |
| $Wt_3, Ht_3$ | = third percentile values for age |

**TABLE 8.1**

**Criteria for Selection of Index Cases and Rationale for Their Use**

| Criteria for selection | Rationale |
|---|---|
| 1. Selected from the Outpatient Clinic at Cambridge Hospital | Families using the Outpatient Clinic would likely be of low socioeconomic status; there is a high prevalence of failure to thrive among this group. |
| 2. Age: 12–59 months | Prevalence of failure to thrive is higher among preschool children than among any other age group. A 12-month baseline was set for practical reasons: The study of behavioral factors in infants 1-year old or younger requires a methodology different from that for preschool children older than 1 year of age. |
| 3. Sex: no restrictions | |
| 4. Anthropometry: height and weight below the third percentile of the Boston growth standards | Operational definition of failure to thrive |
| 5. Birth weight over 2500 gm and ≥36 weeks of gestation | Because prenatal experience may influence postnatal growth, all cases with prenativity or deranged intrauterine growth were excluded. |
| 6. No evidence of birth complications | Birth complications may determine extraordinary postnatal treatments that would have implications for the study. Also, they may affect postnatal growth and may be indicative of faulty intrauterine development. |
| 7. No evidence of physical disability, genetic or organically determined retardation | There is evidence of an association between mental retardation and short stature. Also, a child's mental retardation may regulate in part the parents' behavior and obscure the social–environmental factors that were the target of this study. |
| 8. No evidence of an organic cause of growth retardation | Growth retardation was to be used as an indicator of nutritional deficiency alone. |
| 9. Singleton birth | With twins, there is likelihood of intrauterine undernutrition which could influence postnatal growth. |
| 10. Maternal height: 5'1" or greater | To exclude cases of hereditary short stature |

TABLE 8.2

Anthropometry of the Index and Contrast Children[a]

|  | Index[b] | Contrast[b] | t test[c] | p[d] |
|---|---|---|---|---|
| Age (months) |  |  |  |  |
| Males | 33.4 ± 13.7 | 33.6 ± 13.4 | n.c.[e] | n.c. |
| Females | 38.6 ± 13.6 | 39.0 ± 14.5 | n.c. | n.c. |
| Total | 36.1 ± 13.6 | 36.4 ± 13.8 | n.c. | n.c. |
| Height: percentage of expected[f] |  |  |  |  |
| Males | 93.0 ± 2.2 | 100.5 ± 1.33 | 13.60 | .001 |
| Females | 90.4 ± 2.2 | 102.4 ± 3.2 | 14.70 | .001 |
| Total | 91.6 ± 2.5 | 101.5 ± 2.65 | 13.80 | .001 |
| Weight: percentage of expected[f] |  |  |  |  |
| Males | 78.3 ± 4.3 | 104.1 ± 9.5 | 8.42 | .001 |
| Females | 78.7 ± 4.0 | 108.9 ± 4.1 | 14.16 | .001 |
| Total | 78.5 ± 4.0 | 106.6 ± 7.4 | 15.14 | .001 |

[a] Nine males and ten females in each group.
[b] Values are expressed as means ± $SD$.
[c] Matched pairs.
[d] One-tailed test.
[e] n.c., not calculated.
[f] Expected = height or weight measure at fiftieth percentile for age.

The expression $Wt_A/Wt_E$ reflects the weight appropriateness of the patient, with values below and above 1 indicating degrees of thinness and obesity, respectively. Both contrast and index samples had mean values near 1 ($\bar{M}$ = 1.07, $SD$ = .12 for contrast; $\bar{M}$ = 1.03, $SD$ = .10 for index); the statistical difference between them ($t$ = 1.33, $df$ = 18, .05 > $p$ < .10) did not reach an acceptable level of significance. Thus, given the fact that none of the index cases presented clinical signs of undernutrition or had histories to suggest recent large weight gain, undernutrition could not be implicated as a significant *current* contributor to the short stature of these children. Of course, these data have no bearing on whether *past* undernutrition was partially responsible.

The probability of false positives among the target group is high in a retrospective study such as this. Attempts at identification and reconstruction of the chronology of relevant facts are at constant risk of errors stemming from incomplete records or from informants' errors of recall. These problems are accentuated when the clinical entity to be explained is time-dependent and likely to have multiple causes. Thus, in this study as in almost all other available studies of failure-to-thrive children, the target group may not constitute a homogeneous sample.

To reduce the probability of such errors, longitudinal weight data were obtained on 11 of the 19 index children from their medical records in Cambridge Hospital (see 8.1–8.3). In 7 of these 11 cases, weight data were available from the first 12 months on. The data for 5 of these 7 cases (01, 04, 16, 17, and 18) showed that their weights were around the twenty-fifth percentile isobar during the early months of life, but had dropped below the third percentile by the time of enrollment in the study. Further, in one other case (07), for which the first available data point dates from the second year of life, there is also clear evidence of a downward drift in body weight percentile with time. Only in case 06 was there any strong reason to suspect that the child was small from birth, because all data points beginning in the early months of life fall below the third percentile.

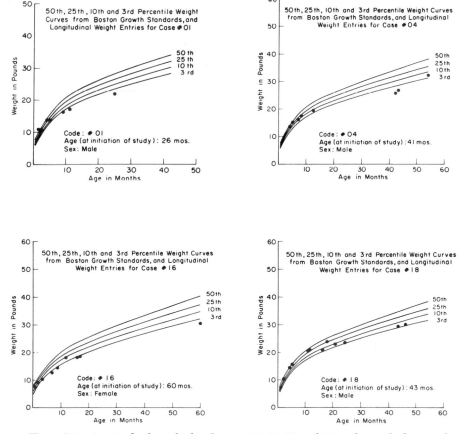

**Figure 8.1.** Longitudinal weight data for cases 01, 04, 16, and 18: evidence of a downward drift in body weight percentile.

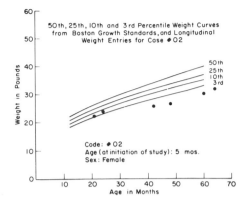

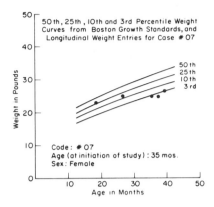

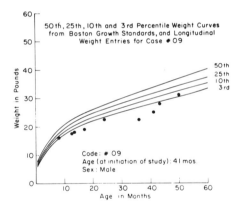

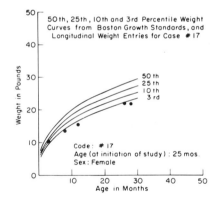

**Figure 8.2.**   Longitudinal weight data for cases 02, 07, 09, and 17: evidence of a downward drift in body weight percentile and of consistent body weight below the tenth percentile.

## Methods

Except for developmental data collected in the hospital by the research physician, data were collected during 7–11 weekly 1½-hr home visits. Interview schedules and guides, informal conversations, and direct observations were used. Data from direct observations and interviews were recorded in narrative form after each visit. There was an average of 9 ($SD = 3$) home visits totaling 13 ($SD = 4$) hr for the index group and 8 ($SD = 3$) home visits totaling 11 ($SD = 4$) hr for the contrast group.

The interviewers were three public health nurses with Masters degrees in child psychiatric nursing and professional experience in interviewing families at home. One interviewer conducted 15 family studies, another 16, and the third the remaining 7. Scheduling problems and budget limitations imposed the uneven distribution of family studies among the three interviewers. They were extensively briefed on the methods of conducting the interviews and given written instructions on the interview procedures. During the first half of the study, the principal investigator met about once a week with each interviewer to ensure that the necessary information was collected and to discuss related questions.

The use of interview schedules and guides unavoidably imposed some common structure to the home visits. For this reason, the interviewers were advised to develop a friendly atmosphere. They encouraged the inter-

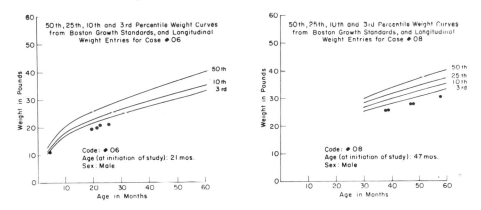

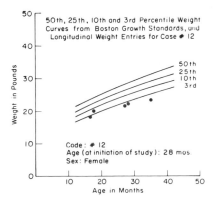

**Figure 8.3.** Longitudinal weight data for cases 06, 08, and 12: evidence of consistent body weight below the tenth percentile.

viewee's comments or elaborations on interview questions, and the initiation of dialogues on topics of interest to the interviewee.

Whenever possible, interviewers answered questions relating to medical and/or nutritional issues. When it seemed helpful, they referred the interviewee to the appropriate department at Cambridge Hospital. In one case, arrangements were made to place a child in a special kindergarten for hyperactive children.

## Variables

The variables described in the following match clearly those included in the hypothetical chain of events previously discussed.

### Socioeconomic Status

Measures of the family's wealth, income, and potential for economic improvement included:

1. Gross family yearly income: sum total of all income included in family budget
2. Per capita yearly income: division of family's gross income by family size
3. Mother's total number of years of schooling
4. Household density: ratio of number of rooms in house (bathrooms excluded) to the number of people living in the house
5. Household facilities: includes vehicles and total number of electrical appliances in the household

The information on gross yearly income and on the mother's schooling was obtained with the aid of two interview guides prepared and pretested for this investigation. Data on household density and facilities were collected by direct observation.

### Family Organization

Family organization deals with historical changes in the structure of the family and household, events that can directly or indirectly affect the child's caretaking:

1. Mother's age at child's birth
2. Mother's marital status at child's birth
3. Number of changes in marital status of mother throughout the child's lifetime
4. Changes in household composition, independent of changes in marital status, throughout the child's lifetime
5. Mobility: changes in address

## Caretaking Competence

Caretaking competence includes the availability and quality of physical care to the child (including aid given to the mother) and the nature of the social and emotional relationship between the mother and child. It also includes the mother's mental health status. A short version of the Spitzer, Endicott, Mesnikoff, and Cohen Psychiatric Evaluation Form (1968) was adapted into an interview schedule and used with all informants in the study. The interview included the following areas: competence in daily routine, anxiety, depression, social isolation, and role of mate.

An interview schedule prepared and pretested for this investigation was used for the data on physical care of the child. The following variables were included:

1. Mother's notion of elevations in body temperature as an indicator of illness
2. Child's record of immunizations
3. Total number of child's physical accidents at home requiring medical attention
4. Number and names of people caring for the child during the following activities: feeding, dressing, bathing, playing, disciplining, and bedtime.

A shortened version of the Inventory of Home Stimulation (Caldwell, Heider, & Kaplan, 1966), including a few items from the Childhood Level of Living Scale (Polansky, 1968), was used to evaluate the interaction between the mothers and their children. This checklist included items in the categories of "development and vocal stimulation," "emotional climate," and "reliable evidence of affection." The scoring system followed Caldwell's instructions.

The results of the checklist were evaluated in two ways: First, the interviewers, after completing the family study, rated each mother. Second, a graduate student in anthropology read all of the narrative records from the family studies, and then rated each mother without knowledge of the results of the first rating or of the group to which a case belonged. The two ratings were so closely correlated ($p < .001$) that they have been averaged for between-group comparisons.

## Dietary Intake

Dietary intake included at least four 24-hr dietary records, based on the mother's recollection, for each child. These data were used to estimate central tendencies in the nutritional intake of the children in the index and contrast groups. Data from the 24-hr records are not intended to be an accurate reflection of actual dietary intake, for although the correlation between the mother's recollection and actual intake may be statistically significant, the errors of measurement are usually high. Replication of the method on the same subjects probably increases the accuracy of the data (Balough, Kahn, & Medalie, 1971), but still is insufficient for diagnostic purposes.

### Developmental: Child's Medical History

The interview was an adaptation of Form 10265 (Child's Medical History) used at the Children's Outpatient Service, Massachusetts General Hospital, Boston, Massachusetts. When they were available, the children's medical records at the Cambridge Hospital were consulted to corroborate and expand the information reported by the interviewee. Birthweight data were always obtained from the medical records.

No routine protocol was used in the medical evaluation except to check that the criteria for selection were met. Biochemical determinations, cultures, and radiographs (including bone age) were left to the discretion of the research physician. The following information was extracted from the medical history:

1. Child's birthweight
2. Child's feeding history: presence or absence of difficulties, age solid food started, age whole milk started
3. Contagious diseases: chicken pox, rubella, measles, mumps
4. Infectious diseases: upper respiratory, ear, gastrointestinal
5. Number of physical accidents

### REDUCTION AND ANALYSIS OF THE DATA

The statistical technique used to differentiate maximally the index from the contrast group was a Stepwise Multiple Discriminant Analysis (Tatsuoka, 1970). A linear function and discriminant scores for each group were calculated. These statistics estimate the classificatory capabilities of the variables, and identify their specific contributions in discriminating between groups.

For the initial between-group comparisons of each of the variables selected, $\chi^2$ or the Student's $t$ test for matched pairs were calculated. Differences between groups were considered to be statistically significant when the probability level was equal to or less than .05. Excluding the calculations for anthropometry, there was a total of 39 $t$ tests and 9 $\chi^2$. Whenever such a large number of comparisons is made, some significant differences are observed that may result from chance alone. The matched-pair study design, however, tends to reduce the standard error of the differences (Blalock, 1972), and the prediction of the direction of results reduces the possible differences that may be attributed to chance alone by one-half. Thus, while not all problems stemming from multiple comparisons were eliminated, our study was designed to decrease them.

All continuous variables that discriminated between groups at statistically significant levels were included in the Stepwise Multiple Discriminant Analysis. However, because residuals in multivariate analysis tend to increase as the number of predictor variables increases (Kerlinger & Pedhazur, 1973), all variables were reduced whenever possible. In the case of one set of variables (socioeconomic), this reduction was accomplished by the formation of new, transformed variables in which two or more variables discriminated between groups. Beta coefficients from a stepwise multiple regression equation were used to construct the new aggregate variable. The regression was calculated by pooling both groups and using the discriminating variables as predictors; the average of height and weight of the standard (fiftieth percentile curve) was used as the dependent variable.

The anthropometric criterion to first classify the index and contrast cases for the discriminant analysis was the median of the distribution of the percentage of standard weight for age for both groups pooled. All cases with a percentage of the standard (fiftieth percentile curve) equal to or less than 90% fell into Group 1; values above 90% identified those cases classified in Group 2.

Although the maximum number of missing observations for any one variable within one group alone is three, some comparisons included only 14 matched pairs. In these cases, the comparisons were limited to 13 degrees of freedom. However, in the one case of multiple regression analysis and in the discriminant functional analysis, the median of the distribution derived from pooling both groups was used as a substitute for the missing observations. In these instances the total number of cases was 38.

## RESULTS

### Socioeconomic Status

The between-group comparison of the gross yearly income (Index $\bar{M}$ = 6493, Contrast $\bar{M}$ = 9451) showed a clear trend toward statistical significance ($t = 1.58$, $df = 13$, $p = .07$); however, it did not reach the level of significance set for the present study ($p \leq .05$). Also, the number of household facilities did not discriminate between groups. The per capita income, however, did differentiate the contrast ($\bar{M}$ = 2648) from the index ($\bar{M}$ = 1557) group in the expected direction ($t = 2.77$, $df = 13$, $p = .01$). The children in the index group were also more likely to live in crowded homes (household density ratio: index $\bar{M}$ = .98, contrast $\bar{M}$ = .83, $t = 1.69$, $df = 18$, $p = .05$)

and have mothers with fewer years of schooling (index $\bar{M} = 11$, contrast $\bar{M} = 12$, $t = 1.88$, $df = 18$, $p = .03$).

Per capita income, mother's education, and household density were therefore used as predictors, and the average of the percentage of standard weight and height as the dependent variable in a stepwise multiple regression analysis aimed at the construction of an aggregate socioeconomic variable. An aggregate variable (labeled SES) was constructed from the beta weights of per capita income and mother's education (per capita income $\beta = .40$, $F = 7.43$, $df = 1/36$, $p < .01$; mother's education $\beta = .24$, $F = 2.72$, $df = 2/35$, $p < .10$). The $F$ level of household density was small enough to be excluded from the regression equation.

## Family Organization

The mean age of the mothers at the time of the child's birth was slightly lower in the index group (21.9, $SD = 4.81$) than in the contrast group (23.6, $SD = 4.25$), but the difference between these two means was not statistically significant ($t = .98$, $df = 17$).

In fact, the only between-group comparison that even approximated statistical significance (Table 8.3) was marital status at the child's birth ($\chi^2 = 4.57$,

**TABLE 8.3**

**Between-group Comparisons of Variables on Family Organization**

| Variable | Variable breakdown | Index | Contrast | $\chi^2$ | $p$ |
|---|---|---|---|---|---|
| | | Frequencies | | | |
| Marital status at child's birth | 1. Married, common law | 12 | 16 | 4.57 | =.10 |
| | 2. Boyfriend | 4 | 0 | | |
| | 3. Single, separated, or divorced | 3 | 3 | | |
| Changes in marital status | 1. No change | 7 | 11 | 1.98 | n.s. |
| | 2. One to two changes | 6 | 5 | | |
| | 3. ≥ Three changes | 6 | 3 | | |
| Mobility | 1. No changes | 8 | 9 | 1.25 | n.s. |
| | 2. One change | 3 | 5 | | |
| | 3. ≥ Two changes | 8 | 5 | | |
| Changes in household composition independent of mobility and changes in marital status | 1. No changes | 10 | 10 | <1.00 | n.s. |
| | 2. ≥ One change | 8 | 9 | | |

**TABLE 8.4**

Between-group Comparisons of Mother's Scores from Psychiatric Interview Schedule

| | Group scores[a] | | $t$ test[b] | $df$ | $p$[c] |
|---|---|---|---|---|---|
| | Index | Contrast | | | |
| Disturbances | | | | | |
| in daily routine | 2.95 ± .71 | 2.68 ± .89 | 1.01 | 18 | n.s.[d] |
| Anxiety | 3.26 ± .56 | 3.05 ± .62 | 1.09 | 18 | n.s. |
| Depression | 3.21 ± .79 | 3.10 ± .99 | .36 | 18 | n.s. |
| Social isolation | 2.63 ± .90 | 2.36 ± .60 | 1.06 | 18 | n.s. |
| Dissatisfaction | | | | | |
| with mate[e] | 3.50 ± 1.02 | 2.71 ± 1.33 | 1.75 | 13 | $.05<p<.10$ |
| Total score | 3.01 ± .54 | 2.76 ± .69 | 1.28 | 18 | n.s. |

[a] Values are expressed as means ± standard deviation.
[b] $t$ test for matched pairs.
[c] One-tail test.
[d] n.s., not significant.
[e] All cases of women who were single, separated, or divorced were excluded (three from each group).

$df = 2$, $p = .10$). More mothers in the contrast group than in the index group were legally married or living under common law. By contrast, more mothers in the index group had a boyfriend or were single, separated, or divorced. There were no differences between groups in their changes in marital status, in mobility, or in the number of changes in household composition since the child's birth.

## Caretaking Competence

Table 8.4 presents the mean total and partial scores for each group on the Psychiatric Interview Schedule. Although all scores for the index group were slightly higher than those for the contrast group, the differences were not statistically significant in any case. The only mean differential that approximated statistical significance at the level set for this study was dissatisfaction with the role of the mate ($.05 < p < .10$).

The mothers of the children in the contrast group were much more likely to have help within their family in taking care of their children than were the mothers of the index group (index = 7.11, $SD$ = 1.15, contrast = 8.10, $SD$ = 1.15; $t$ = 3.77, $df$ = 18, $p$ = .001). There were no statistically significant differences between groups in the other physical care variables, however. Most mothers in both groups (89% in the contrast group, 100% in the index group) said that if their child's temperature were 100°F or above they would assume he or she was sick. No significant differences existed between the number of mothers (contrast = 63%, index = 84%) who claimed that they always kept bandaids, alcohol or other antiseptics, adhesive tape, vaseline, children's aspirin, and a thermometer at home. Immunization records for both groups were also not statistically different, as most children had been immunized. The worst record was for measles among index children (6 of 19 cases had not been immunized). Five of the index and ten of the contrast children had had physical accidents requiring medical attention; this difference was not statistically significant.

The checklist on Mother–Child Interaction revealed a sharp contrast between the index and control groups (Table 8.5). Mothers from the contrast group had significantly more physical and verbal interaction with their children; they were more likely to praise, kiss, or caress them, and less likely to scold, express annoyance with, or slap them. (For details of these findings, see Pollitt *et al.*, 1975.)

### Dietary Intake

Table 8.6 presents data on the dietary intake of both groups (expressed as means of total intake and as percentage of the Recommended Dietary Allowances [National Academy of Sciences, 1974]) and the results of the matched-pairs comparison. The children in the contrast group had a statistically significant higher intake of calories, protein, iron, niacin, and ascorbic acid. Both groups had similar intakes of calcium, thiamine, riboflavin, and vitamin A.

**TABLE 8.5**

**Between-group Comparisons of Mother–Child Interaction Scores**

|  | Index[a] | Contrast[a] | t test[b] | df | p[c] |
|---|---|---|---|---|---|
| Developmental and vocal stimulation | 69.34 ± 30.67 | 94.05 ± 14.45 | 2.87 | 18 | <.01 |
| Emotional climate | 57.02 ± 33.77 | 77.58 ± 23.60 | 2.22 | 18 | <.04 |
| Reliable evidence of affection | 88.90 ± 15.63 | 93.90 ± 13.43 | .88 | 18 | n.s.[d] |
| Total score | 66.23 ± 27.76 | 86.39 ± 15.98 | 2.58 | 18 | <.01 |

[a] Values are expressed as means ± standard deviation.
[b] t test for matched pairs.
[c] One-tailed test.
[d] n.s., not significant.

**TABLE 8.6**

Between-group Comparisons of Nutritional Variables

| Nutritional variable | Total intake[a] Index | Total intake[a] Contrast | t test[b] | df | p[c] |
|---|---|---|---|---|---|
| Calories | 1474 ± 296 (99%)[d] | 1763 ± 484 (125%) | 1.82 | 13 | .05 |
| Protein (gm) | 52 ± 10 (210%) | 64 ± 19 (270%) | 1.97 | 13 | .03 |
| Calcium (mg) | 823 ± 289 (103%) | 856 ± 347 (106%) | .23 | 13 | n.s.[e] |
| Iron (mg) | 6.48 ± 1.86 (52%) | 8.45 ± 3.45 (62%) | 1.84 | 13 | .04 |
| Thiamine (mg) | 877 ± 321 (105%) | 992 ± 309 (133%) | 1.09 | 13 | n.s. |
| Riboflavin (mg) | 1375 ± 413 (155%) | 1585 ± 571 (186%) | .90 | 13 | n.s. |
| Niacin (mg) | 9.7 ± 3.1 (120%) | 15.9 ± 7.5 (171%) | 3.32 | 13 | .001 |
| Ascorbic acid (mg) | 52.2 ± 37.6 (130%) | 104.4 ± 62.8 (261%) | 2.83 | 13 | .007 |
| Vitamin A (IU) | 3508 ± 2756 (163%) | 4906 ± 3899 (236%) | .92 | 13 | n.s. |

[a] Values are expressed as means ± standard deviation.

[b] t test for matched pairs.

[c] One-tailed test.

[d] Numbers in parentheses are percentage of Recommended Dietary Allowances (National Academy of Sciences, 1974).

[e] n.s., not significant.

The data on mean percentage of the Recommended Dietary Allowances show that among the index children the intake of all nutrients except for calories ($\bar{M} = 99\%$) and iron ($\bar{M} = 52\%$) was above 100%. Among the contrast children, the only nutrient with a low mean value was iron ($\bar{M} = 62\%$).

The between-group comparisons of calorie and nutrient intake per kilogram of body weight are reported in Table 8.7. None of the comparisons yielded statistically significant differences, though the children in the index group tended to have higher intakes than did those in the contrast group.

None of the dietary variables that discriminated between groups were transformed into a new aggregate nutritional variable for the discriminant functional analysis. When the data for the two groups were pooled and analyzed separately, their high intercorrelation created a multicollinearity that resulted in spuriously large regression weights. Thus, the contribution of the nutrition variable to the variance of an outcome-anthropometry vari-

**TABLE 8.7**

Between-group Comparisons of Dietary Intake (per Kilogram Body Weight per Day)

| Nutritional variable | Intake (kg/day[a]) | | t test[b] | df | p[c] |
|---|---|---|---|---|---|
| | Index | Contrast | | | |
| Calories (kcal) | 59.03 ± 13.06 | 52.28 ± 16.09 | 1.21 | 13 | n.s.[d] |
| Protein (gm) | 2.14 ± .53 | 1.93 ± .64 | .97 | 13 | n.s. |
| Calcium (mg) | 33.71 ± 13.81 | 25.46 ± 10.71 | 1.65 | 13 | .06 |
| Iron (mg) | .26 ± .07 | .24 ± .11 | .31 | 13 | n.s. |
| Thiamine (mg) | 35.99 ± 15.77 | 29.73 ± 11.85 | 1.59 | 13 | .08 |
| Riboflavin (mg) | 56.29 ± 20.11 | 47.64 ± 19.63 | 1.11 | 13 | n.s. |
| Niacin (mg) | .39 ± .15 | .49 ± .29 | 1.55 | 13 | .07 |
| Ascorbic acid (mg) | 2.03 ± 1.36 | 2.94 ± 1.55 | 1.66 | 13 | .06 |
| Vitamin A (IU) | 139.82± 99.10 | 146.81 ± 126.35 | .14 | 13 | n.s. |

[a] Values are expressed as means ± standard deviation.
[b] t test for matched pairs.
[c] One-tailed test.
[d] n.s., not significant.

able would have been misleading. In addition, among the nutritional variables that discriminated between groups, only calories and protein were likely to influence growth rate. The protein intake of the index group was apparently more than adequate, judging by the group's mean value as a percentage of the Recommended Daily Allowances. Therefore, calorie intake was the only nutritional variable selected for inclusion in the discriminant functional analysis.

### Developmental

This set of variables included the child's birthweight, mother's height, and postnatal medical variables that may have affected growth. The mean birthweights were significantly different (index = 3112 gm, $SD$ = 535; contrast = 3515 gm, $SD$ = 365; $t$ = 2.74, $df$ = 18, $p$ < .01). The number of children who had had measles, chicken pox, or German measles was almost identical in the two groups.

Significantly more children in the index ($N$ = 10) than in the control group ($N$ = 2) had feeding problems during the first 12 months of their lives ($\chi^2$ = 5.97, $df$ = 1, $p$ < .02). These included poor appetite, poor sucking, crying during feedings, vomiting after feedings, and refusal to switch from liquids to solid foods. Two opposite meal patterns were observed among the children in both groups: Type 1, more good-sized meals eaten regularly, and Type 2, meals frequently skimpy and often skipped. Index children had fewer meals of Type 1, and more of Type 2 ($\chi^2 = 8.47$, $df = 1$, $p < .01$).

## Discriminant Functional Analysis

The between-group comparison showed that children in the index group had a lower SES (aggregate socioeconomic variable), birthweight, and calorie intake, and more problems in feeding. Index children also interacted less frequently with their mothers, who had less help in the care of their children. Accordingly, a discriminant functional analysis was calculated to find a linear combination of these discriminating variables that would maximize the differences between index and contrast groups. History of feeding difficulties was excluded from the analysis because it is a dichotomous rather than a continuous variable.

The anthropometric criterion initially used to classify the index and contrast cases for the discriminant analysis was the median of the distribution of the percentage of standard weight for both groups pooled. All cases whose weight was equal to or less than 90% of the standard fell into Group 1 (index); values above 90% identified those cases classified as Group 2 (contrast). The aim thereafter was to estimate a linear combination of SES, birthweight, calorie intake, mother–child interaction scores, and aid-in-caretaking scores that would classify all 38 cases into their respective anthropometric groups.

The discriminating function and discriminating scores for all five social–environmental variables selected are reported in Table 8.8. The stepwise

TABLE 8.8

Discriminant Functional Analysis: Summary Table[a]

| Step number | Variable entered | F value | Coefficients (lambda) | Discriminating scores | |
|---|---|---|---|---|---|
| | | | | Index | Contrast |
| 1 | Mother–child interaction score | 7.52* | −.04 | .1493 | .1988 |
| 2 | Calorie intake | 6.90** | −.01 | .0451 | .575 |
| 3 | Help in caretaking | 4.82** | −.81 | 5.3713 | 6.1905 |
| 4 | Socioeconomic status | 3.16 | −.001 | .0038 | .0050 |
| 5 | Birthweight | 1.40 | −.001 | .0120 | .0132 |

[a] $N = 38$.
*$p < .05$.
**$p < .01$.

order of entry of the variables into this table was determined by the extent to which they maximize the accurate classification of the cases into their anthropometric groups.

The discriminant scores were used to estimate the accuracy with which each variable classified the individual cases. For both index and contrast groups, 16 of the 19 cases (or 32 of 38) were accurately classified into Groups 1 or 2. Thus, the newly transformed variable classified the index and contrast cases with an accuracy rate of 82% ($p < .001$).

The $F$ values for each of the five variables show that all of them except for birthweight made statistically significant contributions to the maximization of differences between groups. Recognizing that the differences in $F$ values between variables are small, no conclusive inferences can be made regarding the competitive causal role and value of any one specific factor in comparison with the other three.

## DISCUSSION

Some of the drawbacks of the research design and samples used, as stated in the "Introduction," is given in the following. First, because of the ex post facto nature of the study, it is impossible to determine whether the growth of the index children was indeed affected by the established covariates. Inferences regarding these covariations must be made without information on their temporal sequence. It is conceivable that most of them are of recent occurrence. Second, the use of the Outpatient Pediatric Clinic at Cambridge Hospital to select the index subjects may have led to the exclusion of failure-to-thrive cases from the most severe multiproblem families in the city. Utilization of health care facilities is often positively correlated with socioeconomic status, and inversely related to prevalence of social-family problems (Leopold, 1974). Finally, selection of and comparisons between two groups contrasting in height and weight may have magnified the relationships between social–environmental factors and body size that exist within the total population. Accordingly, because of this possible overstimation, the chances of generalization beyond samples similar to these studied here is reduced.

In order to test the robustness of the hypothetical chain of causality proposed, the nature and magnitude of the interrelationships among the variables that discriminated between groups should have been established. However, the statistical technique used in this study is a classificatory procedure that establishes only the probability of membership in a particular group on the basis of variables. Path analysis, which depicts the influence of one set of variables over another according to preestablished criteria

(Spaeth, 1975), would have been a more suitable technique for testing the hypothesis. It was not used because it requires a larger sample size to establish accurately the degree of covariations between any pair of variables while controlling for confounding covariate effects. Nonetheless, it must be emphasized that, because the variables that discriminated between groups are of the same nature as those included in the hypothetical chain of causality, the hypothesis cannot be rejected on this basis alone. It may be argued, in turn, that the putative causal factors included in the chain do indeed seem implicated in the etiology of the failure-to-thrive syndrome.

Strictly speaking, the results of this study lead only to covariational statements, which can be summarized as follows: In comparison to children whose physical growth was in keeping with the Boston growth standards for age, underweight–undersized children were more likely to be of lower socioeconomic status and to have less physical and verbal interaction with their mothers, who in turn, have less help in the caretaking of their children. The failure-to-thrive children also had a lower birthweight, more difficulties in feeding during the first 12 months of life, and a lower daily calorie intake at the time of the study. Further, the results of the discriminant functional analysis permit a change of this covariational statement into a classificatory statement as follows: 32 of the 38 children in the study can be correctly classified into groups of short (index) or tall (contrast) children by the use of their discriminant scores on five variables (Mother–Child interaction, calorie intake, aid in caretaking, socioeconomic status, and birthweight).

The usefulness of the discriminant function would be greater if it could be used at an early age to forecast intraindividual changes in growth rate among children. This is particularly true in cases of failure to thrive. In case 01, for example (Figure 8.1), forecasting might have permitted intervention to prevent the abrupt drop in growth during the child's second 6 months of life. However, an analysis of the nature of some of the variables included in the discriminating function indicates the difficulties of forecasting. To forecast the slowed growth pattern of case 01, it would have been necessary to have data on all variables used as predictors before the drop in growth. In the case of the Mother–Child interaction variable, which happens to be the most forceful discriminator between groups, this may have proven impossible. Mother–Child interaction is a plastic and dynamic process shaped through time and affected by both mother and child. Thus, a large error factor may be expected in predictions from cross-sectional analysis of this interaction where the focus is limited to the adult. If it is true that behavioral interaction of mother and child is the strongest predictor of the type of failure to thrive studied here, forecasting would become too costly an endeavor for practical clinical purposes.

The statistical differences between groups in the total daily intake of calories and protein is in keeping with a nutritional explanation for the difference in body size between index and contrast children. However, the strength of the explanation is lost when it is recognized that this difference disappears when data for nutritional intake are corrected for the body weight of the children. Moreover, the data on nutrition, expressed as percentage of the Recommended Dietary Allowances, suggest that the intake of all nutrients except iron was adequate for the weight and age of the small children. Finally, it is pertinent to note once more that the comparisons made on the weight-for-height ratios following correction for the geometry of the growth curves showed no between-group differences. All these data therefore strongly support the contention that the retarded growth of the index children was not likely to be related to undernutrition in the recent past. However, it must be noted that the pattern of growth exhibited by individual cases (see Figures 8.1–8.3) could be related to past deficient dietary intake. Indeed, the data in cases 01, 04, 16, 17, and 18 fall well within growth curves reported for malnourished infants and preschoolers in low-income countries. Under these conditions, the rate of growth decreases progressively as dietary intake becomes quantitatively deficient in calories and protein (Behar, 1968; Guzman, 1968).

The fact that the growth patterns noted here could be related to deficient dietary intake is not necessarily strong support for the nutritional explanation of failure to thrive. A progressive neuroendocrine derangement with an inhibition of growth hormone release may result in growth patterns similar to those observed in Figure 8.1.

In view of the apparently adequate nutritional status of these children and the fact that the Mother–Infant interaction was the most potent discriminator between groups, a neuroendocrine mechanism may best explain the failure to thrive of the children in question. Moreover, the clinical descriptions of these children fit well with the clinical data reported by Powell *et al.* (1967) in their cases of reversible growth hormone deficiency associated with emotional deprivation. An in-depth analysis of disturbances in the eating, sleeping, elimination, autoerotic, and self-harming behavior of index and contrast cases showed a strong statistical difference between groups. The number of children exhibiting atypical behavior was ten in the index group and only one in the contrast group (Pollitt & Eichler, 1976).

A detailed description of the disturbances in the Mother–Child interaction of the index group has been reported previously (Pollitt *et al.*, 1975). In comparison to the mothers of the children in the contrast group, the mothers in the index group were less affectionate, related less often to their children, and were more prone to use physical punishment. These data agree with previous reports on failure-to-thrive children that have had little physical handling by the mother or no appreciable social contact with her (Fischhoff, Whitten, & Pettit, 1971). Mothers of such children have also been reported rarely to hold, cuddle, play with, or communicate with their children (Coleman & Provence, 1957; Leonard *et al.*, 1966).

The discussion to now has been restricted to the immediate antecedents of growth failure: nutrition or emotional deprivation. However, from the discriminant functional analysis and from the nature of the variables assessed, we see that other environmental variables also have a causal role. Even if we accept the Mother–Child interaction as the most important causal agent, and regardless of whether the nutritional or the neuroendocrine or both explanations are validated, it is apparent that future research must consider other variables. In agreement with the hypothetical chain of causality originally proposed and with an ecological view of this syndrome, it is apparent that, in order to trace to the origin of the problem, it is necessary to consider the family.

The data on caretaking competence showed that, in contrast to previous reports (Fischhoff *et al.*, 1971), the prevalence of psychopathology among the mothers in the index group was in no way unusually high. Thus, the disturbances in Mother–Child interaction found could not be explained by derangements in the mental health of the mothers. It appears that these disturbances reflect a restricted incompetence in childrearing or a malfunction in the maternal role. Conceivably, as suggested by Garbarino (1977) and Parke and Collmer (1975), this selective incompetence may be related to traumatic experiences of the individuals in question. In the case of this study it is most interesting that, as reported elsewhere (Pollitt *et al.*, 1975), the mothers of the children in the index group had had more stressful experiences in childhood than had the mothers of the contrast children, and were more likely to have been raised by parents who were psychiatrically ill, alcoholic, addicted to drugs, separated, or divorced.

Selective incompetence in child care may be exacerbated and its effects intensified by conditions in the immediate family environment (see also Garbarino, 1977). In comparison to the mothers of the contrast cases, the index mothers had less aid in caretaking of the children. Moreover, as suggested by the socioeconomic data, it appears that they were more likely to be exposed to economic stress. Conceivably, these conditions could contribute to the difficulties in child care.

In summary, this study demonstrates that the origins of failure to thrive when it occurs in the context of a pathologic social ambience cannot be found in a single etiological agent. To clarify its etiology, a multifactorial approach with heavy emphasis on the social ecology of the patient is required. As such, the syndrome is not only biomedical but also social in its very nature. The relevance of these data for treatment purposes should be obvious, as they strongly suggest that a monofocal, biomedical approach to therapy will be ineffective.

## REFERENCES

Apley, J., Davies, J., Davis, D. R., & Silk, B. Dwarfism without apparent physical cause. *Proceedings of the Royal Society of Medicine*, 1971, *64*, 135–138.

Balough, M., Kahn, H., & Medalie, J. Random repeat 24-hour dietary recalls. *The American Journal of Clinical Nutrition*, 1971, *24*, 304–310.

Barbero, G. J., & Shaheen, E. Environmental failure to thrive: A clinical view. *Journal of Pediatrics*, 1967, *71*, 639–644.

Behar, M. Prevalence of malnutrition among preschool children of developing countries. In N. S. Scrimshaw & J. Gordon (Eds.), *Malnutrition, learning and behavior*. Cambridge: M.I.T. Press, 1968. P. 30.

Blalock, H. M. *Social statistics* (2nd ed.). New York: McGraw Hill, 1972. P. 235.

Brasel, J. A. Review of findings in patients with emotional deprivation. In L. I. Gardner & P. Amachier (Eds.), *Endocrine aspects of malnutrition*. Kroc Foundation Symposia No. 1. Kroc Foundation, Santa Inez, Calif., 1973. P. 115.

Bronfenbrenner, U. Toward an experimental ecology of human development. *American Psychologist*, 1977, *32*, 513–531.

Brown, G. M. Endocrine aspects of psychological dwarfism. In E. J. Sachar (Ed.), *Hormones, behavior and psychopathology*. New York: Raven Press, 1976. Pp. 253–261.

Caldwell, B., Heider, J., & Kaplan, B. *Home observation for measurement of the environment*. Paper presented at the meeting of the American Psychological Association, New York, 1966.

Coleman, R. W., & Provence, A. Environmental retardation (hospitalism) in infants living in families. *Pediatrics*, 1957, *19*, 285–292.

Daughaday, W. H. Hormonal regulation of growth by somatomedin and other tissue growth factors. *Clinics in Endocrinology and Metabolism*, 1977, *6*, 117–135.

Department of Health, Education and Welfare. *Interdisciplinary glossary on child abuse and neglect: Legal, medical, social work terms*. DHEW Publication No. (OHDS) 78-30137, 1978.

D'Ercole, A. J., Underwood, L. E., & Van Wyk, J. J. Serum somatomedin-C in hypopituitarism and in other disorders of growth. *Journal of Pediatrics*, 1977, *90*, 375–381.

Elmer, E. Failure to thrive: Role of the Mother. *Pediatrics*, 1960, *25*, 717–725.

Evans, S. L., Reinhart, J. B., & Succop, R. A. Failure to thrive: A study of 45 children and their families. *Journal of the American Academy of Child Psychiatry*, 1972, *11*, 440–457.

Fischhoff, J., Whitten, C., & Pettit, M. A psychiatric study of mothers of infants with growth failure secondary to maternal deprivation. *Journal of Pediatrics*, 1971, *79*, 209–215.

Garbarino, J. A preliminary study of some ecological correlates of child abuse: The impact of socioeconomic stress on mothers. *Child Development*, 1976, *47*, 178–185.

Garbarino, J. The human ecology of child maltreatment: A conceptual model for research. *Journal of Marriage and the Family*, 1977, *39*, 721–735.

Gardner, L. I. Deprivation dwarfism. *Scientific American*, 1972, *227*, 76–82.

Gardner, L. I. The endocrinology of abuse dwarfism. *American Journal of Diseases of Children*, 1977, *131*, 505–507.

Guzman, M. A. Impaired physical growth and maturation in malnourished populations. In N. S. Scrimshaw & J. Gordon (Eds.), *Malnutrition, learning and behavior*. Cambridge: M.I.T. Press, 1968. P. 42.

Hintz, R. L., Suskind, R., Amatayakul, K., Thanangkul, O., & Olson, R. Plasma somatomedin and growth hormone values in children with protein–calorie malnutrition. *Journal of Pediatrics*, 1978, *92*, 153–156.

Hollowell, J. G., & Gardner, L. I. Rumination and growth failure in male fraternal twins. *Pediatrics*, 1965, *36*, 565–571.

Kerlinger, F. N., & Pedhazur, E. J. *Multiple regression in behavioral research*. New York: Holt, Rinehart & Winston, 1973.

Kreiger, I. Endocrines and nutrition in psychosocial deprivation in the U.S.A.: Comparison with growth failure due to malnutrition on an organic basis. In L. I. Gardner & P. Amachier (Eds.), *Endocrine aspects of malnutrition*. Kroc Foundation Symposia No. 1. Kroc Foundation, Santa Inez, Calif., 1973.

Kreiger, I. Food restriction as a form of child abuse in ten cases of psychosocial deprivation dwarfism. *Clinical Pediatrics*, 1974, *13*, 127–133.

Kreiger, I., & Mellinger, R. C. Pituitary function in the deprivation syndrome. *Journal of Pediatrics*, 1971, *79*, 216–225.

Leonard, M., Rhymes, J., & Solnit, A. Failure to thrive in infants: A family problem. *American Journal of Diseases of Children*, 1966, *111*, 600–612.

Leopold, E. A. Who do we reach? A study of health care utilization. *Pediatrics*, 1974, *53*, 341–348.

McCarthy, D. Effects of emotional disturbance and deprivation (maternal rejection) on somatic growth. In J. A. Davis & J. Dobbing (Eds.), *Scientific foundations of Pediatrics*. Philadelphia: Saunders, 1974.

McCarthy, D., & Booth, E. M. Parental rejection and stunting of growth. *Journal of Psychosomatic Research*, 1970, *14*, 259–265.

National Academy of Sciences–National Research Council. *Recommended dietary allowances* (8th ed.). Food and Nutrition Board, 1974.

Nelson, W. E., Vaughn, V. C., & McKay, J. R. *Textbook of pediatrics*. Philadelphia: Saunders, 1968. Pp. 42–53.

Parke, R., & Collmer, C. W. Child abuse: An interdisciplinary analysis. In E. M. Hetherington (Ed.), *Review of child development research* (Vol. 5). Chicago: University of Chicago Press, 1975. Pp. 509–590.

Polansky, N. A. *Childhood level of living scale*. Unpublished manuscript, School of Social Work, the University of Georgia, Athens, Georgia, 1968.

Pollitt, E., & Eichler, A. Behavioral disturbances among failure-to-thrive children. *American Journal of Diseases of Children*, 1976, *130*, 24–29.

Pollitt, E., Eichler, A., & Chan, C. K. Psychosocial development and behavior of mothers of failure-to-thrive children. *American Journal of Orthopsychiatry*, 1975, *45*, 525–537.

Powell, G. G., Brasel, J. A., & Blizzard, R. M. Emotional deprivation and growth retardation simulating idiopathic hypopituitarism: I: Clinical evaluation of the syndrome. *The New England Journal of Medicine*, 1967, *276*, 1271–1283.

Reed, R. B., & Stuart, H. C. Patterns of growth in height and weight from birth to eighteen years of age. *Pediatrics*, 1959, *24*, 904–921.

Shaheen, E., Alexander, D., Truskowsky, M., & Barbero, G. J. Failure-to-thrive: A retrospective profile. *Clinical Pediatrics*, 1968, *7*, 255–261.

Silver, H. K., & Finkelstein, M. Deprivation dwarfism. *Journal of Pediatrics*, 1967, *70*, 317–324.

Spaeth, J. L. Path analysis. In D. J. Amick & H. J. Walberg (Eds.), *Introductory multivariate analysis*. Berkeley, Calif.: McCutchan, 1975.

Spitzer, R. L., Endicott, J., Mesnikoff, A., & Cohen, G. *Psychiatric evaluation form*. Unpublished manuscript, Department of Psychiatry, Columbia University, New York, 1968.

Tatsuoka, M. M. *Discriminant analysis. The study of group differences* (Vol. 6). In *Selected topics in advanced statistics*. Champaign, Ill.: Institute for Personality and Ability Testing, 1970.

Whitten, C. F., Pettit, M. G., & Fischhoff, J. Evidence that growth failure from maternal deprivation is secondary to undereating. *Journal of the American Medical Association*, 1969, *209*, 1675–1682.

# 9

# The Dynamics of Malnutrition
# in Jamaica[1]

THOMAS J. MARCHIONE AND FRED WILLIAM PRIOR

## INTRODUCTION

Protein–energy malnutrition (PEM) in infants and young children will probably remain the most serious nutritional problem facing the world in the latter half of the twentieth century (Bengoa, 1973; cf. Morley, 1973). Although it seems clear that gross estimates of child nutritional status reflect aggregate differences in wealth and level of technological development between the continents, nations, and regions in which children reside, detailed social epidemiological investigations *within* human populations are perhaps more important in public health programs and to national health and nutritional planners. The key to generating information on the epidemiology of PEM that is not only true but also useful lies in detailed knowledge of why children become malnourished. Many of the questions concerning the etiology of PEM remain unanswered. Are causes proximate to the child or distant? In what ways do distant and proximate causes articulate? What combination of intrafamilial, interfamilial, national, and international factors are important to child nutrition? In order to approach these problems effec-

[1]This research was carried out in 1973 and 1975 with support from the Caribbean Food and Nutrition Institute in Kingston, Jamaica, the Jamaican Ministry of Health and Environmental Control, and by a grant from the National Center for Health Services Research, United States Department of Health, Education and Welfare.

*Social and Biological Predictors of*
*Nutritional Status, Physical Growth,*
*and Neurological Development*

tively, it is important to understand the ways in which the changing world system and the flow of national policy affect the microenvironments to which the child must adapt.

Jamaica provides a unique opportunity to study a society which has attempted to grapple with its national food and nutrition problems along with its general development problems (Jamaican Nutrition Advisory Council, 1974; Marchione, 1977a). Although Jamaica is not faced with the overwhelming nutrition-related problems of many Third World nations, for example, those of its neighbor, Haiti, the early 1970s brought a series of disturbing research reports on the continuing seriousness of young child malnutrition. In 1972, after 10 years of political independence, there was growing recognition of continuing high mortality, morbidity, growth retardation, and possible mental and behavioral retardation due to infant and young child malnutrition (Ashworth & Picou, 1974; Birch & Richardson, 1972; Cook, 1971; Fox, Campbell, & Harris, 1968; Gurney, Fox, & Neill, 1972; Puffer & Serrano, 1973).

This study is based on data collected in 1973 and 1975 during the period when Jamaica was undergoing numerous changes due to new policies, partly in response to its recognition of the persistence of PEM and partly in response to the threats posed by the world food crisis of 1974. We will describe the complex of factors that influence the growth of 1-year-old children and the difficulty of tracing these factors through time as Jamaican society underwent major, if not revolutionary, social and cultural change.

## THE CHANGING PARISH OF ST. JAMES

The geographical focus of this research is the Parish of St. James in the western part of the Republic of Jamaica, one of the island's 13 parishes (Figure 9.1). Its population was estimated by the Jamaican Department of Statistics at 115,000 in 1975, representing 6% of the nation's population of 2.01 million people. The parish capital, Montego Bay, was the major population center with 40% of the parish population and was growing rapidly according to the 1970 census (Jamaican Department of Statistics, 1975, pp. 123–125). The parish well represents Jamaican life. Its history and current social structure are typical of both the urban and rural experience of the island as a whole.

In 1972 a new government was elected in Jamaica promising major changes in the colonial social and economic patterns that had persisted during the 10 years following independence. However, not more than a year elapsed before the island had to contend with the world food crisis. Food import prices accelerated (Figure 9.2) and overall food prices nearly doubled. Between 1967 and 1973 the consumer price index for food items increased 70%, but in the 24 months from mid-1973 to mid-1975 the index

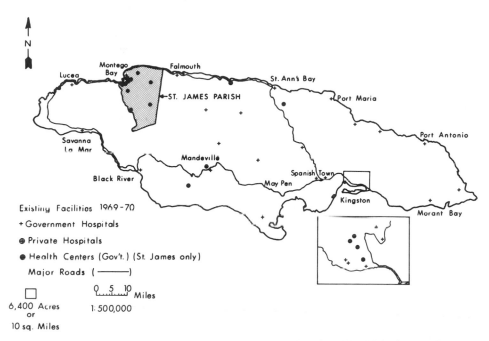

**Figure 9.1.** The Island of Jamaica showing parish capitals, selected health facilities, and St. James Parish. (Adapted from Jamaican Department of Statistics, *Statistical yearbook for 1974.*)

leaped by 90%. This reflected the fact that, according to 1972 food balance sheets, Jamaicans had continued to depend on food imports for over half of both their protein and energy requirements. In addition, banana export prices, a potential source of income for Jamaica's many small producers, remained virtually constant. A nutrition crisis seemed inevitable. Even in our rural household sample in St. James, 70% of the average household income was spent on food, and in over one-third of these households more than 90% of their incomes were spent on food in 1973 (Marchione, 1977a).

The Jamaican Government instituted a number of policies in response to the economic situation affecting St. James. One was the creation of public service employment including the creation of a community health aide program with nutritional education objectives (Marchione, 1977b). Part of the financing for the employment programs came from increased taxation on foreign bauxite companies. In addition, as the food import bill rose, a policy of "grow our own food" was initiated. Rural food marketing was supported and land was redistributed to small farmers by leasing and purchasing idle acreage from large landholders. To aid the nonfarmer, the government tacitly supported aggressive union demands on larger businesses. Higher wage increases were being granted in new contract agreements (Marchione, 1977a, pp. 67–71).

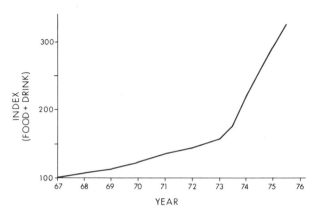

**Figure 9.2.**   Consumer price index for food and drink in Jamaica for 1967 to June of 1975 (from Jamaican Department of Statistics, *Annual Report of 1974* and 1975 Quarterly Reports.)

## FIELD METHODS AND SAMPLING

The overall study assessed the impact of this changing situation through two field surveys examining social and cultural conditions and the nutritional status of children in St. James Parish. The surveys involved two samples of 500 children under 36 months of age, one in 1973 and the other in 1975 (Figure 9.3). Random, cluster, stratified sampling was used. Enumeration districts (EDs) were randomly selected from those defined in the 1970 census of St. James. The EDs were first stratified by the urban–rural designation provided by the Department of Statistics, then all households with children under 3 were located within the sample EDs. This chapter reports on a subsample of *1-year-olds* and their households. Only one child per household is included in this analysis.

In Montego Bay, both middle-class and shanty-town neighborhoods were represented. The rural sample included the large towns, banana plantations, and peasant farming areas. The diversity of settlement typologies found relevant to PEM incidence by Foneroff (1969) (i.e., urban, town, isolated rural, and plantation) were all represented in both samples. Both samples of 1-year-olds compared remarkably well on characteristics such as age, sex, household size, land resources, distance to piped water supply, and use of health facilities.

The surveys were conducted in two parts using health workers from the sampled areas. They completed sociocultural interview protocols in households with young children and arranged to have children examined at nearby health facilities. In the second part of the survey, professional personnel checked interview results and did anthropometric measurements. There was

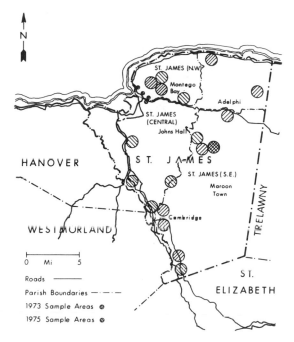

Figure 9.3.    Survey areas in the Parish of St. James in 1973 and in 1975.

a concerted effort to achieve total coverage of each area chosen. When it was found that children were not brought to the centers, the household was visited and measurements were done using portable equipment. Anthropometry was obtained on over 90% of both groups of children.


## NUTRITIONAL STATUS OF CHILDREN

Early observations on the nutritional status of Jamaican children focused on cases of florid kwashiorkor which is most common during the second year of life. These children were reported to have low intakes of protein relative to energy because of the consumption of high-carbohydrate, low-protein foods such as sugar and teas, diluted sweetened condensed milk, and starchy porridges, and were referred to as "sugar babies" by the medical nutritionist Platt (Waterlow, 1974, p. 151). A number of recent crosssectional and longitudinal studies in Jamaica have documented growth failure among children 12–24 months of age (Alderman & Minott, 1973; Desai, Standard, & Miall, 1969; Gurney et al., 1972, p. 654). These community studies report a prevalence of severe weight and height deficits not exceeding 2 or 3%, and suggest that the prevalence of severe PEM with clinical signs of kwashiorkor or marasmus is relatively rare outside of hospital settings. Most cases found represent moderate or slight degrees of PEM, and assessment of nutritional status is usually based on anthropometric measures of weight and height.

In our study, weight and height for age are determined relative to the fiftieth percentile of the Boston standards (Habicht, 1974; Jelliffe, 1966). These continue to be considered reliable and valid indicators of nutritional status because of the existence of accurate birth documentation throughout the island and because of evidence indicating height and weight distributions similar to those standards among privileged Jamaicans of African, Afro-European, and European origin (Ashcroft, Heneage, & Lovell, 1966, pp. 36–41). Furthermore, the degree of PEM rated according to the classification of Gomez, Galvan, Cravioto, and Frank (1955) is widely used by researchers and Jamaican health authorities. Recent data comparing the growth of American Blacks and Whites suggest that the Boston standards may underestimate the nutritional problems of the 90% of Jamaican children who are primarily of African origin (Garn & Clark, 1976). In any case, all nutritional measures in this study and in those studies cited are comparisons principally between different Afro-Jamaican population segments. Therefore, they can be viewed as relative indications of nutritional status.

Anthropometric measurements utilized in this study were height for age and weight for age. In the samples of 500 children, from birth to 36 months of age, combined Gomez II and III grades of malnutrition were 7.4% in 1973 and 4.5% in 1975. This was not a statistically significant change at the .05 level according to $\chi^2$ test; however in the rural areas a change from 9.5% in 1973 to 4.5% in 1975 was significant at the .05 level (Marchione, 1977a). Taking the *1-year-old subsample* separately, the combined Gomez II and III grades show 10.9% malnourished in 1973 and 9.2% in 1975 (Table 9.1). Generally, both the height and weight measures confirmed the persistent growth problem in the 12- to 24-month age group (Table 9.2). Changes were

**TABLE 9.1**

**Gomez Grade of 1-year-old Children in St. James in 1973 and 1975**

| Gomez grade[a] | 1973 | | 1975[b] | |
|---|---|---|---|---|
| | No. | % | No. | % |
| Normal | 67 | 52.3 | 55 | 46.2 |
| Gomez I | 47 | 36.7 | 53 | 44.5 |
| Gomez II | 14 | 10.9 | 8 | 6.7 |
| Gomez III | 0 | .0 | 3 | 2.5 |
| Total | 128 | 100.0 | 119 | 100.0 |

[a] Gomez I is 75 to 89% of standard weight for age, Gomez II is 60 to 74%, Gomez III is under 60%.

[b] Differences are not significant from 1973 to 1975 ($\chi^2 = 5.86$, $p = .1188$).

**TABLE 9.2**

Height for Age of 1-year-old Children in St. James from 1973 to 1975

| Percentage of standard height for age | 1973 | | 1975[a] | |
|---|---|---|---|---|
| | No. | % | No. | % |
| >104 | 1 | .9 | 7 | 7.1 |
| 100–104 | 34 | 31.2 | 24 | 24.5 |
| 95–99 | 55 | 50.5 | 43 | 43.9 |
| 90–94 | 14 | 12.8 | 13 | 13.3 |
| 85–89 | 4 | 3.7 | 7 | 7.1 |
| <85 | 1 | .9 | 4 | 4.1 |
| Total | 109 | 100.0 | 98 | 100.0 |

[a] Differences from 1973 to 1975 are not significant ($\chi^2 = 9.79$, $p = .08$).

not significant in this age group. Increases shown in Tables 9.2 and 9.3 in taller (>104%) and in severely malnourished (Gomez III) children are difficult to reliably interpret because of the small cell numbers which are highly subject to sampling error.

## SOCIAL EPIDEMIOLOGY OF MALNUTRITION

### Zero-order Correlations

In the present study, data were gathered on a number of household-level social, economic, dietary, demographic, and other variables which were thought to be potentially important to a child's nutritional status. These data included information on family size and structure, economic status, dietary history, as well as the child's age, sex, and frequency of illness. The variables selected are shown in Table 9.3. These 31 variables were chosen on the basis of their importance in previous epidemiological studies in Jamaica and the Caribbean (Desai, Miall, & Standard, 1968; Desai, Standard, & Miall, 1970; Pan American Health Organization, 1972).

In the 1973 sample, 15 of the 31 variables were significantly correlated with the height for age or weight for age of the child (Table 9.4). In the 1975 analysis, the correlation coefficients were significant on 8 variables. One of these, father's support, was not significant in 1973. Thus, 7 variables proved to be consistently associated with nutritional status through time. Growth attainment in height or weight of 1-year-old children in both 1973 and 1975 was positively correlated with (a) household food expenses, (b) household income, (c) meal-makers dietary variety, (d) the presence of the child's father in the household, (e) the age of the mother, (f) the dietary adequacy of

**TABLE 9.3**

**Operational Definitions of Household Social Epidemiological Variables Used in the Analysis**

| Variable name | Definition[a] |
|---|---|
| Location | House place (urban, 1; rural, 2) |
| Household size | Number of residents and meal sharers over previous week |
| Dependency ratio | Number of residents under 15 ÷ number of residences over 15 years |
| Employment history | Proportion of past year main provider was employed |
| School lunches | Number of children currently receiving lunches |
| Agricultural resources | None, land or livestock, both land and livestock |
| Home food use | Number of home-grown items in weekly diet |
| Food expenditures | Cash per person over previous week |
| Income | Cash per person over previous week |
| Distance to piped water | Distance to functioning pipe |
| Distance to health facility | Distance to public facilities |
| Relationship of mealmaker and child | Consanguinous, affinal, other |
| Age of mealmaker | Age categories |
| Age of child | Age categories |
| Diet variety | Number of different items in 24-hr recall of mealmaker |
| Diet sharing | Item comparison of mealmaker and child recall records |
| Diet complexity | Guttman-type scale of recalled food items. |
| Mother's presence | Current membership in household (absent, present). |
| Father's presence | Current membership in household (absent, present). |
| Mother's employment | Job outside home, no, part-time, full-time. |
| Father's child support | None, partial, full, economic support |
| Age of mother | Age classifications ( < 20, 20–26, 27–34, > 34) |
| Siblings under 5 | Number of siblings under 5-years-old |
| Mother's literacy | No, yes |
| Milk type | Quality of current type most frequently used |
| Illness of child | Yes, no, episode in past month |
| Child welfare clinic attendance | Attendance at most recent local public session |
| Family planning attendance | Attendance at most recent local public session |
| Sex of child | Female, male |
| Dietary adequacy of child | Based on diet recall portion counts |
| Dietary adequacy of mealmaker | Based on diet recall portion counts |

[a] More complete definitions can be found in Appendix B of Marchione, 1977b.

the child, and (g) negatively correlated with the number of home grown foods used in the household diet.

We exercise caution in drawing conclusions about etiology of malnutrition from these low, zero-order correlations because of the interrelationships existing among the set of household measures. The correlation matrix existing between the 31 measures demonstrates that household conditions are complexly interwoven (Marchione, 1980). On the order of 200 significant correlations exist among the 31 measures. Some correlations may be merely reflections or proxy expressions of others which are more powerfully related to nutritional status. In addition, a close examination of these relationships shows that variables with no apparent relationship to height or weight for age are frequently correlated with at least one other variable that is significantly related to these measures (e.g., employment history is related to income and food expenditure which are, in turn, related to child nutritional status). It is highly probable that under proper control new associations not demonstrated would appear. In fact, changes in category cutting points or slight changes in samples cause new low-value correlations to appear (Marchione, 1980).

TABLE 9.4

Household Measures Correlated[a] with the Weight and Height for Age of 1-year-old Children By Year of Survey

| | Weight for age[b] | | Height for age[b] | |
|---|---|---|---|---|
| Household measures | 1973 (N = 128) | 1975 (N = 119) | 1973 (N = 109) | 1975 (N = 98) |
| Location | −.19 | — | −.18 | — |
| Household size | — | — | −.20 | — |
| Dependency ratio | — | — | −.15 | — |
| Agricultural resources | −.14 | — | −.24 | — |
| Home food use | — | −.14 | −.15 | — |
| Food expenses | .24 | .22 | .20 | — |
| Income | .13 | .26 | — | — |
| Distance to piped water | −.14 | — | −.18 | — |
| Diet variety | .15 | .15 | .20 | .17 |
| Mother's presence | .15 | — | — | — |
| Father's presence | .21 | .17 | — | — |
| Mother's age | .14 | .18 | — | .16 |
| Siblings under 5 | — | — | −.15 | — |
| Child welfare clinic attendance | −.13 | — | — | — |
| Diet adequacy of child | — | .14 | .16 | — |
| Father's support of child | — | .17 | — | — |

[a] Correlations are Kendal's $\tau$ significant at $p$ less than .05, one-tailed.

[b] Percentage of standard using seven value ordinal rankings.

## Factor Analysis

Factor analysis is a useful tool for reducing the number and controlling for the interrelationships between variables (Rummel, 1970). Factors are new variables composed of mathematical combinations of the original variables. Classical or common factor analysis with rotation provides a particular solution composed of a set of new variables fewer in number than the original number of variables in the matrix. Factor analytical solutions using the 31 epidemiological variables in 1973 and in 1975 yielded 12 and 11 factors, respectively. The factor procedure used produced orthogonal factors, or variables which were uncorrelated with each other (see Marchione, 1980; Nie, Hull, Jenkins, Steinbrenner, & Bent, 1975, pp. 468–514). The character of a factor is determined by the original variables correlated with it or "loading" on it.

In both the 1973 and 1975 analyses, similar factors were derived, except that the family social variables tended to be expressed in two factors using 1975 data. Overall, the two-factor structures were very stable for the 1973 and 1975 factor analyses. Nearly eight identical factors that we expected to predict either height for age or weight for age are defined in the following, and reliable variable loadings from 1973 to 1975 are compared.

### Agricultural Subsistence

Five variables combined to form this factor, which represents a *measure of the degree to which the household is dependent on its own agricultural production*. The variables loading on this factor and the major factor loadings for 1973 and 1975, respectively, are agricultural resources (.79, .83); home food use (.73, .71); location (.53, .76); household size (.41, .33); and food expenditures (−.40, −.31). Those households using more home-grown food in their own diets obviously had food resources to draw from even though the resources might be meager ones. It is important to note that more households made use of home-grown food items in their diets in 1975 than in 1973 (44 versus 37%, $\chi^2 = 20.9$, $df = 2$, $p < .0001$). This increase seems understandable considering the rising food prices during the period. The negative loading of food expenditures on the factor confirms that home-grown food use lowers overall food expenditures, and/or, conversely, being short of cash for food purchases induced more families to start home gardens. However, this argument is somewhat compounded by the fact that farm families can also benefit from higher food prices. The number of farm families *heavily dependent* on home-grown foods appeared to decrease in this period, suggesting that they entered into the cash economy. In other words, they benefited from the sale of food products due to rising prices, better rural marketing, and shortages of competitively priced imported foods.

## Maternal-Guardian Maturity

This factor is composed of the age of the mother of the child (.70, .82) and the age of the mealmaker for the child (.95, .75). In both 1973 and 1975 these tended to be the same person. Most of the mothers were 20–34 years of age: one in six were above 34, and one in six were below 20. We have labeled the factor as such to suggest that the age of the mother and/or guardian relates to the biocultural development of the child.

## Family Demographic Stress

This variable is primarily a combination of the dependency ratio (.60, .70) and the number of siblings under five (.50, .60), both of which reflect the number of children in the household. Slightly less important in the factor's definition was household size (.37, .69). From 1973 to 1975 there was no significant increase either in dependency ratio (one-fifth of households exceeded 2.0) or in family size (one-third had eight or more persons). However, there was a significant increase in the siblings under 5 ($\chi^2 = 12.35$, $df = 4$, $p = .02$).

## Family Cohesion

This factor is composed of three variables: father's presence in the household (.87, .78); father's support of the child (.72, .92); and mother's presence in the household (.50, .53). These three measures relate to the relative stability, integrity, and coherence of the child's family. It highlights the fact that in households in which the father did not reside with his child, he often was not a regular economic supporter. Also, the mother's and father's absence often occurred together when the child was residing with the grandmother while both parents were working abroad or in other parts of the island. It is important to note that family cohesion improved from 1973 to 1975 according to this study. Mothers and fathers were significantly more likely to be present in 1975. For example, the father's presence increased from 47% to 63% present ($p = .02$).

## Monetary Wealth

Numerous variables loaded on this factor. Income (.68, .72) and food expenditures (.62, .61) were the more consistent components in both years. Other loadings proved less stable because of changing income and food expenditure: distance to piped water (−.59, −.12), employment history of the main provider (.46, .08), and location (−.44, −.17). The factor largely reflects the current budget of the household because the cash-flow figures were gathered for the previous week. In the more stable situation the regularity of the main provider's employment over the past year closely correlated with current wealth, and the presence of water connections reflected the past ability of wealthier householders to afford such luxuries or to live where piped water was more accessible. As might be expected from the food price increases previously discussed, the food expenditures increased significantly from 1973 to 1975. Those households spending more than $4 per person per week increased from 16 to 33%. However, income also increased so that the average percentage of income spent on food remained about 70%.

## Age Transition

This factor is merely the age of the child (.89, .95). It reflects the transition of the child from age 12 months to 24 months not only biologically but also culturally. Jelliffe (1968) has referred to children around this age as "biocultural transitionals."

## Clinic Care

This factor is composed of the single variable, child welfare clinic attendance (.83, .96). It reflects the demand for and the availability of government child-welfare clinics. We found that in both 1973 and in 1975 about 30% of the 1-year olds were regularly brought to local clinics held in their areas of residence.

## Household Diet

This factor reveals the interrelationship of dietary variables. Two loadings proved to be reliable, dietary variety (.80, .61) and the dietary adequacy of the mealmaker (.48, .68). Other variables, such as diet sharing between mealmaker and child (−.31, −.55) and dietary adequacy of the child, were somewhat less closely related to the factor. Both 1973 and 1975 samples demonstrated that less than half of the mealmakers had diets consisting of 10 or more items per day. Some indications of slight improvements in dietary adequacy of children were observed.

Although the 1973 and 1975 factor structures were quite similar, the 1973 factors were originally derived to be *predictors* of nutritional status. Consequently, the 1973 factor-score coefficient matrix was utilized to calculate factor scores in 1975.[2] Children in each sample were assigned a value for each factor (including those not defined here) in place of the original 31 measures, and correlations with nutritional anthropometry were calculated (Rummel, 1970, pp. 433–445). Table 9.5 shows that six factors were associated with at least one of the anthropometric variables in either 1973 or 1975. Two of the factors proved to be consistent predictors of weight for age

[2]When using the 1973 factor-score coefficient matrix with 1975 data, factors ceased to be entirely orthogonal, and were therefore not completely uncorrelated with each other. Nevertheless, the analysis using 1975 factors, which are orthogonal but not strictly comparable, demonstrated significant correlations similar to those reported in Table 9.5. Only "age transition" did not reach significance.

TABLE 9.5

Correlation (r) between Factors and Nutritional Status of the 1-year-olds in 1973 and in 1975

| | Nutritional status | | | |
|---|---|---|---|---|
| | Weight for age | | Height for age | |
| Factors | 1973 $(N = 103)^a$ | 1975 $(N = 82)^a$ | 1973 $(N = 103)$ | 1975 $(N = 82)$ |
| Agricultural subsistence | $-.25^b$ | $-.21^c$ | $-.28^b$ | .02 |
| Maternal–guardian maturity | $.22^b$ | $.19^c$ | .11 | .16 |
| Family demographic stress | $-.22^b$ | $-.14$ | $-.35^b$ | $-.14$ |
| Family cohesion | $.23^b$ | .08 | .15 | .01 |
| Monetary wealth | .12 | $.29^c$ | .07 | .12 |
| Age transition | $-.03$ | $.26^c$ | $-.14$ | $-.23^c$ |
| Clinic care | $-.08$ | .17 | $-.14$ | .17 |
| Household dietary | .09 | $-.05$ | .03 | $-.02$ |
| Multiple R | .49 | .42 | .53 | .33 |
| $R^2$ variance accounted for (%) | 24 | 17 | 28 | 11 |

[a] Substantial data loss occurs because of list-wise deletion of missing data in the factor analysis.
[b] Pearson's r significant at $p < .05$, two-tailed tests.
[c] Pearson's r significant at $p < .05$, one-tailed tests.

through time. The degree of agricultural subsistence was negatively associated with weight for age in both 1973 and 1975. Similarly, maternal–guardian maturity was positively associated with weight for age in both years. Two other factors, family demographic stress and family cohesion, were negatively associated with weight for age in 1973 but not in 1975. Two factors that were insignificant predictors in the 1973 analysis, age transition and monetary wealth, were significant predictors in 1975: Wealth was positively related to weight for age while child age was negatively related to both weight and height for age. Also, in 1973 but not in 1975, children experiencing greater agricultural subsistence and family demographic stress were significantly shorter. Two expected predictive factors, household diet and clinic care, proved to have no association with nutritional status at either time. Overall, the significant factors predicted 24% of the variation in weight for age and 28% of the variation in height for age in 1973, but in 1975 only 17% of weight for age and 11% of height for age variation was predicted by these factors.[3]

[3]Because of the relationship between some factors in 1975, a multiple regression analysis was performed to obtain the multiple $R^2$, or proportion of variance explained. In 1973, however, the variance explained can be estimated by the sum of squares of each individual correlation with the factors.

## DISCUSSION AND IMPLICATIONS

### Subsistence Agriculture and Nutritional Status

It should not be surprising to find that the degree of agricultural subsistence practiced proved a consistent predictor of malnutrition in Jamaica. The combination of dietary dependence on home-grown food and the low food expenditures of the households was deleterious to growth of 1-year-olds. The factor identified the households with few alternative means of survival except for a small inadequate piece of land. Similar results have been reported in other studies (Bantje, 1974; Desai, *et al.*, 1970, pp. 140–141). At the micro-level, this retarded growth could be considered an adaptational response to scarce resources (Alland, 1970, pp. 74–75; Stini, 1971). For the sake of the overall survival of the household, child growth was not maximized but rather optimized. However, the marginalization of child nutrition often results in serious clinical malnutrition in Jamaica. Furthermore, examination of the macrostructures reveals that key environmental conditions have been and continue to be very much manipulated by human action.

This observation reveals the articulation of persistent, inequitable colonial socioeconomic structures with the microecology of child-rearing households. In keeping with its history as a plantation economy, Jamaican policies favored cultivation of export crops up to the early 1970s. Sugar estates comprised 56% of farm land, but represented only 1% of all farms on the island (Beckford, 1972, p. 25). In St. James, 80.5% of all farms ($N=8064$) were under five acres in size in 1968. These farms averaged 1.3 acres and utilized only 12% of the cultivated land in the parish. Farms over 500 acres constituted .19% of all farms, but monopolized 48.1% of all cultivated land. Furthermore, from 1962 to 1968 the small farms decreased in average land area by 27% (Jamaican Department of Statistics, 1975; p. 726). Since 1972, the Government of Jamaica has attempted to remedy land maldistribution as part of a general self-reliance strategy. Abandoned estates were purchased or leased by the government, then parcels were released or government-managed cooperatives were set up. In St. James, this affected only 5% of the land by mid-1975 (Ministry of Agriculture, 1975).

Government policies combined with the rising food costs were probably responsible for the significant increase in the number of households using home grown foods between 1973 and 1975, what has been called an increase in "semi-subsistence farming" (Marchione, 1977a, pp. 66–68). However, the predicted increase in young child malnutrition did not occur. The reason appears to be that the practice of some form of food production for home use is a necessary but not sufficient condition for high agricultural subsistence stress. It strengthens the view that the relation of the factor to young child malnutrition is nonlinear. When a household began to use home-grown foods in their diets to supplement purchased foods and to substitute for inappropriate and ever more costly imported foods, they probably reaped some nutritional benefit. Also, the sales of local food products were an increasingly lucrative income supplement to the rural producer. These conditions *do not,* however, constitute agricultural subsistence *stress.* The conditions of stress occur when the household is unable to purchase needed food in the market and is forced to live almost exclusively on home production derived from inadequately sized land plots. Such conditions are reflected in the direction of the five simple variables which compose high scores on the factor: possession of agricultural resources, *many* home-grown foods in the diet, low food expenditure, larger family size, and rural residence. Both the job creation programs, the improved market for local food products, and other redistribution policies appear to have combined to prevent and even reduce agricultural subsistence stress.

That agricultural subsistence was in great flux over this period is indicated by the fact that agricultural subsistence stress is no longer associated with height for age. Chronic nutritional stress on child growth tends to be revealed by a height for age shortfall (Seone & Latham, 1971). This relationship was undermined as households shifted into food production from other pursuits, with some farmers becoming less, and others more, stressed by the changing situation.

The analysis confirms the fact that early child nutrition is linked to many aspects of food and nutrition policy: land use and distribution, dependence on imported foods, food prices, marketing, and wage income. It suggests that a large proportion of rural Jamaican households cannot be expected to be food self-reliant unless more adequate land parcels are provided, or supplemental farm or nonfarm income is made available.

## Mother–Guardian Maturity and Nutritional Status

Child weight for age was higher in households with mature mothers and guardians. Mothers under 20 tended to have lighter 1-year-old children than mothers in their thirties in both samples. This finding may be a consequence of better child-care experience, although dietary measures do not load on the factor. The subtleties of good care and appropriate feeding were not measured in this analysis. For instance, longer and more complete breast feeding during infancy may be practiced by older mothers following more traditional patterns, whereas younger mothers may be more inclined to use costly modern foods such as formula milks, more for their prestige value than their nutritional value. It is also possible that the higher prematurity rates of teenage mothers may be reflected here. If younger mothers have low-birthweight children, the weight and length for age of their 1-year-olds are also likely to be low. However, in Jamaica, Desai *et al.* (1968) report no statistically significant relationship between birthweights and later growth attainment, especially after 12 months of age.

These data suggest that older women would be better as nutrition educators. Another analysis showed that the community acceptability and performance of older community health aides was better than younger, more inexperienced women (Marchione, 1973).

### Family Demographic Stress and Nutritional Status

Child growth tended to fail as the number of preschool siblings increased, dependency ratios increased, and family size grew larger. That is, malnutrition tended to occur where family demographic stress was greatest, an observation that corroborates similar findings on the effects of fertility and family size in the Caribbean (Antrobus, 1971). These observations are similar to those of Boodoo and Standard (1970) in rural St. Andrew near Kingston, where young child mortality due to malnutrition was found to increase sharply as the number of siblings under 5 years exceeded two. The growth of the Jamaican population is in large measure due to a decrease in the infant mortality rate without a concomitant decrease in the birth rate, a common pattern throughout the Third World. Jamaica's crude birth rate (35 per thousand) was among the highest in the Americas (Sivard, 1974). However, because of emigration, the annual population growth rate has been relatively low (1.5% annually). There is still no generalized food shortage for all people due to overpopulation, but in 1973 there appeared to be an overload of dependents in poor households with marginal resources and income (Marchione, 1980).

The remarkable fact is that there was a significant increase in the number of children under 5 in the parish households between 1973 and 1975 (p. 211). However, the relationship between family demography and malnutrition found in 1973 did not reliably predict young child malnutrition in 1975; in fact, the relationships between family demographic stress and weight for age and height for age were not replicated. This result suggests a fundamental reinterpretation of the relationship found in 1973. It implies that family demographic stress, especially family size variables, may not be a reliable predictor of nutritional status because nutritional deficiency also strongly affects the survival of young children.

One has to bear in mind that children in the second year of life are the survivors of infancy. In Jamaica, Garrow and Pike (1967, p. 4) found that faster-growing children were more likely to suffer life-threatening malnutrition under a restricted diet. In Peru, Frisancho, Sanchez, Pallardel, and Yanez (1973) found that under poor economic conditions shorter mothers had about 9% more surviving offspring than taller mothers. Therefore, in St. James, family demography, especially the number of siblings in the household, is *a cause* of retarded growth not only because of the dilution of food resources in larger households but is also a *result* of the greater survival of children of shorter mothers, as such children require less food.

When economic, and consequently nutritional, conditions improve, we would expect that there would be more children surviving, and we would also expect that a larger number of taller children would survive. We have some evidence to support this hypothesis. Table 9.2 indicates that children exceeding 104% of standard height for age increased from .9 to 7.1% between 1973 and 1975. Collapsing Table 9.2 to a two-by-two table shows this to be a significant increase ($\chi^2 = 5.45$, $df = 1$, $p < .05$). This mechanism, if true, would account for the following observations made in this study: (*a*) a greater number of surviving children per mother; (*b*) an attenuation in the association of the number of siblings with the anthropometric measurements, because of the greater phenotypic diversity of offspring; (*c*) the lack of dramatic overall nutritional improvement of the 1-year-old children, because resources are turned to increasing the number of individuals in the family rather than improving the nutritional status of a limited number of offspring.

In summary, this factor is too interwoven with nutritional status to be a reliable predictive independent variable. Nevertheless, the result implies that Jamaica's family planning efforts should be continued, and the integration with nutritional improvement programs should be intensified.

## Family Cohesion and Nutritional Status

In 1973, family cohesion, the residence and support of the child's parents in the household, was clearly important to the child's nutritional status. In 1975, however, this relationship was not demonstrated although the bivariate correlations between the anthropometry and father's presence and support do indicate some consistency through time. The data previously discussed (p. 211) suggest that household cohesion did improve through time. Thus, the factor would have predicted improved nutritional status. The loss of association in 1975 suggests that the use of family cohesion as a predictor may be an oversimplification. Other observers have viewed family structure as an adaptive response to local economic circumstances (Bantje 1974; Clarke 1957, p. 78; Comitas 1973; Marchione, 1980). If this is indeed the case, then the association of nutrition and family cohesion may be an artifact of their mutual relation to the availability of local employment.

## Monetary Wealth and Nutritional Status

The correlations between the anthropometric measures and income and food expenditures was significant in both 1973 and in 1975. However, in 1973 the factor of monetary wealth was not significantly related to either height for age or weight for age although it was the most powerful predictor of standard weight for age in 1975. The reason for this change may be that in 1973 the children of wealthier households suffered negative nutritional consequences from the use of commercial infant foods with high cost per nutrient value (Marchione, 1977b; pp. 258, 314). A more probable explanation is that with the inflation in food prices in 1975 these foods were exceptionally costly and less likely to be utilized. Also, by this time government countermeasures to the promotion of these products had begun.

An alternative explanation is that income deficits are compensated for through time by sociocultural adaptations. In the short-term, changing economic conditions have direct and overt effects on nutritional status. This appears to have been the case in 1975. In 1973, however, the research followed 10 years of economic stagnation during which time family structure, food production and employment were modified to blunt the direct consequences of the chronic income shortage in the poorer households.

We have demonstrated the obvious, that current income is an extremely important predictor of weight for age and will appear so when economic changes have been recent and relatively dramatic. The subtle point is that researchers relying upon cross-sectional data and synchronic analyses could very well underestimate the importance of wealth. The implications are that wealth is a pervasive influence on many aspects of household life which directly or indirectly influence the nutritional status of young children as well as the quality of their lives in general. Therefore, governmental employment, income supplementation, and price subsidization policies should be key elements in improving child health and growth (Jamaican Nutritional Advisory Council, 1974).

## Age Transition and Nutritional Status

Older children appeared to be more poorly nourished in 1975, while age was not related to nutritional status in 1973. One possible reason for this finding is that during the second year of life the child is adjusting to more and more demanding postweaning life conditions. Since the association held in 1975, but not in 1973, we suggest a more situational explanation. The sample of children in 1973 had experienced a relatively stable economic situation throughout their lifetimes. However, the 1975 sample had been born during a highly volatile time economically. Children aged 18–24 months at the time of the 1975 survey were born in the latter half of 1973, just when food prices began rising sharply, yet before any sociocultural or governmental remedial actions could have much of an effect. The children born in the following 6 months were not as stressed, and therefore children aged 12–18 months were better off in 1975.

### Diet and Clinic Care

Diet or clinic care factors did not prove to be significantly related to nutritional status of children either in 1973 or in 1975. Although in Table 9.4 two bivariate correlations between dietary and anthropometric measures were significant, they proved to be so only because of their mutual relationship to income, subsistence agriculture, or some other factor in the analysis. Perhaps these variables might take on greater significance if more precise definitions and methodologies were utilized, such as food weighing rather than 24-hr recall, or if weekly cycles or longer periods of food intake were measured.

Similarly, the lack of association between welfare clinic-care per se and child nutritional status does not prove that such care is unimportant. It suggests that the clinic for the well baby is used not only to maintain child health but also to seek cures for illness, as mothers do not always perceive or accept the neat distinctions between well-baby and sick-baby clinics made by health officials in Jamaica (Desai & Clarke, 1970). If so, the measurable growth benefits from one group of children using the clinic would tend to be offset by the growth deficits of children frequently ill. The use of a measure of the frequency of diarrhea might have provided the analysis with a variable that was a better indicator of child health status (Grantham-McGregor & Back, 1970, p. 407; Latham, 1975). Therefore, one cannot conclude from the present analysis that greater attention to child diet or child health is unimportant for growth among Jamaican children.

### SUMMARY AND CONCLUSION

This analysis has shown that the nutritional status of Jamaican 1-year-old children (measured by percentage of standard height for age and percentage of standard weight for age) was not consistently associated through time with a set of variables in the child's microenvironment. According to bivariate, zero-order, rank correlations, 15 of 31 possible independent variables were significantly associated with either height for age or weight for age in 1973, but in 1975 only 8 of 31 variables were significantly associated.

In both periods, weight for age was positively associated with household food expenditures, income, dietary variety, presence of the father, and the mother's age. In both periods, height for age was positively associated only with dietary variety of the meal maker. Qualitative measures of dietary adequacy were associated with weight for age in 1973 and height for age in 1975. Also, use of home-grown foods was negatively associated with weight for age in 1973 and height for age in 1975.

To control for the interrelationships of the 31 variables, a factor analysis was performed and yielded six orthogonal factors which proved to be significantly associated with nutritional status in either 1973 or 1975. Two consistent predictors of weight for age through time were the factors of agricultural subsistence stress and mother–guardian maturity. The former factor demonstrated the persisting importance of the maldistribution of land and wages in influencing child growth in Jamaica. The latter factor pointed to the continuing biocultural problems associated with very young women bearing and raising children. The analysis also demonstrated that two factors, family cohesion and family demographic stress, were significantly associated with nutritional status measures in 1973 but not in 1975. Furthermore, two additional factors, the household's monetary (cash) wealth and the child's age, did not associate with malnutrition in 1973 but were strong predictors in 1975. In fact, age was the only predictor of height for age in 1975.

The inconsistency of the predictive capacity of the variables in this analysis was explained by the underlying dynamics of the changing society of Jamaica between the years 1973 and 1975. During the period under study, Jamaica instituted many new agricultural, economic, and food policies, and the island came under the influence of the massive food-price increases occurring in the international food market. These changes were expressed at the local level in the child's microenvironment in a manner that complicated the straightforward causal linear assumptions of the mathematical method. It was found that so-called "independent variables" such as family-size variables could also be seen as outcomes of nutritional stress rather than as merely predictors. Also some variables may appear to be causally related to nutritional status only because of their mutual relation to a third variable, for example, family structure and nutritional status may appear to be causally related because both are responsive to economic conditions. In summary, the various time lags and interrelationships of cultural and biological adaptive strategies were relevant to the understanding of the predictors. Although the simple epidemiological model of seeking independent variables as predictors of malnutrition seems very practical, such an approach is no substitute for a thorough understanding of the true nature of the relationships of social–cultural and biological phenomena.

In conclusion, predictors of nutritional status derived from synchronic analyses based on cross-sectional data should be used with caution. Even when the potential spuriousness of zero-order correlations is recognized, social etiological predictors can be quite misleading unless the diachronic dynamics of the society under study are understood.

## REFERENCES

Alderman, M., & Minott, O. D. A Young-Child Nutrition Programme in rural Jamaica. *Lancet,* 1973, *1,* 1160–1169.

Alland, A. *Adaptation in cultural evolution: An approach to medical anthropology.* New York. Columbia University Press, 1970.

Antrobus, A. C. K. Child growth and related factors in a rural community in St. Vincent. *Journal of Tropical Pediatrics and Environmental Child Health,* 1971, *17,* 188–210.

Ashcroft, M. T., Heneage P., & Lovell, H. G. Heights and weights of Jamaican school children of various ethnic groups. *American Journal of Physical Anthropology,* 1966, *24,* 35–44.

Ashworth, A., & Picou, D. *Nutrition status in Jamaica (1968–73).* Unpublished monograph, Tropical Metabolism Research Unit, University of the West Indies, 1974.

Bantje, H. *Household circumstances and infant malnutrition in Western Hanover, Jamaica.* Unpublished Monograph, Kingston, Caribbean Food and Nutrition Institute, 1974.

Beckford, G. L. *Persistent poverty: Underdevelopment in plantation economics of the Third World.* London: Oxford University Press, 1972.

Bengoa, J. M., The state of world nutrition. In M. Recheigle (Ed.), *Man, food and nutrition.* Cleveland: CRC Press, 1973. Pp. 1–13.

Birch, H. G., & Richardson, S. The functioning of Jamaican school children severely malnourished during the first two years of life. In *Nutrition, the nervous system, and behavior.* Scientific Publication No. 251, Washington, D.C.: Pan American Health Organization, 1972.

Boodoo, V., & Standard, K. *An investigation of child mortality in rural St. James, June 1968–May 1970.* Unpublished Monograph, Kingston: Department of Social and Preventative Medicine, University of the West Indies, 1970.

Clarke, E. *My mother who fathered me.* London: Allen and Unwin, 1957.

Comitas, L. Occupational multiplicity in rural Jamaica. In L. Comitas & D. Lowenthal (Eds.), *Work and family life: West Indian perspectives.* Garden City, N.Y.: Anchor Books, 1973. Pp. 157–173.

Cook, R. The cost of malnutrition in Jamaica. *Ecology of Food and Nutrition,* 1971, *1,* 61–66.

Desai, P. L., & Clarke, L. Do child welfare clinics influence growth? *Journal of Biosocial Science,* 1970, *2,* 305–315.

Desai, P. L., Miall, W. E., & Standard, K. Jamaica: The social background of malnutrition. *Maternal and Child Care,* 1968, *4,* 161–165.

Desai, P. L., Standard, K., & Miall, W. E. Socio-economic and cultural influences on child growth in rural Jamaica. *Journal of Biosocial Science,* 1970, *2,* 133–143.

Desai, P. L., Standard, K., & Miall, W. E. A five year study of infant growth in rural Jamaica. *The West Indian Medical Journal,* 1969, *18,* 210–221.

Foneroff, L. S. Settlement typology and infant malnutrition in Jamaica. *Tropical and Geographical Medicine,* 1969, *21,* 177–185.

Fox, H. C., Campbell, V. S., & Harris, J. The dietary and nutritional status of Jamaican infants and toddlers. *Bulletin of the Scientific Research Council,* 1968, *8,* 31–51.

Frisancho, R. A., Sanchez, A. J., Pallardel, D., & Yanez, L. Adaptive significance of small body size under poor social-economic conditions in southern Peru. *American Journal of Physical Anthropology,* 1973, *2,* 255–260.

Garn, S. M., & Clark, D. C. Problems in the nutritional assessment of Black individuals. *American Journal of Public Health*, 1976, *66*, 262–267.

Garrow, J. S., & Pike, M. C. The longterm prognosis of severe infantile malnutrition. *Lancet*, 1967, *1*, 1–4.

Gomez, F. R., Galvan, R., Cravioto, J., & Frank, S. Malnutrition in infancy and childhood with special references to kwashiorkor. *Advances in Pediatrics*, 1955, *8*, 131–169.

Grantham-McGregor, S. M., & Back, E. H. Breast feeding in Kingston, Jamaica. *Archives of Disease in Childhood*, 1970, *45*, 404–409.

Gurney, J. M., Fox, H., & Neill, J. A rapid survey to assess the nutrition of Jamaican infants and young children in 1970. *Transactions of the Royal Society of Tropical Medicine and Hygiene*, 1972, *66*, 653–662.

Habicht, J. Height and weight standards for preschool children. How relevant are differences in growth potential? *Lancet*, 1974, *1*, 611–614.

Jamaican Department of Statistics. *Statistical yearbook of 1974*. Kingston: Government Printer, 1975.

Jamaican Nutrition Advisory Council. *A food and nutritional policy for Jamaica with a programme for incorporation into the national development plan 1975/76–1977/78*. Kingston: National Advisory Council, 1974.

Jelliffe, D. B. *The assessment of the nutritional status of the community (with a special reference to field surveys in developing regions of the world)*. Geneva: World Health Organization, 1966.

Jelliffe, D. B. The preschool child as a bio-cultural transitional. *Journal of Tropical Pediatrics and Environmental Child Health*, 1968, *14*, 217–227.

Latham, M. C. Nutrition and infection in national development. *Science*, 1975, *188*, 561–565.

Marchione, T. J. *An evaluation of the nutritional and family planning components of the community health aide programme in St. James Parish*. Kingston: Caribbean Food & Nutrition Institute, 1973.

Marchione, T. J. Factors associated with malnutrition in the children of Western Jamaica. In N. Jerome, Gretel Pelto, & R. Kandel (Eds.), *Nutritional anthropology*. New York: Redgrave, 1980.

Marchione, T. J. Food and nutrition in self-reliant national development: The impact on child nutrition of Jamaican government policy. *Medical Anthropology*, 1977, *1*, 57–59. (a)

Marchione, T. J. *Health and nutrition in self-reliant national development. An evaluation of the Jamaican community health aide programme*. Unpublished doctoral dissertation, University of Connecticut, 1977. (b)

Ministry of Agriculture, Project Lend Lease Report. July, 1975.

Morley, D. *Pediatric priorities in the developing world*. London: Butterworths, 1973.

Nie, N. H., Hull, C. H., Jenkins, J. G., Steinbrenner, K., & Bent, D. H. *Statistical package for the social sciences* (2nd ed.). New York: McGraw-Hill, 1975.

Puffer, R. R., & Serrano, C. V. *Patterns of mortality in childhood*. Washington, D.C.: Pan American Health Organization, 1973.

Rummel, R. J. *Applied factor analysis*. Evanston: Northwestern University Press, 1970.

Seone, N., & Latham, M. Nutritional anthropometry in the identification of malnutrition in childhood. *Journal of Tropical Pediatrics and Environmental Child Health*, 1971, *17*, 98–104.

Stini, W. Evolutionary implications of changing nutritional patterns in a human population. *American Anthropologist*, 1971, *73*, 1019–1030.

Sivard, R. L. *World military and social expenditures. 1974*. New York: Institute for World Order, 1974.

Waterlow, J. C. The history of the tropical metabolism research unit, University of the West Indies. *The West Indian Medical Journal*, 1974, *13*, 151–159.

# 10

# Social and Biological Predictors of Physical Growth and Neurological Development in an Area Where Iodine and Protein–Energy Malnutrition Are Endemic

## INTRODUCTION

In the early part of this century it was recognized that nutritional stress has a significant effect on physical growth in experimental animals (Dye & Maughan, 1929; Jackson, 1915; Jackson & Stewart, 1920). Later studies suggested that environmental factors probably account for many of the anthropometric differences that have long been observed among human populations (Beals, 1972; Boas, 1911; Greulich, 1958; Little & Hochner, 1973; Roberts, 1953, 1973; Tanner, 1962). However, it is only recently that the importance of nutrition among those environmental stresses affecting human physical variability has been established with any degree of rigor (Cravioto, DeLicardie, & Birch, 1966; Frisancho, Sanchez, Pallardel, & Yanez, 1973; Lechtig, Delgado, Lasky, Klein, Engle, Yarbrough, & Habicht, 1975; Naeye, Blanc, & Paul, 1973; Scrimshaw & Gordon, 1968; Stini, 1972; Stoch & Smythe, 1963). Thus Habicht, Martorell, Yarbrough, Malina, and Klein (1974) now suggest that most of the observed differences in stature

Social and Biological Predictors of
Nutritional Status, Physical Growth,
and Neurological Development

Copyright © 1980 by Academic Press, Inc.
All rights of reproduction in any form reserved.
ISBN 0-12-299750-6

among human populations are the consequence of environmental stresses, especially nutritional and disease stress, during the course of growth and development. Recent studies also indicate that nutritional stress, particularly if it occurs early in life, may have a significant effect on neurological development and behavior in human populations (Botha-Antoun, Babayan, & Harfouche, 1968; Champakam, Srikantia, & Gopalan, 1968; Chase & Martin, 1970; Cravioto *et al.*, 1966; Geber & Dean, 1956; Mönckeberg, Tisler, Toro, Gattás, & Vega, 1972; Winick, 1970; Winick & Rosso, 1969a, 1969b).

Although malnutrition is a stress that produces both physical and behavioral variation in human populations, it is only in the last decade that systematic research efforts have attempted to delineate the specific social and biological factors that are determinants of nutritional status, physical growth, and neurological development in human populations (Chavez, Martinez, & Yashine, 1975; Christiansen, Vouri, Mora, & Wagner, Cravioto & DeLicardie, 1972, 1975; DeLicardie & Cravioto, 1974; Latham, 1971; Pollitt, 1969, 1973; Richardson, 1974, 1976). It is this area of investigation with which we are concerned.

The primary intent of our overall research program was to describe the effect of a widespread nutritional stress on physical growth, neurological development, and behavioral capacity in a human population and to contrast such a situation with populations living under more favorable nutritional circumstances (Greene, 1973, 1974, 1976, 1977a). We were thus interested in the effect of nutritional stress in producing interpopulation physical, neurological, and behavioral variability. A second goal was to describe intrapopulation variability in growth and development and to evaluate the hypothesis that this variability was, to a significant degree, a consequence of nutritional differences. A third goal, which is the objective of this chapter, is to ascertain the causes of this variability. In order to realize this goal we will attempt to determine which of a number of social and biological factors are significant statistical predictors of intrapopulation variation in nutritional status, physical growth, and neurological development in the communities under study. We will also attempt to elucidate the causal links through which these factors become developmental determinants.

We chose to carry out our study in two populations in which iodine malnutrition is severe and goiter (enlargement of the thyroid gland) and cretinism (short stature, deaf-mutism, and severe mental retardation) is endemic. Protein–energy malnutrition (PEM) is also common. In selecting populations living under severe nutritional stress, we were maximizing the likelihood that we would be able to describe a broad continuum of neurological and behavior effect. Given the wide range of environmentally produced developmental defects in these populations, it was also likely that we would be able to isolate the major predictors of this variation with moderate sample sizes.

The data which we will report were collected between 1970 and 1972; however, the present study was part of a larger public health program evaluating the effect of depot iodine supplementation on physical growth and neuromotor development (Fierro-Benítez, Penafiel, DeGroot, & Ramírez, 1969a; Fierro-Benítez, Ramírez, Estrella, Jaramillo, Díaz, & Urresta, 1969b; Fierro-Benítez, Ramírez, Garcés, Jaramillo, Moncayo, & Stanbury, 1974; Fierro-Benítez, Ramírez, & Suárez, 1972).

The following sections will present an overview of the problem of iodine malnutrition and its developmental effects. This should serve as a background to the data that will follow.

## IODINE MALNUTRITION, ENDEMIC GOITER, AND ENDEMIC CRETINISM

Iodine malnutrition is widespread and severe in the *parroquias* of Tocachi and La Esperanza as well as in many other communities in the northern portion of the Ecuadorian Andes (Fierro-Benítez & Recalde, 1958; Fierro-Benítez *et al.* 1969a, 1969b). This is primarily due to the extremely low iodine content of the local soil and drinking water. At the beginning of these studies 52.8% of the population of La Esperanza and 69.7% of that of Tocachi had goiters, while 6.0% of the people living in La Esperanza and 8.2% of those in Tocachi were deaf-mute "cretin" individuals (Fierro-Benítez *et al.*, 1969a, 1969b). The following sections will present a brief outline of iodine malnutrition and its effect on thyroid function and growth and development in human populations.

### External Iodine Cycle

Most of the Earth's iodine is concentrated in ocean waters and reaches land masses in two ways (Goldschmidt, 1959). The first is through the uplifting of marine sediments. The second and more important is the evaporation of iodine from the sea to the atmosphere as hydrogen iodide (HI) and iodine ($I_2$). It is then carried inland in a gaseous state or affixed to dust particles and returns to the earth with rain or snow. This iodine passes through the uppermost soil layers and becomes preferentially fixed in these surface layers. If a soil is saturated with iodine, much of the additional airborne iodine will filter through and appear in the drainage, thus adding iodine to the local water supply. The iodine content of the local flora reflects that of the soils in which it grows. The treatment of soil with fertilizers derived from seaweed, fish products, or Chilean nitrate (caliche) can increase their iodine content from 10 to 100 times. Sea salt is a poor source of iodine since most of it is lost in the process of solar evaporation. The same is true for most crude rock salts, although some of these do have moderate iodine contents.

The iodine intake of animals, including humans, is a function of what is obtained from the drinking water, plant and animal matter, and salt that they consume. One of the major determinants of the iodine content of the diet of a population is its access to seafoods (both animals and plant) in which iodine is greatly concentrated. Populations located considerable distances from the coast usually have limited access to sea products and are thus totally dependent upon the local availability of environmentally derived iodine.

In addition to differential consumption of sea products, Goldschmidt (1958) has noted a number of geochemical factors which may lead to an insufficiency of environmental iodine. Experiments suggest that less airborne iodine reaches those areas more distant from the ocean and that a limited annual amount of precipitation may also contribute to a low iodine content of local soils. It has also been demonstrated that areas subjected to late Pleistocene glaciations presently have soils which have marginal or deficient iodine contents. This is because the glaciers remove the iodine-rich soils, and, following their retreat, the iodine content of new soils is replenished only after tens of thousands of years. Merke (1967) has shown that areas of Switzerland that had been severely glaciated in the late Pleistocene corresponded quite closely to those areas in which iodine malnutrition, goiter, and cretinism had, until recently, been hyperendemic.

The iodine content of soils is also greatly reduced by erosion, which is especially common in mountainous areas. It has also been suggested that there is a relationship between the iodine content of a soil and its substratum, with limestone being unfavorable for iodine retention.

In addition to the geochemical influences on iodine availability, other factors may limit the thyroidal uptake and utilization of iodine. A large number of naturally occurring antithyroid substances of plant origin, and some organic water pollutants, interfere with these processes and may greatly exacerbate the iodine deficiency experienced by certain human populations. This will be discussed more fully in the following section.

As a consequence of these factors, iodine deficiency tends to be most severe in mountainous areas of the world where the soils have been eroded, having been subjected to the effect of late Pleistocene alpine glaciations. The Pyrenees, Swiss and Italian Alps, Himalayas, highland New Guinea, and the Andean region of South America are all areas where severe iodine malnutrition and its sequelae, goiter, hypothyroidism, and cretinism, have been common.

## Internal Iodine Cycle

### Thyroid Hormones

The major nutritional significance of iodine is that it is a micronutrient necessary for the normal production of thyroid hormones—thyroxine ($T_4$), containing four atoms of iodine, and 3,5,3'-triiodothyronine ($T_3$), containing three. These hormones are necessary for normal physical growth, nervous system development, temperature regulation, nerve conduction, and a variety of other important functions (DeGroot & Stanbury, 1975; Hoch, 1968). Reverse $T_3$ ($rT_3$; 3,3'5'-triiodothyronine) is also normally produced in small amounts by the thyroid gland, but is metabolically inactive.

The iodine intake of adults varies from less than 10 to over 1000 $\mu$g daily with the average being about 500 $\mu$g on the eastern coast of the United States (Matovinovic, Child, Nichaman, & Trowbridge, 1974). An intake of 100–300 $\mu$g/day is considered desirable (Matovinovic et al., 1974).

Ingested iodine is reduced to iodide, is absorbed in the small intestine, and enters the inorganic iodine pool together with about 70 $\mu$g of iodide/day from the daily degradation of thyroid hormones. The normal plasma inorganic iodide (PII) level is about .5 $\mu$g/100 ml and thyroid iodide uptake is approximately 75 $\mu$g/day. In the thyroid gland, iodide is oxidized to iodine and rapidly bound to the 3-position of the tyrosine molecule attached to thyroglobulin. This monoiodotyrosine is then iodinated in the 5-position to form diiodotyrosine. Two diiodotyrosine moledules undergo an oxidative condensation to form thyroxine ($T_4$). Oxidative condensation of a molecule of monoiodotyrosine and diiodotyrosine leads to the formation of triiodothyronine, $T_3$. $T_3$ is approximately two to four times more metabolically active than $T_4$, but the normal ratio of circulating $T_3:T_4$ is around 1:30 (De Groot & Stanbury, 1975; Oppenheimer & Surks, 1971; Sterling & Lazarus, 1977). Recent studies indicate that thyroidal production accounts for only about 25% of circulating $T_3$ with the remainder being the consequence of the peripheral monodeiodination of $T_4$ (Chopra, 1976; Sterling & Lazarus, 1977). This is the normal metabolic pathway for $T_4$.

The thyroid gland in humans secretes approximately 80 $\mu$g of free thyroxine daily. This free thyroxine is bound to plasma proteins, mainly thyroxine-binding prealbumin (TBPA) and thyroxine-binding globulin (TBG), with smaller amounts being attached to albumin. The amount of protein-bound iodine (PBI) in the plasma normally ranges from about 4.0 to 8.0 $\mu$g/100 ml, averaging about 6.0 $\mu$g/100 ml. Ninety-five percent of the protein-bound iodine is in the form of thyroxine (De Groot & Stanbury, 1975; Ingbar, 1971; Tong, 1971). An adequate production of thyroid hormones is referred to as euthyroidism, while hypo- and hyper thyroidism refer to conditions of insufficient and excessive levels of thyroid hormones, respectively.

## Thyroid Control

The endocrine control of the activity and enlargement of the thyroid gland is the result of a complex negative feedback mechanism. The blood level of thyroid hormone is dependent on the dietary intake of iodine and the trapping and synthesizing capacity of the thyroid gland. The blood level of "free" thyroid hormones acts directly at the level of both the hypothalamus and adenohypophysis to affect hypothalamic thyrotropic hormone-releasing factor (TRF) secretion and thyroid-stimulating hormone (TSH) release from the adenohypophysis. Insufficient dietary iodine intake lowers the level of thyroid hormones in the blood, thereby stimulating an increase in secretion of TSH by the adenohypophysis. The increases secretion of TSH produces a cellular hypertrophy of the thyroid gland with a concomitant increase in the secretion and release of thyroid hormones, thus maintaining the euthyroid state (Dumont, Neve, & Otten, 1969; De Groot & Stanbury, 1975).

## Nutritional and Disease Stress and Thyroid Function

Nutritional factors also have a significant effect on the metabolism of thyroid hormones. In protein-energy malnutrition and under conditions of systemic illness there is a decrease in serum $T_3$ and an increase in serum levels of reverse $T_3$ (Chopra, 1976; Merimee & Fineberg, 1976; Palmblad, Levi, Burger, Melander, Westgren, von Schenck, & Skude, 1977; Vagenakis, Burger, Portnay, Rudolph, O'Brien, Azizi, Arky, Nicod, Ingar, & Braverman, 1975). This is a consequence of a shift in the peripheral monodeiodenation of $T_4$ away from metabolically active $T_3$ and toward the metabolically inactive $rT_3$ form (Merimee & Fineberg, 1976). This shift appears to be an important biological adaptation to a limitation in protein and energy supply; however, it suggests that alterations in thyroid function may be a significant factor in the etiology of the developmental abnormalities associated with severe protein-energy malnutrition of long duration. Furthermore, protein-energy malnutrition may impair the thyroidal response to low iodine availability because the high blood level of metabolically inactive $rT_3$ prevents an increase in secretion of TSH by the adenohypophysis. Thus, the thyroid gland does not enlarge under conditions of nutritional or disease stress even though the blood level of metabolically active hormone is decreased. We would therefore expect to see an extremely high prevalence of developmental abnormalities in populations living under the dual stress of iodine and protein-energy malnutrition, which is the case in the communities of Tocachi and La Esperanza in highland Ecuador.

## Naturally Occurring Goitrogens

Although environmental iodine deficiency is the major cause of iodine malnutrition and goiter, many food crops, especially those of the *Brassica* genus (cabbage, kale, brussel sprouts, turnip, rutabaga, and many others) contain small amounts of antithyroid compounds (goitrogens) which interfere with thyroid function (Van Etten, 1969). There are two major classes of goitrogens: those that interfere with the iodide-trapping mechanism of the thyroid gland and those that block the organic binding of iodine to thyroglobulin within the gland. The first group consists of monovalent anions which compete with iodide for transportation into the thyroid gland. The inhibition of iodide uptake is a function of the relative concentrations of iodide and the competing anion, with ingestion of adequate amounts of iodine overcoming the goitrogenic effect of the anion. Thiocyanate occurs commonly in nature as a product of the hydrolysis of thioglucosides which are contained in virtually all edible plants.

The second group of goitrogens interferes with the binding of iodine to thyroglobulin, possibly by competing with iodide as a substrate for thyroid peroxidase. This group consists of organic compounds containing a thiocarbamide group (thioureas, N–C–N; thiothiazolines, N–C–S; thiooxazolines, N–C–O)

$$\overset{\displaystyle \|}{\text{S}} \qquad\qquad \overset{\displaystyle \|}{\text{S}} \qquad\qquad \overset{\displaystyle \|}{\text{S}}$$

(Astwood, 1949). The thiocarbamides occur commonly in nature as hydrolysis products of thioglucosides contained in most edible plants. Goitrin (l5-vinyl-2-thiooxazolidone) is particularly common among the *Brassica* and is a potent antithyroid compound.

## Endemic Goiter

When thyroid hormone production is insufficient for bodily needs a hypothyroid state ensues—a condition that is defined both biochemically and clinically. In response to this situation the thyroid gland undergoes a hypertrophic enlargement under the influence of an increase in secretion of TSH from the adenohypophysis (see preceding). If the thyroid gland enlarges beyond two to five times its normal size of 25 gm, it is called a goiter (De Groot & Stanbury, 1975). The enlarged thyroid gland, or goiter, is more efficient in trapping the small amount of available iodine and in synthesizing thyroid hormone, and is thus a positive adaptation. Goiter is approximately seven times more prevalent among females than males and it is least common during childhood and progressively more frequent during puberty and adulthood. "Sporadic" goiter occurs with some frequency in almost all populations and is indistinguishable from endemic goiter. Clements (1960) estimated that its prevalence may be as high as 4% of all preadolescent and adolescent girls in nongoitrous areas.

Goiter is considered to be endemic (as opposed to sporadic) when a distinct enlargement of the gland can be detected in more than 10% of the individuals in a population (De Smet, 1960). In areas where goiter is hyperendemic, from 50 to more than 90% of the adults have enlarged thyroid glands, many of which vary in size from that of a baseball to occasionally that of a football (Ermans, Thilly, Vis, & Delange, 1969; Fierro-Benítez *et al.*, 1969a; Gajdusek, 1962).

### The Effect of Hypothyroidism on Growth and Development

Thyroid hormones have a significant effect on physical growth, nervous system development, nerve conduction, body temperature regulation, and a number of other physiological processes. Their main influence on growth and development is a consequence of their stimulation of protein synthesis via their action at the level of the cell mitochondria. The effect of thyroid hormones is to produce both incremental growth and also maturational changes which affect shape, fine structure, and ultimately function (Hoch, 1968; Sterling & Lazarus, 1977).

Hypothyroidism induced in experimental animals during the neonatal period leads to marked deficits in linear growth and a characteristic brachycephalization of the skull (Dye & Maughan, 1929; Eayrs & Taylor, 1951; Scow & Simpson, 1945). Brain size and dendritic interconnectivity are decreased (Eayrs & Taylor, 1951; Nicholson & Altman, 1972), amino acid incorporation into the immature brain is hampered (Gelber, Campbell, Deibler & Sokoloff, 1964; Sokoloff, 1967), brain neurochemistry is altered (Balázs, Kovács, Cocks, Johnson, & Eayrs, 1971; Balázs, Kovács, Treichgräber, Cocks, & Eayrs, 1968), and there is a significant deficit in adult brain cell number as measured by total brain DNA (Bass & Netsky, 1969; Bass & Young, 1973).

### Hypothyroidism, Cretinism, and Developmental Retardation in Human Populations

The effect of hypothyroidism is time dependent, especially with respect to the nervous system. The somatic effects appear to be largely reversible (if iodine or thyroid hormone is later supplied), but the neurological consequences of hypothyroidism within a critical period of the first 14 days in the rat and within the first 18–24 months in the human infant are generally less alterable or are irreversible (Eayrs, 1961, 1968; Smith, Blizzard & Wilkins, 1957). The degree of any effect, especially a neurological one, is dependent on the time during growth and development at which the hypothyroid stress occurs, its duration, and its severity. This largely irreversible neurological effect is reflected in a permanent behavioral deficit in the experimental animal or child so affected (Davenport, 1970, 1976; Essman, Mendoza, & Hamburgh, 1968; Smith, Blizzard, & Wilkins, 1957). The effect of hypothyroidism on human neurological development thus appears to be generally similar to that produced by protein–energy malnutrition, with the period of greatest vulnerability being during the time of rapid brain growth (Dobbing, 1972; 1973; Dobbing & Sands, 1971;Winick & Rosso, 1969a, 1969b; Winick, Rosso, & Brasel, 1972).

Cretinism caused by environmental lack of iodine is called endemic cretinism and is as prevalent as 7–10% in some human populations (Fierro-Benitez et al., 1969a; Gajdusek, 1962; Stanbury, 1977). It is usually associated with a spectrum of physical and neurological retardation characterized by varying degrees of irreversible neuromuscular deficits, irreversible abnormalities in hearing and speech often leading to deaf-mutism, and retarded physical growth (Dumont, Delange, & Ermans, 1969). This clinical spectrum is frequently separated into two syndromes: nervous endemic cretinism and myxedemetous endemic cretinism (Delange, Costa, Ermans, Ibbertson, Querido, & Stanbury, 1972; McCarrison, 1908; Stanbury, 1977).

Endemic cretinism is the most dramatic developmental abnormality in areas where iodine malnutrition is severe and goiter is hyperendemic. Several recent studies have provided empirical evidence indicating that endemic cretins are only the most severely affected end of a continuum of neurological deficit (Greene 1973, 1976, 1977a; Querido & Swabb, 1975). In previous publications we have presented data from the Ecuadorian Andean community of La Esperanza indicating that besides the 5.7% of the adult population who were deaf-mute "cretins," an additional 17.4% of the adults showed evidence of moderate neurological and behavioral deficits (Greene, 1973, 1976, 1977a). Thus, iodine malnutrition, like protein-energy malnutrition, has a widespread and significant effect on physical growth, neurological maturation, and behavioral development in human populations.


## THE COMMUNITIES UNDER STUDY

The *parroquias* of Tocachi and La Esperanza are located in the Andean region of Ecuador in the northeast portion of the province of Pichincha. Both communities are situated along the southern wall of Mt. Mojanda, approximately 2 km north of the equator. They extend from the edge of the Pisque River at about 2500 m to the crest of Mojanda near 4300 m and encompass three altitudinal-ecological zones (upper zone 2950 to 3200 m; middle zone, 2700 to

2950 m; lower zone, 2500 to 2700 m). The higher portion of the *parroquias* over 3200 m is páramo grazing lands. Both iodine and protein-energy malnutrition are common in these populations.

The *parroquia* is the smallest legal civil administrative unit in Ecuador and is usually made up of a number of distinct *barrios* and *anejos* (Greene, 1976). In 1971 the size of the populations, as determined by a household census and adjusted for absent individuals, was 1600 in La Esperanza and 1100 in Tocachi. The ethnic composition of the populations was 78% *indígena* and 22% *blanco* and *mestizo* in La Esperanza and 63% *indígena* and 37% *blanco* and *mestizo* in Tocachi. Most individuals were semisubsistence agriculturalists-pastoralists who grew corn, potatoes, peas, beans, and squash for domestic consumption and barley and wheat for both domestic consumption and as a cash crop. Households involved in herding were mainly those *indígenas* affiliated with the *haciendas* in the upper altitudinal zone who had rights of pasture in the *páramo* grasslands. Six large *haciendas* (over 1500 acres) and a smaller one (150 acres) accounted for approximately one-half of the arable land in La Esperanza and an even greater portion in Tocachi. A survey of 119 of the 368 households in La Esperanza indicated that the average amount of land owned was 2.5 acres. Forty-two percent of the households surveyed owned no land at all. Many of the landless individuals, most of whom were indigenous, were involved in sharecropping arrangements which were frequently extremely exploitative. Opportunities for wage labor were extremely limited, especially for the indigenous individuals. In 1971 adult males working full-time on the *haciendas* earned approximately 60–68¢ per day. This was then considered an extremely desirable wage, approximately twice that paid by the *blanco* and *mestizo* small landholders. A most extensive description of the community of La Esperanza, its sociocultural system, and the pattern of interethnic relations has been presented elsewhere (Greene, 1976, 1977a).

## GOITER, CRETINISM, AND DEVELOPMENTAL
## RETARDATION IN THE STUDY POPULATIONS

### Goiter and Cretinism in Tocachi and La Esperanza

As noted, iodine malnutrition is severe and goiter and cretinism are endemic in the Ecuadorian Andean communities of Tocachi and La Esperanza (Fierro-Benítez *et al.* 1969a, 1969b, 1974; Stanbury, 1972a). At the beginning of these studies, 52.8% of the population of La Esperanza and 69.7% of that of Tocachi had enlarged thyroid glands, while the prevalence of cretinism was 6.0% in La Esperanza and 8.2% in Tocachi (Fierro-Benítez *et al.*,

1969a, 1969b). Protein-energy malnutrition was also common among children.

## The Iodization Program

In 1966 a public health program of depot iodization was commenced in Tocachi, with La Esperanza serving as a noniodized control population. This program evaluated the safety and efficacy of intramuscular injections of iodine in oil in eradicating goiter and preventing cretinism at a time when there was only limited success in iodizing the domestic salt supply in Ecuador. The isolation of these populations and the initial resistance of many of the inhabitants to the use of iodized salt were other factors suggesting this type of public health approach.

## Physical Growth and the Continuum of Neurological Deficit

Adult stature in these communities is extemely small, even in comparison with other Andean populations living at similar, or greater, altitude (Table 10.1); some of the deaf-mutes in these populations attain statures barely over 120 cm. Of the adult population of La Esperanza, 23.1% also show moderate to severe neurological deficits (5.7% "cretins" and 17.4% moderately affected individuals) (Greene, 1973; Fierro-Benítez et al., 1969a). This retardation in physical growth and neurological development is the final consequence of long-term iodine and protein-energy malnutrition acting in synergism with high rates of intermittent diarrheal disease early in life.

TABLE 10.1

Adult Stature in the Indigenous Segments of Two Andean Communities

|  | La Esperanza | Nuñoa, Peru[a] |
|---|---|---|
| | *Males* | |
| $\bar{X}$ (cm) | 155.6 | 160.0 |
| SD | 6.1 | 4.9 |
| N | 70 | 50 |
| | *Females* | |
| $\bar{X}$ (cm) | 145.0 | 148.0 |
| SD | 6.4 | 5.2 |
| N | 79 | 50 |

[a] Frisancho and Baker (1970).

## INDEPENDENT AND DEPENDENT VARIABLES

The following sections will evaluate the relative importance of a number of biological and social factors affecting nutritional status and growth and development in Tocachi and La Esperanza. This data are based on a study of 348 children 6–15 years of age. Half of the children were from Tocachi and the other half from La Esperanza, with the sample containing approximately equal numbers of male and female children in both populations at all age levels. The samples were drawn from all ethnic, socioeconomic, and altitudinal segments of both communities. Occasional reference is also made to data on 313 adult individuals 15–64 years of age from La Esperanza. The sampling procedure and the age-sex characteristics of the samples are discussed more fully elsewhere (Greene, 1976).

We are reporting data on two dependent developmental variables both of which are affected by nutritional stress. Stature is being used as a reflection of the cumulative effect of nutritional factors on an individual's physical growth, and an individual's score on the Bender–Gestalt test as an indication of how nutritional stress may have affected neurological maturation in visual–motor perception. The rationale for the use of the Bender–Gestalt test in this population and data utilizing a variety of other anthropometric and psychometric indices have been presented in previous publications (Greene, 1973, 1976).

We will first consider the issue of inbreeding and its possible effect on growth and development and then proceed to a statistical evaluation and discussion of the effect of the other independent variables on physical growth and neurological maturation in the children under study.

### Inbreeding

Although environmental factors (nutritional and disease stress) appear to be the major causes of the high prevalence of developmental deficits in these two populations, we were concerned that the relatively strong cultural preference for marriage within the community, and more specifically for marriage within certain subdivisions (*barrios* and *anejos*) of the community, might be associated with some degree of inbreeding depression affecting both physical growth and/or neurological development (Bashi, 1977; Cavalli-Sforza & Bodmer, 1971; Dewey, Barrai, Morton, & Mi, 1965; Mange, 1964; Schull & Neel, 1965; Schull, Neel, Yamamoto, Uchida, Yanase, & Fujiki, 1970). We thus decided to evaluate inbreeding in these communities.

The coefficient of inbreeding ($F$) of an individual is the probability that this individual receives two genes at a given locus that are identical by descent

(Cavalli-Sforza & Bodmer, 1971). The amount of inbreeding that takes place in most human populations is extremely small with the most common types of consanguineous marriages being somewhere between first cousins ($F = \frac{1}{16}$) and second cousins ($F = \frac{1}{64}$). Average consanguinity in a population is usually measured by calculating the average inbreeding coefficient of its individuals (Cavalli-Sforza & Bodmer, 1971). This quantity, usually called $\alpha$, is obtained by averaging the $F$ values of the progeny of all consanguineous matings. The average inbreeding coefficient ($\alpha$) in human populations is generally around 1 per 1000 (.001) and is rarely higher than .01 except in small "genetic isolates" that have little or no gene exchange with other populations.

The average inbreeding coefficients in Tocachi and La Esperanza were estimated on the basis of isonymy, the frequency of marriages between persons of the same surname (Crow & Mange, 1965; Friedl & Ellis, 1974; Lasker, 1968; Lasker, Chiarelli, Masali, Fedele, & Kaplan, 1972). Calculated on the basis of isonymy, this value is referred to as $f$ (Cavalli-Sforza & Bodmer, 1971). In La Esperanza the average relationship between individuals, as estimated from isonymy ($f = .0222$), is midway between that of first cousins once removed ($F = .0313$) and second cousins ($F = .0156$), while in Tocachi the average relationship between individuals ($f = .0179$) is slightly greater than that of second cousins ($F = .0156$).

These figures compare with average inbreeding coefficients, estimated from isonymy, of .0445 in the Hutterite population (Crow & Mange, 1965), .0102 in coastal Peru (Lasker, 1969), .0221 and .0107 in two Italian alpine populations (Lasker, *et al.*, 1972), and .0267 in a Swiss alpine community (Friedl & Ellis, 1974). None of these other communities shows the high rates of developmental retardation observed in Tocachi and La Esperanza. It is thus unlikely that inbreeding per se is a major determinant of these deficits in the communities under study.

If anything, inbreeding in La Esperanza seems to be associated with a lower prevalence of developmental deficits. Although inbreeding, as estimated on the basis of isonymy, is much greater in the social units of the upper zone ($f = .0437$) than in those of the middle ($f = .0214$) or lower ($f = .0029$) zones, the adult *indigenas* living in the upper altitudinal-ecological zone (above 2950 m) were significantly taller ($F = 6.54$, $df = 2/143$, $p < .01$) and scored significantly better on the Bender–Gestalt test of visual–motor maturation ($F = 3.27$, $df = 2/176$, $p < .05$) than *indigenas* living in the middle (2700–2950 m) and lower (2500–2700 m) altitudinal-ecological zones (Table 10.2).

These data strongly argue against inbreeding depression as a significant explanation for the high prevalence of physical retardation and neurological deficits in these populations. Data to be presented indicate that economic

**TABLE 10.2**

Mean Stature, Bender–Gestalt Error Score, and Coefficient of Inbreeding among the Indigenous Inhabitants of the Three Altitudinal–Ecological Zones in La Esperanza

| | Upper zone | | Middle zone | | Lower zone | |
|---|---|---|---|---|---|---|
| | Males | Females | Males | Females | Males | Females |
| Stature (cm) | 158.6 | 148.7 | 155.6 | 143.6 | 153.3 | 143.3 |
| Bender–Gestalt error score | 1.3 | 4.9 | 2.1 | 3.5 | 2.9 | 5.3 |
| Coefficient of inbreeding $(f)$ estimated on the basis of isonymy | .0437 | | .0214 | | .0029 | |

and microenvironmental differences across these zones are likely to be the causal factors producing this intrapopulation variation in development.

### Developmental Predictors

Table 10.3 lists those biological, nutritional, and social factors (independent variables) that were evaluated as predictors of physical and visual–motor development (dependent variables) in the sample of children 6–15 years of age.

#### Biological Factors

*Birthorder.* Birthorder is an important determinant of development in the prenatal period as the birthweight of subsequent pregnancies tend to average 150 gm heavier than those of first pregnancies (Naeye *et al.*, 1973). This situation appears to be due to hormonal and anatomical changes that occur as a consequence of pregnancy. Increase in parity is usually accompanied by an increase in ease of delivery, thus reducing the pressure on the infant cranium, a factor which could be hypothesized to be of some significance for subsequent neurological development especially under non-Western medical circumstances. Nutritional factors are also nested in this variable, as with increased parity the parents are often somewhat older and more established economically, thus increasing the likelihood of adequate nutrition to the infant. Conversely, increased parity with limited economic resources if *often* associated with chronic maternal and infant protein–energy malnutrition.

*Ethnicity.* Individuals in Tocachi and La Esperanza define themselves, and are classified by others, as belonging to either the *blanco, mestizo,* or *indígena* ethnic, or "racial" group. While biological characteristics are certainly important in their definition, these are basically social categories that are determined by manner of dress and speech, place of residence, sentiment of affiliation, type of work, and type of food eaten. The term *mestizo* is actually not utilized to any degree in the local classificatory system, and anyone who is not considered to be indigenous is classified as *blanco*. The ethnic categorization of children was based on a judgment by our two main informants, both of whom had lived in these communities all their lives and who knew the children and their families intimately. The categorization of adults was based on an ethnic classification of surnames (Greene, 1976).

*PTC taste sensitivity.* Perhaps the major conceptual issue posed by the problem of endemic goiter and cretinism is the question of why certain individuals in a population show neurological deficits and others do not. Since iodine deficiency is basically environmentally determined, and availability appears to vary only slightly, why are some individuals deaf-mute "cretins," others only moderately affected, and still others apparently free of neurological deficits? Genetic differences between individuals in their ability to taste and avoid dietary factors that interfere with iodine utilization by the thyroid gland would help account for the observed variation in neurological development in these populations. We are suggesting that the PTC taste system serves that function.

In previous publications we have discussed how the well-known genetically determined variation in human taste sensitivity to the bitter-tasting substance phenylthiocarbomide (PTC) is highly correlated with taste sensitivity to structurally similar bitter-tasting naturally occurring thiocarbamide-like antithyroid compounds of plant origin (Greene, 1974, 1976). We have further argued that what is called the "PTC taste polymorphism" actually reflects a differential ability of individuals to detect, and thus, reject or modify prior to ingestion, a large class of food products containing these goitrogens. Thus, an individual's genetically determined ability to taste PTC may be a

**TABLE 10.3**

**Independent Variables Evaluated as Predictors of Dependent Developmental Variables**

| Social | Nutritional | Biological |
|---|---|---|
| Amount of travel | Total Resource Index | Thyroid size |
| SES rating | Age at weaning | Sex |
| Marital status of mother | Type of salt used | Age |
| | Altitudinal zone | Birthorder |
| | | PTC taste sensitivity |
| | | Ethnic group |

significant determinant of his or her exposure to antithyroid compounds. In an area where iodine intake is extremely low (as in highland Ecuador), this biological factor may then become an important determinant of degree of iodine stress and consequently of physical and neurological growth and development.

Several bitter-tasting food crops were locally consumed in moderate quantities. Oca (*Oxalis tuberosa*) and quinoa (*Chenopodium quinoa*) are grown on a small scale by a limited number of households, mostly in the upper altitudinal–ecological zone. 'Chocho beans' (*Lupinus mutabalis*) were grown much more widely and in greater quantities. We suspected that chocho beans were strongly goitrogenic, but animal studies proved equivocal (J. T. Dunn, personal communication, 1971). Problems with the manner in which the beans were prepared and difficulty in maintaining the experimental animals on a low iodine diet made interpretation of the results difficult.

In La Esperanza the mean harvest of *chochos* in 1971 was 67.1 lb per household. These beans are quite bitter tasting. They are boiled for 24 hr or longer and then put in a sack and washed in running water (in the river, a gully, or in an irrigation ditch) for 3 to 5 days, which partially eliminates the bitter taste. The beans are eaten along with salt or in heavy soups (*coladas*) made from *maiz*. Consumption is greatest after the harvest in October and November and lowest between March and July. *Chochos* are grown in greater quantity in the lower altitudinal–ecological zone where the soil is much more sandy and the temperature slightly warmer. The *chocho* is apparently more resistant to heavy rains than is *maiz*. Thus in those years in which the corn crop is damaged by excess rainfall, *chochos* constitute a significantly larger portion of the diet of many families. Cabbage (*Brassica oleracea* var. *capitata*) is also consumed almost daily as a constituent of most *coladas*.

In order to evaluate the relationship between PTC taste sensitivity and our dependent developmental measures, we determined PTC taste thresholds (the lowest concentration at which a solution of the test substance can be distinguished from water) on a subsample of 264 of the 348 children using serial dilutions of phenylthiocarbamide at .625, .312, .156, .078, .039, .019, .009, .0045 mM. Thresholds were determined using a 20-cup scoring technique based on signal detection theory. This procedure is discussed in greater detail elsewhere (Greene, 1974, 1976).

### Nutritional Factors

*Age at weaning.* The process of supplementing mother's milk begins around 4–6 months of age and the mean age at weaning for these children is 1 year and 9 months. Infants are slowly weaned onto a diet consisting mostly of thick soups (*coladas*) made from ground corn, Lima bean, and *chocho*. The sweet sap of the *maguey* plant or crude brown sugar is often added as a sweetener.

Given the low-protein content of the local diet (Fierro-Benítez *et al.*, 1969a), the child who is nursed for a longer period of time might be expected to be better nourished and more resistant to disease (due to its receiving passive immunity from the mother) than children weaned at an early age under these environmental circumstances. Since nervous system development is most rapid, and thus vulnerable to nutritional stress, during the first year of life, it is reasonable to evaluate the hypothesis that age at weaning is a significant predictor of neurological development in these children.

*Thyroid size.* Thyroid size was determined using the classification of Pérez, Scrimshaw, and Muñoz (1960) as modified by Fierro-Benítez *et al.* (1969a).

Grade 0a   —   not palpable;
Grade 0b   —   palpable, but not visible with the head raised;
Grade I    —   easily palpable with the head in the normal position and visible with the head raised;
Grade II   —   easily visible with the head in the normal position;
Grade III  —   visible at a distance;
Grade IV   —   monstrous goiters.

The distribution of thyroid sizes in this sample of children is shown in Table 10.4. This variable should give some indication of degree of thyroid stress or the adequacy of adaptation to that stress. It thus may reflect differential iodine nutriture or constitutional differences in adaptation to low iodine intake.

*Type of salt used.* Two basic types of salt were available in these communities: refined iodized salt, which was sold in plastic bags of 1–5 lb, and

**TABLE 10.4**

Distribution of Thyroid Size among Children 6 to 15 Years of Age in Tocachi (Iodized) and La Esperanza (Noniodized)

| Thyroid size | Tocachi (%) | La Esperanza (%) |
|:---:|:---:|:---:|
| 0A | 40.4 | 12.2 |
| 0B | 56.0 | 64.6 |
| 1 | 3.0 | 21.1 |
| 2 | .6 | 2.0 |
| 3 | .0 | .0 |
| 4 | .0 | .0 |

**TABLE 10.5**

Type of Salt Used in the Households of the Children under Study

| Type of salt used | Tocachi (%) | La Esperanza (%) |
|---|---|---|
| Iodized | 34.9 | 46.1 |
| Noniodized | 33.7 | 29.2 |
| Both | 31.4 | 24.7 |

crude rock salt, which was sold loosely by the pound. Iodized salt had been available only for about 2–3 years prior to the time of this study. Table 10.5 shows the pattern of salt usage by the households of the children under study.

*Total Resource Index (TRI).*    This index attempts to quantitatively measure the economic circumstance of the household of each child in the study by adding together its wealth in animals (in *sucres*), the total yearly wage income of the household, and the *sucre* value of its total harvest in 1971. It was hypothesized that children from more affluent households (as measured by this index) would be better nourished and thus show higher levels of physical and neurological development.

*Altitudinal–ecological zone.*    This variable evaluates possible differences in iodine availability and goitrogen intake across the three altitudinal–ecological zones. It also covaries with socioeconomic differences between residents of the three zones as will be described in the following section.

### Social Factors

*Socioeconomic status (SES).*    This variable was a product of a rating of the household of each child by our main informants, two respected adult individuals who had lived their entire lives in these communities. The rating was on a six-point scale (*muy rico, rico, corriente, medio pobre, pobre, muy pobre*) that basically reflected economic judgments.

*Geographical mobility.*    This variable attempted to evaluate the effect of experiential differences between children on neurological development. Geographical mobility was ascertained by calculating the number of times children had visited several cities and towns each of which had received a weighted factor for distance. Several of these children had never been outside of their natal *parroquia* at 12–15 years of age.

*Marital status of mother.*    The marital status of a woman may have an effect on the experiential environment of her children and may also have economic implications which affect their nutritional status and consequent development.

## SOCIAL AND BIOLOGICAL PREDICTORS OF NUTRITIONAL STATUS, PHYSICAL GROWTH, AND NEUROLOGICAL DEVELOPMENT

### Visual–Motor Maturation

The relationship between the independent and dependent variables was evaluated through a stepwise, multiple regression analysis utilizing the Data-Text statistical package (Armor & Couch, 1972). Table 10.6 shows those variables that account for a significant portion of the total variance in the Bender–Gestalt scores in the 348 children 6–15 years of age in both populations. It also shows the multiple correlation ($R$) and the squared multiple correlation ($R^2$) for these variables. $R^2$ is generally considered to indicate the proportion of the variation in the dependent variable (Bender–Gestalt score) accounted for by association with the independent variables (McNemar, 1962). The standardized partial regression coefficients reflect adjustments in the scale of measurement of each of the independent variables and can be compared to one another to determine the relative predictive power of each independent variable with the others held constant (Armor & Couch, 1972). For the combined populations $R = .65$ and $R^2 = .43$. This means that these four independent variables account for 43% of the variation in the Bender–Gestalt scores. None of the other independent variables account for a significant amount of variation.

In addition to age, the analysis identifies two independent variables, one economic (SES rating) and the other biological (PTC taste sensitivity), as being most important in "explaining" the variation in the Bender scores. A second biological variable (sex) accounts for somewhat less of the variation.

TABLE 10.6

Independent Variables Which Are Significant Predictors of the Bender–Gestalt Test Score of Children 6–15 Years of Age in Tocachi and La Esperanza

| Variable | Standardized partial regression coefficient | $t$ test | DF | $p$ | Variance |
|---|---|---|---|---|---|
| Age | −.55 | 13.27 | 341 | .001 | .293 |
| SES rating | .19 | 4.66 | 341 | .001 | .036 |
| PTC taste sensitivity | .18 | 4.40 | 341 | .001 | .032 |
| Sex | −.14 | 3.30 | 341 | .002 | .018 |

$R = .66$
$R^2 = .43$

Thus, children from households with a higher (better) SES rating scored better than those from households with low ratings; sensitive tasters of PTC scored better than nontasters; and males scored better than females. The standardized partial regression coefficients for these variables are .19, .18, and .14 and reflect their relative predictive strengths. Therefore, we can say for the combined populations that across all age ranges the best predictors of a child's level of visual–motor development are his or her socioeconomic status and PTC taste sensitivity and then his or her sex.

### PTC Taste Sensitivity

The relationship between PTC taste sensitivity, the ingestion of naturally occurring goitrogens, thyroid function, and neurological maturation has already been discussed. These data suggest that sensitive "tasters" of PTC eat fewer goitrogens than "nontasters" and less sensitive "tasters" and are thus less likely to be under thyroid stress. Thus, thyroid function and neurological maturation (as measured by the Bender–Gestalt test) is maximized as a function of increasing taste sensitivity to PTC (see also, Greene 1974, 1976).

### Socioeconomic Class Rating

The interpretation of the SES rating as a predictor of the Bender scores is somewhat more complex. The scale is basically economic, thus in these communities the children from poorer households are most likely to be malnourished while those from wealthier households are apt to be better nourished. Therefore, this measure *probably* reflects some aspect of the effect of protein–energy malnutrition on neurological maturation. The scale also involves social judgments and thus incorporates behavioral and educational evaluations of the children's parents. These cultural factors are certainly important influences on the development of the child. Experimental studies with laboratory animals suggest that experiential factors have significant effects on several aspects of brain development (Greenough, 1975; Rosenzweig, Bennett, & Diamond, 1972; Walsh & Cummins, 1976) and behavior (Levitsky & Barnes, 1972; Wells, Geist, & Zimmermann, 1972) and that these factors may be equally operable in humans (Chavez et al., 1975, Greene 1977b).

We were somewhat surprised that our informant's subjective evaluation of socioeconomic status had such high predictive value for Bender scores while our quantitative Total Resource Index had no predictive utility. There are, of course, obvious questions about the construct validity of the TRI variable as a measure of wealth. Information on number of animals, wage income. and amount of various crops harvested was solicited from the head of each household by our informants as part of a general socioeconomic questionnaire. The information appeared to be reliable as our informants knew the members of each household intimately; however, we were not able to verify the harvest data in any precise way, and we found it difficult to determine how wage income entering extended households—or closely associated households—was actually dispersed. Our decision to weight the three components equally and in terms of a year's wage income and year's value in harvest may also be questioned. Unfortunately, we had insufficient data to estimate net income from the yearly harvest. For that matter, the householders' estimation of their harvest was only an approximation.

Another problem with the TRI index is that it is synchronic, measuring only what it pretends to measure at a single point in time. It does not tell us much about the economic status of the household over time, especially during the early critical years for the children under study. This particular quantitative index is probably also subject to marked fluctuations as wage earners enter and leave extended households, and as large animals are sold off for cash (which the index does not measure).

In contrast, the subjective SES rating, while lacking the apparent "rigor" of a quantitative measure, appears to have certain advantages under these circumstances. First, being done by a member of the community who knew all of these households intimately, the SES rating contains a diachronic dimension and is not unduly influenced by momentary changes in the economic situation of a household, or by the particular mix of its assets. Because it reflects how the household is perceived by another member of the community, it avoids some of the reliability problems that are inherent in the TRI, although it certainly does introduce another set of questions concerning validity and reliability. A third and most important point is that although primarily economic, the SES variable also incorporates educational and behavioral judgments which are not readily discernible factors. These judgments may provide important information on the experiential dimension of the household environment, a factor which we have noted may actually have a direct effect on behavioral development.

## Sex

Sex is a significant predictor of visual–motor development in these children with males scoring better than females at all ages. The effect of sex on Bender scores is seen even more clearly among the La Esperanza adults where possible sex differences in rates of visual–motor development cannot obscure the comparisons. The mean Bender scores for all adult subjects in the 15–54 year age range was 1.8 for the males and 3.8 for the females and are outstanding in terms of their significant difference ($F = 40.28$, $df = 1/268$, $p < .001$). Five times as many adult females (40) as males (8) showed evidence of "moderate" deficits in visual–motor maturation. These were individuals 15–54 years of age whose scores fell below the fifth percentile among 10-year-old North American children (Greene, 1973, 1976).

These effects may be a consequence of the female's greater vulnerability to low iodine intake due to hormonal factors. Estrogen causes a marked increase in thyroxine-binding globulin (TBG) levels. With more binding sites to saturate, it may be more difficult for the female to maintain adequate blood levels of "free" $T_3$ and $T_4$ when iodine intake is low (see Stanbury, 1972b). This phenomenon may thus account for the markedly higher prevalence of goiter in females than males, and possibly for the higher prevalence of neurological deficits under these environmental conditions.

These same differences existed between the sexes among children 6–15 years of age in La Esperanza ($F = 15.22$, $df = 133$, $p < .001$) even when the large majority of both sexes were attending the local school and were certainly equally familiar with the use of pencil and paper which is required in the Bender–Gestalt test. No such sex differences appear in Koppitz' standardization data on North American children (Koppitz, 1964), nor did these sex differences exist among the sample of children from Tocachi who had been receiving supplementary injections of iodine in oil over a 5–7 year period.

### Ethnicity

Ethnic group (*blanco-mestizo* or *indígena*) was not a significant predictor of visual–motor development in the combined populations; however, when the data from La Esperanza were considered separately, ethnic group was as strong a predictor of visual–motor maturation as was SES (standardized partial regression coefficients, -.25 and .21) with *blanco* children scoring significantly better than *indígena* children. An analysis of variance of the Bender–Gestalt scores of the La Esperanza *adults* also indicates that *blanco* individuals had significantly better scores than *indígenas* ($F = 5.63$, $df = 1/213$, $p < .05$). We will comment further on these findings in the following section.

### Summary of Regressions on Bender Scores

SES rating and PTC taste sensitivity, the independent variables that account for the greatest proportion of variance in neurological maturation in the children in these two populations, probably largely represent the effect of two nutritional stresses, protein–energy malnutrition and iodine malnutrition, on nervous system development. The portion of the variance in the Bender scores accounted for by sex is likely to be another manifestation of iodine malnutrition via its greater effect on females due to their apparent difficulty in adapting to low iodine availability because of endocrine factors.

The variance in Bender Scores accounted for by these three variables is shown in Table 10.6. These data indicate that the two variables reflecting the effect of iodine malnutrition account for about one and a half times the variance in visual–motor development in these children than does the variable which we believe is associated with the effect of protein–energy malnutrition.

It is interesting to note that all of the other independent variables accounted for little or no variance in the Bender scores. This was somewhat surprising. A child's birthorder, age at weaning, and thyroid size were all weak predictors. Ethnic group was stronger, particularly in La Esperanza (see preceding). Altitudinal–ecological zone, travel experience of the child, marital status of the mother, and Total Resource Index were all poor predictors.

The type of salt used (iodized, noniodized, or both) by the child's household also was unimportant. All three salt categories were used in this analysis. The effect of salt type on Bender scores using only the iodized and noniodized categories was evaluated through an analysis of variance. The analysis indicated that children from households using iodized salt had significantly better Bender scores than those from households using noniodized salt ($F = 9.15$, $df = 1/178$, $p = .003$). Although salt type (iodized versus noniodized) has a significant effect on neurological maturation of children in these two populations, its effect is weaker than that of the three main predictors: SES, PTC taste sensitivity, and sex. If the Bender–Gestalt scores of the individuals at the *extremes* of either the SES or PTC variables were to be compared, their predictive strengths would also undoubtedly increase.

## Physical Growth—Stature

The result of the multiple regression of the independent variables on height (dependent variable) is shown in Table 10.7. After age, ethnicity is the best predictor with *indígena* children being smaller than *blanco* and *mestizo* children. The SES rating is a significant, but weak, predictor of stature, with children from poorer households being shorter. PTC taste sensitivity has no predictive value for stature.

The fact that PTC taste sensitivity is not a predictor of stature, but of visual–motor maturation, is undoubtedly associated with the relative irreversibility of neurological deficits incurred during *early critical phases* of brain growth, compared to the ease of reversibility of statural deficits ("catch-up" growth) throughout growth and development. Thus, a high seasonal intake of goitrogens by a "nontaster" of PTC early in life may have enduring neurological effects, but the resultant deficits in statural growth (consequent to the intermittent hypothyroidism that would be produced) would be almost entirely reversible if subsequent iodine intake is adequate, or when the goitrogen-induced hypothyroidism passes.

### Association Between the Dependent Variables

Height-for-age is a useful index of the cumulative effect of nutritional stress on the child and is frequently used to differentiate well- from poorly nourished children in studies done retrospectively. Children with poor nutritional histories (as reflected in low height-for-age) are more likely to show neurological deficits as a consequence of this stress than are better nourished children. We thus evaluated this relationship in the children under study.

Table 10.8 shows the partial correlations between height and Bender–Gestalt score controlling for age in both sexes in Tocachi and La Esperanza. When age is controlled, shorter children perform more poorly than taller children in both sexes in both populations. The correlation coefficients are large and highly significant. These data indicate that children who are smaller (most likely as a consequence of lifelong nutritional and disease stress) lag significantly behind better nourished children in visual–motor development. Although there is a wide range of normal variation in rate of visual–motor maturation, it is likely that some portion of the retardation among the smaller children reflects the consequence of nutritional stress.

The correlation between stature and a measure of neurological maturation is useful as an indication of how individuals who have been malnourished (low height-for-age) may also show neurological deficits. However, these correlations generally underestimate the effect of malnutrition on neurological development since neurological deficits are relatively irreversible, while statural deficits can be greatly ameliorated if the child is subsequently well nourished. Consequently, some of those children who are operationally defined as being "malnourished" on the basis of height-for-age may not have

**TABLE 10.7**

**Independent Variables Which Are Significant Predictors of Stature among Children 6–15 Years of Age in Tocachi and La Esperanza**

| Variable | Standardized partial regression coefficient | $t$ test | DF | $p$ | Variance |
|---|---|---|---|---|---|
| Age | .86 | 33.30 | 343 | .001 | .728 |
| Ethnic group | .14 | 5.49 | 343 | .001 | .020 |
| SES rating | −.09 | 3.28 | 343 | .002 | .007 |

$R = .88$
$R^2 = .78$

TABLE 10.8

Partial Correlation of Stature and Bender–Gestalt Score Controlling for Age among Children 6–15 Years of Age in Tocachi and La Esperanza

| | Tocachi | | La Esperanza | |
| | Males | Females | Males | Females |
|---|---|---|---|---|
| $r$ | −.36 | −.44 | −.33 | −.25 |
| $N$ | 85 | 85 | 85 | 79 |
| $p$ | <.001 | <.001 | <.001 | .01 |

sustained neurological deficits, while others with profound impairment may be of average height. Thus, in a population in which malnutrition is endemic, the prediction of neurological development from height-for-age will always be less than perfect.

## Iodine Malnutrition, Protein–Energy Malnutrition, and the Pattern of Developmental Retardation in Areas Where Goiter and Cretinism Are Endemic

We noted that under conditions of protein–energy deprivation the peripheral monoiodination of $T_4$ shifts away from the highly metabolically active $T_3$ form to the metabolically inactive $rT_3$. Even though there is a lower blood level of metabolically active hormone, the high level of $rT_3$ prevents an increase in secretion of TSH. Consequently, we would expect that TSH secretion and thyroid enlargement (a positive adaptation to increase the iodide-trapping and hormine-synthesizing capacity of the gland) would be impeded in iodine-deficient individuals who were also experiencing protein–energy malnutrition. Therefore, protein–energy malnutrition would greatly exacerbate the effects of severe iodine malnutrition and may well be an extremely important factor in accounting for the geographic pattern of endemic cretinism as well as the intrapopulation variability in developmental deficits in areas in which goiter and cretinism are endemic.

## DISCUSSION

The data presented throughout this chapter indicate that there is significant intrapopulation variation in physical growth and neurological maturation among the children and adults in the communities under study, and that this variation is not random, being strongly influenced by a number of biological, nutritional, and social factors. Under the conditions of iodine and protein–energy malnutrition that exist in these populations, an individual's taste sensitivity to PTC and his or her sex become important determinants of visual–motor maturation; yet, these factors would not be determinants of neurological development in circumstances in which iodine intake is adequate and few goitrogenic food crops are consumed.

## PTC Taste Sensitivity

The interrelationship between PTC taste sensitivity and goitrogen intake may be operative at several different levels. Ingestion of goitrogens by a pregnant woman suppresses the maternal and possibly fetal thyroid glands, and it is not uncommon for an infant to be born with an enlarged thyroid gland as a consequence of casual or purposeful (therapeutic) maternal intake. Suppression of fetal thyroid function can also be accomplished in laboratory animals through the incorporation of antithyroid substances in the diet of the pregnant dam. Thus, it is likely that the PTC taste sensitivity of a mother is also a significant determinant of neurological development in her children. Maternal PTC taste sensitivity would determine the exposure of the fetus to naturally occurring goitrogens early in life when brain development is most rapid and vulnerable. Since these goitrogens can pass into the maternal milk supply, the mother's taste sensitivity to these substances would also be the primary interface between her infant and this portion of the environment during the first 6 months of life, because bitter taste sensitivity in human infants appears to be late developing (Desor, Maller, & Andrews, 1975). More sensitive tasters of PTC may eat fewer goitrogenic food crops or they may prepare these foods (wash and boil longer) in such ways as to greatly diminish their antithyroid content. Variation in *chocho* preparation as a function of a woman's PTC taste sensitivity would be an interesting area of investigation.

## Ethnicity and Socioeconomic Status

Ethnicity was not a predictor of visual–motor development, but was a determinant of stature in the children from the combined populations. That this difference in stature is independent of SES would suggest a genetic explanation or may reflect differences in rates of development.

A comparison of adults (where development is completed) in La Esperanza indicates that the *blancos* had significantly better Bender scores ($F = 5.63$, $df = 1/213$, $p < .05$) and the females were significantly taller ($t = 2.42$, $df = 101$, $p < .02$) than *indígenas*. However, a different pattern of variation emerged when the data were analyzed according to altitudinal–ecological zone. *Indígenas* living in the upper zone were significantly taller ($F = 6.54$, $df = 2/143$, $p < .01$) and had significantly better Bender scores ($F$

$= 3.27$, $df = 2/176$, $p < .05$) than those living in the middle and lower zones. Upper zone *indígenas* were actually taller (but not significantly so) than the primarily middle zone *blancos* and their Bender scores were not significantly different.

We did not collect detailed socioeconomic data on the specific households of the La Esperanza adults in our sample; however, data from the children's households (which greatly overlap with those of the adults) indicate that there is a significant pattern of variation in wealth (as measured by the Total Resource Index) across the three zones, with upper zone *indígenas* being significantly better off than both the middle and lower zone *indígenas* ($F = 12.37$, $df = 2/93$, $p < .001$) and at least as well-off as the primarily middle zone *blancos*.

Therefore, among the adults, the mean developmental data on stature and Bender scores previously described appear to covary quite clearly with differences in economic circumstances, although microenvironmental variations in iodine availability or goitrogen intake across the three zones are other, but less likely, causal factors. Although we have questioned the utility of the Total Resource Index of each household as a developmental predictor in the multiple regression analysis (see preceding), we feel that the *averaged* data on this variable do provide a rough, but useful, indication of *group* economic differences.

The superior economic position of the upper zone *indígenas* is undoubtedly a consequence of their affiliation with the *haciendas* which are located in that zone. During the Colonial period the original *haciendas* were established on the best lands, and this certainly is the case in La Esperanza. Historically, the *hacienda* system has been exploitative in that it obligated the Indian inhabitants (*huasipungeros*) to work on the *hacienda* and gave them only usufruct rights to small plots of land (*huasipungos*). However, this land is located in the best zone and the Agrarian Reform law of 1963 gave these upper zone *indígenas* ownership of their *huasipungos* while 42% of the inhabitants of the *parroquia* remain landless.

Their larger and more productive landholdings, a small payment in wages which they presently received for their labor on the *hacienda* (in an area where other opportunities for wage labor for significant numbers of individuals are literally nonexistent), and their rights of pasture in the high *páramo* grasslands on the *haciendas* (thus enabling them to maintain relatively large flocks of sheep and goats and as many as 10–15 head of cattle) puts the upper zone *indígenas* in a superior economic position relative to other *indígenas* and many *blancos* alike.

However, these observed socioeconomic and developmental differences between the ethnic groups should be interpreted with caution as a sampling problem has influenced our data in several ways. This relates to the fact that the socioeconomic survey of the households of the children in our study does not include information on the five wealthiest *blanco* families due to the fact that they did not have any children within the 6–15 age range, or below for that matter. This is a consequence of a differential rate of out-migration from La Esperanza on the part of *blancos* compared to the *indígenas.* The married children of the wealthy *blancos* have all emigrated to Quito while their parents have stayed behind. If these families are included in the analysis it would be seen that wealth in the *blanco* segment of the population is highly concentrated among a limited number of individuals. The remaining *blancos* are, on an average, in a slightly inferior economic position to the wealthiest (upper zone) *indígenas,* a fact reflected in their shorter mean stature.

## CONCLUSION

Data presented throughout this chapter indicate that both iodine and protein–energy malnutrition have significant effects on both inter- and intra-population variation in physical growth and neurological maturation. Specific biological and social factors are important predictors of the pattern of these effects within the populations under study. The predictive strengths of these factors differ for physical and neurological development due to differences in the rate and timing of these processes. Although multivariate techniques are extremely useful in "boiling down" and controlling a large number of independent variables, univariate manipulations are still useful in disentangling an often complex web of relationships. Finally, we strongly believe that the interpretation of these developmental data is possible only through a thorough understanding of the ethnographic context in which they occur, including an appreciation of the historical dimensions of the community under study.

## ACKNOWLEDGEMENTS

I wish to thank Dr. John B. Stanbury, Department of Nutrition and Food Science, Massachusetts Institute of Technology, and Dr. Rodrigo Fierro-Benítez, Department of Radioisotopes, Escuela Politecnica Nacional, Quito, for their help in all aspects of this study. Special thanks are also due to the people and authorities of the *parroquias* of La Esperanza and Tocachi whose kind cooperation has made these studies possible.

## REFERENCES

Armor, D. J., & Couch, A. J. *Data-text primer.* New York: Free Press, 1972.
Astwood, E. The natural occurrence of antithyroid compounds as a cause of simple goiter. *Annals of Internal Medicine,* 1949, *30,* 1087–1103.

Balázs, R., Kovács, S., Cocks, W., Johnson, A., & Eayrs, J. Effect of thyroid hormone on the biochemical maturation of the rat brain: Postnatal cell formation. *Brain Research,* 1971, *25,* 555–570.

Balázs, R., Kovács, S. Treichgräber, W., Cocks, W., & Eayrs, J. Biochemical effects of thyroid deficiency on the developing brain. *Journal of Neurochemistry,* 1968, *15,* 1335–1349.

Bashi, J. Effects of inbreeding on cognitive performance. *Nature (London),* 1977, *266,* 440–442.

Bass, N., & Netsky, M. Microchemical pathology of adult rat cerebrum following neonatal nutritional deprivation and hypothyroidism. *Transactions of the American Neurological Association,* 1969, *94,* 216–219.

Bass, N., & Young, E. Effects of hypothyroidism on the differentiation of neurons and glia in the developing rat cerebrum. *Journal of Neurological Sciences,* 1973, *18,* 155–173.

Beals, K. Head form and climatic stress. *American Journal of Physical Anthropology,* 1972, *37,* 85–92.

Boas, F. *Changes in bodily form in descendents of immigrants. Final Report.* Washington, D.C.: U. S. Government Printing Office, 1911.

Botha-Antoun, E., Babayan, S., & Harfouche, J. Intellectual development related to nutritional status. *Journal of Tropical Pediatrics,* 1968, *14,* 112–115.

Cavalli-Sforza, L., & Bodmer, W. *The genetics of human populations.* San Francisco: Freeman, 1971.

Champakam, S., Srikantia, S., & Gopalan, C. Kwashiorkor and mental development. *American Journal of Clinical Nutrition,* 1968, *21,* 844–850.

Chase, P., & Martin H. Undernutrition and child development. *New England Journal of Medicine,* 1970, *282,* 933–939.

Chavez, A., Martinez, C., & Yashine, T. Nutrition, behavioral development, and mother–child interaction in young rural children. *Federation Proceedings,* 1975, *34,* 1574–1582.

Chopra, I. An assessment of daily production and significance of thyroid secretion of 3,3′,5′-triiodothyronine (reverse $T_3$) in man. *Journal of Clinical Investigation,* 1976, *58,* 32–40.

Christiansen, N., Vouri, L., Mora, J., & Wagner, M. Social environment as it relates to malnutrition and mental development. In J. Cravioto, L. Hambracus, & B. Valquist (Eds.), *Early malnutrition and mental development.* Uppsala, Sweden: Almqvist & Wiksell, 1974, pp. 186–199.

Clements, F. Health significance of endemic goitre. In *Endemic goitre.* World Health Organization Monograph No. 44. Geneva: World Health Organization, 1960.

Cravioto, J., & DeLicardie, E. Environmental correlates of severe clinical malnutrition and language development in survivors from kwashiorkor and marasmus. In *Nutrition, the nervous system, and behavior.* Pan American Health Organization Scientific Publication No. 251. Washing, D.C.: World Health Organization, 1972. Pp. 73–94.

Cravioto, J., & DeLicardie, E. Longitudinal study of language development in severely malnourished children. In G. Serban (Ed.), *Nutrition and mental functions.* New York: Plenum, 1975, Pp. 143–191.

Cravioto, J., DeLicardie, E., & Birch, H. Nutrition, growth and neurointegrative development: An experimental and ecologic study. *Pediatrics,* 1966, *38,* 319–372.

Crow, J., & Mange, A. Measurement of inbreeding from the frequency of marriages between persons of the same surname. *Eugenics Quarterly,* 1965, *12,* 199–203.

Davenport, J. Cretinism in rats: Enduring behavioral deficit induced by tricyanoaminopropene. *Science,* 1970, *167,* 1007–1008.

Davenport, J. Environmental therapy in hypothyroid and other disadvantaged animal populations. In R. N. Walsh & W. T. Greenough (Eds.), *Environments as therapy for brain dysfunction.* New York: Plenum, 1976. Pp. 71–114.

DeGroot, L., & Stanbury, J. *The thyroid and its diseases* (4th ed.). New York: Wiley, 1975.

Delange, F., Costa, A., Ermans, A., Ibbertson, H., Querido, A., & Stanbury, J. A survey of the clinical and metabolic patterns of endemic cretinism. In J. B. Stanbury & R. L. Kroc (Eds.), *Human development and the thyroid gland. Relation to endemic cretinism.* New York: Plenum, 1972. Pp. 175–187.

DeLicardie, E., & Cravioto, J. Behavioral responsiveness of survivors of clinical severe malnutrition to cognitive demands. In J. Cravioto, L. Hambracus, & B. Vahlquist (Eds.), *Early malnutrition and mental development.* Stockholm: Almqvist & Wiksell, 1974. Pp. 134–154.

De Smet, M. Pathological anatomy of endemic goitre. In *Endemic goitre.* World Health Organization Monograph No. 44. Geneva: World Health Organization, 1960.

Desor, J., Maller, O., & Andrews, K. Ingestive responses of human newborns to salty, sour and bitter stimuli. *Journal of Comparative and Physiological Psychology,* 1975, *89,* 966–970.

Dewey, W., Barrai, I., Morton, N., & Mi, M. Recessive genes in severe mental defect. *American Journal of Human Genetics,* 1965, *17,* 237–256.

Dobbing, J. Vulnerable periods of brain development. In Ciba Foundation Symposium No. 3. *Lipids, malnutrition and the developing brain.* Amsterdam: Elsevier, 1972. Pp. 9–29.

Dobbing, J. Nutrition and the developing brain. *Lancet,* 1973, *1,* 48.

Dobbing, J., & Sands, J. Vulnerability of developing brain. 9. The effect of nutritional growth retardation on the timing of the brain growth spurt. *Biologia Neonatorum,* 1971, *19,* 363–378.

Dumont, J., Delange, F., & Ermans, A. Endemic cretinism. In J. B. Stanbury (Ed.), *Endemic goiter.* Pan American Health Organization Scientific Publication No. 193. Washington, D.C.: World Health Organization, 1969. Pp. 91–98.

Dumont, J., Neve, P., & Otten, J. Recent advances in the knowledge of the control of thyroid growth and function. In J. B. Stanbury (Ed.), *Endemic goiter.* Pan American Health Organization Scientific Publication No. 193. Washington, D.C.: World Health Organization, 1969. Pp. 14–29.

Dye, J., & Maughan, G. Further studies of the thyroid gland. 5. The thyroid gland as a growth promoting and form-determining factor in the development of the animal body. *American Journal of Anatomy,* 1929, *44,* 331–368.

Eayrs, J. Age as a factor determining the severity and reversibility of the effects of thyroid deprivation in the rat. *Journal of Endocrinology,* 1961, *22,* 409–419.

Eayrs, J. T. Developmental relationship between brain and thyroid. In R. P. Michal (Ed.), *Endocrinology and human behavior.* London: Oxford University Press, 1968. Pp. 239–255.

Eayrs, J., & Taylor S. The effect of thyroid deficiency induced by methyl thiouracil on the maturation of the central nervous system. *Journal of Anatomy,* 1951, *85,* 350–358.

Ermans, A., Thilly, C., Vis, H., & Delange, F. Permissive nature of iodine deficiency in the development of endemic goiter. In J. B. Stanbury (Ed.), *Endemic goiter.* Pan American Health Organization Scientific Publication No. 193. Washington, D.C.: World Health Organization, 1969. Pp. 101–117.

Essman, W., Mendoza, L., & Hamburgh, M. Critical periods of maze acquisition development in euthyroid and hypothyroid rodents. *Psychological Reports,* 1968, *23,* 795–800.

Friedl, J., & Ellis, W. Inbreeding, isonymy, and isolation in a Swiss community. *Human Biology,* 1974, *46,* 699–712.

Fierro-Benítez, R., Penafiel, W., DeGroot, L., & Ramírez, I. Endemic goiter and endemic cretinism in the Andean region. *New England Journal of Medicine,* 1969, *280,* 296–302. (a)

Fierro-Benítez, R., Ramírez, I., Estrella, E., Jaramillo, C., Díaz, C., & Urresta, J. Iodized oil in the prevention of endemic goiter in the Andean region of Ecuador. I. Program design, effects on goiter prevalence, thyroid function, and iodine secretion. In J. B. Stanbury

(Ed.), *Endemic goiter*. Pan American Health Organization Scientific Publication No. 193. Washington, D.C.: World Health Organization, 1969. Pp. 306–340. (b)

Fierro-Benítez, R., Ramírez, I., Garcés, J., Jaramillo, C., Moncayo, F., & Stanbury, J. The clinical pattern of cretinism as seen in highland Ecuador. *American Journal of Clinical Nutrition*, 1974, *27*, 531–543.

Fierro-Benítez, R., Ramírez, I., & Suárez, J. Effect of iodine correction early in fetal life on intelligence quotient. A preliminary report. In J. B. Stanbury & R. L. Kroc (Eds.), *Human development and the thyroid gland. Relation to endemic cretinism*. New York: Plenum, 1972. Pp. 239–247.

Fierro-Benítez, R., & Recalde, F. Estudios previos y planificación de los trabajos de investigación sobre bocio endémico en la Región Andina. *Revista de Facultad de Ciencias Médicas* (Quito), 1958, *9–10*, 55–67.

Frisancho, R., & Baker, P. Altitude and growth: A study of the patterns of physical growth of a high altitude Peruvian Quechua population. *American Journal of Physical Anthropology*, 1070, *32*, 279–292.

Frisancho, R., Sanchez, J., Pallardel, D., & Yanez, L. Adaptive significance of small body size under poor socio-economic conditions in southern Peru. *American Journal of Physical Anthropology*, 1973, *39*, 255–261.

Gajdusek, C. Congenital defects of the central nervous system associated with hyperendemic goiter in a Neolithic society of Netherlands New Guinea. I. Epidemiology. *Pediatrics*, 1962, *29*, 345–363.

Geber, M., & Dean, R. The psychological changes accompanying kwashiorkor. *Courrier*, 1956, *6*, 3–13.

Gelber, S., Campbell, P., Deibler, G., & Sokoloff, L. Effects of l-thyroxine on amino acid incorporation into protein in mature and immature rat brain. *Journal of Neurochemistry*, 1964, *11*, 221–229.

Goldschmidt, V. M. *Geochemistry*. Oxford: Clarendon, 1958.

Greene, L. Physical growth and development, neurological maturation and behavioral functioning in two Ecuadorian Andean communities in which goiter is endemic. I. Outline of the problem of endemic goiter and cretinism. Physical growth and neurological maturation in the adult population of La Esperanza. *American Journal of Physical Anthropology*, 1973, *38*, 119–134.

Greene, L. Physical growth and development, neurological maturation and behavioral functioning in two Ecuadorian Andean communities in which goiter is endemic. II. PTC taste sensitivity and neurological maturation. *American Journal of Physical Anthropology*, 1974, *41*, 139–152.

Greene, L. Nutrition and behavior in highland Ecuador (Doctoral dissertation, University of Pennsylvania, 1976). (University Microfilms, No. 76–695).

Greene, L. Hyperendemic goiter, cretinism, and social organization in highland Ecuador. In L. S. Greene (Ed.), *Malnutrition, behavior, and social organization*. New York: Academic Press, 1977. Pp. 55–94. (a)

Greene, L. Toward an appreciation of the biological bases of behavioral variation and its influence on social organization. In L. S. Greene (Ed.), *Malnutrition, behavior, and social organization*. New York: Academic Press, 1977. Pp. 267–291. (b)

Greenough, W. Experiential modification of the developing brain. *American Scientist*, 1975, *63*, 37–46.

Greulich, W. Growth of children of the same race under different environmental conditions. *Science*, 1958, *127*, 515–516.

Habicht, J. P., Martorell, R., Yarbrough, C., Malina, R., & Klein, R. Height and weight standards for preschool children. How relevant are ethnic differences in growth potential? *Lancet*, 1974, *1*, 611.

Hoch, F. Biochemistry of hyperthyroidism and hypothyroidism. *Postgraduate Medical Journal*, 1968, *44*, 347–362.

Ingbar, I. Clinical considerations. In S. Werner & S. Ingbar (Eds.), *The thyroid*. New York: Harper and Row, 1971. Pp. 243–255.

Jackson, C. Effects of acute and chronic inanition on the relative weights of the various organs and systems of adult albino rats. *American Journal of Anatomy*, 1915, *18*, 75–116.

Jackson, C., & Stewart, C. The effects of inanition in the young upon the ultimate size of the body and of the various organs in the albino rat. *Journal of Experimental Zoology*, 1920, *30*, 97–128.

Koppitz, E. *The Bender Gestalt test for young children*. New York: Grune & Stratton, 1964.

Lasker, G. The occurrence of identical (isonymous) surnames in various relationships in pedigrees: A preliminary analysis of the relation of surname combinations to inbreeding. *American Journal of Human Genetics*, 1968, *20*, 250–257.

Lasker, G. Isonymy (recurrence of the same surnames in affinal relatives): A comparison of rates calculated from pedigrees, grave markers and death and birth registers. *Human Biology*, 1969, *41*, 309–321.

Lasker, G., Chiarelli, B., Masali, M., Fedele, F., & Kaplan, B. Degree of human genetic isolation measured by isonymy and marital distances in two communities in an Italian alpine valley. *Human Biology*, 1972, *44*, 351–360.

Latham, M. The effects of malnutrition on intellectual development and learning. *American Journal of Public Health*, 1971, *61*, 1307–1324.

Lechtig, A., Delgado, H., Lasky, R., Klein, R., Engle, P., Yarbrough, C., & Habicht, J.-P. Maternal nutrition and fetal growth in developing societies. Socioeconomic factors. *American Journal of Diseases of Children*, 1975, *129*, 434–437.

Levitsky, D., & Barnes, R. Nutritional and environmental interactions in the behavioral development of the rat: Long term effects. *Science*, 1972, *176*, 68–71.

Little, M., & Hochner, D. *Human thermoregulation, growth, and mortality*. Reading, Mass.: Addison-Wesley, 1973.

Mange, A. Growth and inbreeding in a human isolate. *Human Biology*, 1964, *36*, 104–133.

Matovinovic, J., Child, M., Nichaman, M., & Trowbridge, F. Iodine and Endemic goiter. In J. Dunn & G. Medeiros-Neto (Eds.), *Endemic goiter and cretinism: Continuing threats to world health*. Pan American Health Organization Scientific Publication No. 292. Washington, D.C.: World Health Organization, 1974. Pp. 67–94.

McCarrison, R. Observations on endemic cretinism in the Chitral and Gilgit valleys. *Lancet*, 1908, *2*, 1275–1280.

McNemar, Q. *Psychological statistics* (3rd ed.). New York: Wiley, 1962.

Merimee, T., & Fineberg, E. Starvation induced alterations in circulating thyroid hormone concentrations in man. *Metabolism*, 1976, *25*, 79–83.

Merke, F. Weitere belege für die eiszeit als primordiale ursache des endemisehen Kropfes: Eiszeit und Kropf in Wallis. *Schweizerische Medizinische Wochenschrift*, 1967, *97*, 131–140.

Mönckeberg, F., Tisler, S., Toro, S., Gattás, V., & Vega, L. Malnutrition and mental development. *American Journal of Clinical Nutrition*, 1972, *25*, 766–772.

Naeye, R., Blanc, W., & Paul, C. Effects of maternal nutrition on the human fetus. *Pediatrics*, 1973, *52*, 494–503.

Nicholson, J., & Altman, J. The effects of early hypo- and hyper-thyroidism on the development of the rat cerebellar cortex. II. Synaptogenesis in the molecular layers. *Brain Research*, 1972, *44*, 25–46.

Oppenheimer, J., & Surks, M. Kinetics of iodine metabolism: Hormonal distribution and turnover. In S. Werner & S. Ingbar (Eds.), *The thyroid*. New York: Harper and Row, 1971. Pp. 66–78.

Palmblad, J., Levi, L., Burger, A., Melander, A., Westgren, U., von Schenck, H., & Skude, G. Effects of total energy withdrawal (fasting) on the levels of growth hormone, thyrotropin, cortisol, adrenaline, noradrenaline, $T_4$, $T_3$, and $rT_3$ in healthy males. *Acta Medica Scandinavica*, 1977, *201*, 15–22.

Pérez, C., Scrimshaw, N., & Muñoz, A. Techniques of endemic goiter surveys. In *Endemic goitre*. World Health Organization Monograph No. 44. Geneva: World Health Organization, 1960. Pp. 369–383.

Pollitt, E. Ecology, malnutrition, and mental development. *Psychosomatic Medicine*, 1969, *31*, 193–200.

Pollitt, E. Behavior of infant in causation of nutritional marasmus. *American Journal of Clinical Nutrition*, 1973, *26*, 264–270.

Querido, A., & Swabb, D. (Eds.). *Brain development and thyroid deficiency* Amsterdam: North-Holland, 1975.

Richardson, S. The background histories of children severely malnourished in infancy. *Advances in Pediatrics*, 1974, *21*, 167–195.

Richardson, S. The relation of severe malnutrition in infancy to the intelligence of school children with differing life histories. *Pediatric Research*, 1976, *10*, 57–61.

Roberts, D. Body weight, race and climate. *American Journal of Physical Anthropology*, 1953, *11*, 533–558.

Roberts, D. *Climate and human variability*. Reading, Mass.: Addison-Wesley, 1973.

Rosenzweig, M., Bennett, E., & Diamond, M. Brain changes in response to experience. *Scientific American*, 1972, *226*, 22–29.

Schull, W., & Neel, J. *The effects of inbreeding on Japanese children*. New York: Harper and Row, 1965.

Schull, W., Neel, J., Yamamoto, M., Uchida, T., Yanase, T., & Fujiki, N. The effects of parental consanguinity and inbreeding in Hirado, Japan. Physical development, tapping, blood pressure, intelligence quotient and school performance. *American Journal of Human Genetics*, 1970, *22*, 263–286.

Scow, R., & Simpson, M. Thyroidectomy in the newborn rat. *Anatomical Record*, 1945, *91*, 209–226.

Scrimshaw, N., & Gordon, J. (Eds.). *Malnutrition, learning and behavior*. Cambridge, Mass.: Massachusetts Institute of Technology Press, 1968.

Smith, D., Blizzard, R., & Wilkins, L. The mental prognosis in hypothyroidism of infancy and childhood. *Pediatrics*, 1957, *19*, 1011–1022.

Sokoloff, L. Action of thyroid hormones and cerebral development. *American Journal of Diseases of Children*, 1967, *114*, 498–505.

Stanbury, J. The clinical pattern of cretinism as seen in highland Ecuador. In J. B. Stanbury & R. L. Kroc (Eds.), *Human development and the thyroid gland. Relation to endemic cretinism*. New York: Plenum, 1972. Pp. 3–17. (a)

Stanbury, J. Cretinism and the fetal-maternal relationship. In J. B. Stanbury & R. L. Kroc (Eds.), *Human development and the thyroid gland. Relation to endemic cretinism*. New York: Plenum, 1972. Pp. 487–500. (b)

Stanbury, J. The role of the thyroid in the development of the human nervous system. In L. S. Greene (Eds.), *Malnutrition, behavior, and social organization*. New York: Academic Press, 1977. Pp. 39–54.

Sterling, K., & Lazarus, J. The thyroid and its control. *Annual Review of Physiology*, 1977, *39*, 349–371.

Stini, W. Reduced sexual dimorphism in upper arm muscle circumference associated with protein deficient diet in a South American population. *American Journal of Physical Anthropology*, 1972, *36*, 341–351.

Stoch, M., & Smythe, P. Does undernutrition in infancy inhibit brain growth and subsequent intellectual development? *Archives of Disease in Childhood*, 1963, *38*, 546–552.

Tanner, J. *Growth at adolescence*. Oxford: Blackwell, 1962.

Tong, W. Thyroid hormone synthesis and release. In S. Werner & S. Ingbar (Eds.), *The thyroid*. New York: Harper and Row, 1971. Pp. 24–40.

Vagenakis, A., Burger, A., Portnay, G., Rudolph, M., O'Brian, J., Azizi, F., Arky, A., Nicod, P., Ingar, S., & Braverman, L. Diversion of peripheral thyroxine metabolism from activating to inactivating pathways during complete fasting. *Journal of Clinical Endocrinology and Metabolism*, 1975, *41*, 191–194.

Van Etten, C. Goitrogens. In L. Liener (Ed.), *Toxic constituents of plant food stuffs*. New York: Academic Press, 1969. Pp. 103–142.

Walsh, R., & Cummins, R. Neural responses to therapeutic environments. In R. Walsh & W. T. Greenough (Eds.), *Environments as therapy for brain dysfunction*. New York: Plenum, 1976. Pp. 171–200.

Wells, A., Geist, C., & Zimmermann, R. Influence of environmental and nutritional factors on problem solving in the rat. *Perceptual and Motor Skills*, 1972, *35*, 235–244.

Winick, M. Nutrition and nerve cell growth. *Federation Proceedings*, 1970, *29*, 1510–1515.

Winick, M., & Rosso, P. The effect of severe early malnutrition on cellular growth of human brain. *Pediatric Research*, 1969, *3*, 181–184. (a)

Winick, M., & Rosso, P. Head circumference and cellular growth of the brain in normal and masculine children. *Journal of Pediatrics*, 1969, *74*, 774–778. (b)

Winick, M., Rosso, P., & Brasal, J. Malnutrition and cellular growth in the brain: Existence of critical periods. In *Lipids, malnutrition, and the developing brain*. Ciba Foundation Symposium No. 3. Amsterdam: Elsevier, 1972. Pp. 199–206.

# 11

## Maternal Adaptation and Fetal Growth at High Altitude in Bolivia

Jere D. Haas

### INTRODUCTION

Prediction of fetal growth and newborn nutritional status from information on the maternal phenotype depends on a knowledge of the relationship between mother and fetus as well as the multitude of factors that affect this relationship. From the point of view of evolution, it seems reasonable to assume that natural selection has worked to optimize the efficiency of the maternal–fetal unit under certain environmental conditions. Consequently, one would expect to encounter a certain degree of interpopulation variation in the measurable characteristics of this Maternal–Infant interaction, especially if we look at populations living under environmental stress in which adaptation and selection are ongoing. If we recognize that both the selection pressures and the mechanisms for adaptation vary with the nature and severity of the environmental stresses, it becomes obvious that the best maternal predictors of pregnancy outcome in one population may not necessarily be the best predictors for another population living in a different environment. Particularly appropriate for the investigation of the differential effects of maternal adaptation and contribution to fetal growth and neonatal maturity is an extreme high-altitude environment.

High-altitude stresses, especially hypoxic stress, have been shown to affect many aspects of physiological functioning in humans (Baker & Little, 1976; Mazess, 1975). Adaptations to high-altitude hypoxia include short-

*Social and Biological Predictors of*
*Nutritional Status, Physical Growth,*
*and Neurological Development*

term reversible acclimatization and irreversible developmental adaptations (Frisancho, 1975). Genetic adaptations are more difficult to demonstrate and have not been well documented for high-altitude populations. However, if one can show that developmental responses to stress during fetal life increase the probability of survival, and that variation in these characteristics is dependent upon variation in the mother's physiological response to pregnancy at high altitude, we will have made a significant step toward an understanding of adaptive mechanisms that may have a genetic basis.

The purpose of this chapter is to present a framework for analyzing the contribution of maternal phenotypic variation to pregnancy outcome at high altitude. We will develop this framework through a review of the scientific literature dealing with the effects of high altitude on (a) growth during childhood and puberty, (b) female fertility and reproduction, (c) fetal growth and development, and (d) infant growth and mortality. Preliminary analysis of data from a study currently being conducted in Bolivia will be presented. This study relates several parameters of maternal phenotype and high-altitude adaptation with pregnancy outcome.

## Effects of High Altitude on Child Growth

High-altitude hypoxia may affect the maternal phenotype well before reproduction is possible. Much of adult phenotypic variation is the result of the interaction between genes and the environment during the period of growth. Nutritional variation during this period is probably the major factor associated with differential growth within human populations (Tanner, 1966), and much of the variation in adult physique and physiological function can be attributed to the nutritional environment during infancy, childhood, and puberty.

Several studies of human growth observed at high altitude in Peru have reported that hypoxic stress appears to be a major factor explaining the slow growth, small body size for age, delayed puberty, and late attainment of adult body size. These effects of hypoxia on growth have been documented for well-nourished infants (Beall, 1976; Haas, 1973, 1976), preschool and school age children (Frisancho & Baker, 1970), and adolescents (Beall, Baker, Baker, & Haas, 1977; Frisancho & Baker, 1970; Hoff, Baker, Haas, Garruto, & Spector, 1974). The adolescent growth patterns are of particular importance because they relate more directly to the adult phenotype, are apparently very sensitive to the stresses of high altitude (Beall et al., 1977), and may be critical to the interpretation of how the female reproductive system develops to the point at which it is called upon to initiate and support childbearing.

At high altitude, menarche occurs at about 13.6 years or approximately 1 year later than comparable low-altitude samples (Bouloux, 1968; Peñaloza, 1971). This later menarche implies a later attainment of physiological maturity for conception and childbearing. Altitude-related growth retardation is comparable to growth retardation due to poor nutrition, and the relationship between childhood nutritional deprivation and subsequent malfunctioning of the female reproductive system has been documented (Baird, 1974; Birch & Gussow, 1970; Drillien, 1957; Emanual & Sever, 1974; Gruenwald, 1974; Habicht, Yarbrough, Lechtig, & Klein, 1974b; NAS, 1970). In a population under hypoxic stress, one could hypothesize genetic selection for women who have responded favorably to high-altitude environments during childhood so that they retain an adaptive advantage through their childbearing years. Evidence from a study of recent migrants (i.e., two generations or less) to high altitude in Leadville, Colorado (alt. 3200 m) suggests that women of European low-altitude ancestry may not respond favorably to hypoxic stress when exposed during childhood. The birthweights of their offspring were found to be significantly lower than weights of infants born to high-altitude women who had grown as children at low altitude (Weinstein & Haas, 1977).

Delayed attainment of adult body size at high altitude may prolong the period of physiological maturation and thus compromise the pregnancies of young women who are still growing. In highland Peru, women of 16 or 17 years are within the age of socially prescribed marriage and are capable of conceiving at high altitude. Many first and second pregnancies occur during late teenage years in high-altitude Peruvian native populations (Abelson, Baker, & Baker, 1974); however, since puberty is delayed at high altitude, these women are likely to be at-risk to develop pregnancy complications observed in 14- or 15-year old girls at low altitude. Teenage pregnancies in the United States are at higher risk to fetal death, low birthweight, and infant mortality than the pregnancies of older women (NAS, 1970).

## Female Fertility and Reproduction

Studies of female fertility in the high Andes of Peru and Bolivia (Abelson et al., 1974; Dutt, 1976; Baker & Dutt, 1972; Cruz-Coke, Cristoffanini, Aspillaga, & Biancani, 1966) and the highlands of Nepal (Weitz, Pawson, Weitz, Lang, & Lang, 1979) report reduced fertility of women at high altitudes when compared to low-altitude norms. Just how much of this reduction in fertility is due to reduced fecundity and how much to increased fetal wastage has not been demonstrated due to questions concerning the reporting of early abortions. Several investigators suggest that both factors may be operating (Abelson *et al.*, 1974; Baker & Dutt, 1972; Clegg & Harrison, 1971; Dutt, 1976). Furthermore, there is no information on differential female fertility related to physiological or morphological variation in high-altitude populations.

## Fetal Growth and Development

When conception is achieved at high altitude, there is evidence that the subsequent physical development of the fetus is affected, directly or indirectly, by the high-altitude environment. Specifically, at high altitude, the newborn infant who survives the 266 days of embryonic and fetal development in the uterus of a hypoxically stressed mother is significantly smaller than babies born at low altitude (Haas, Baker, & Hunt, 1977; Lichty, Ting, Bruns, & Dyar, 1957; McClung, 1969; Weinstein & Haas, 1977). Birthweights are approximately 200 to 300 gr lower at high altitude than at low altitude and crown-heel length, crown-rump length, head circumference, and subcutaneous fat thickness are also reduced. These differences in newborn morphology have been reported in Peru (Haas *et al.*, 1977; McClung, 1969), where lower and middle socioeconomic classes were compared at high and low altitudes. Studies by Lichty *et al.*, (1957), Grahn and Kratchman (1963) and Weinstein and Haas (1977) in Leadville, Colorado, at 3200 m altitude, indicate that, even for middle socioeconomic class mothers, birthweights are 300–500 gr lower for high-altitude women than for low-altitude United States women of similar social class.

Researchers in fetal growth recognize the importance of factors other than birthweight in assessing biological maturity at birth (cf. Habicht *et al.*, 1974b). The minimally acceptable research in this area should include the gestational age of the fetus or newborn (Lubchenco, Searls, & Brazie, 1972; Yerushalmy, 1967), since the combination of birthweight and gestational age permits the assessment of prematurity or immaturity in the case of infants weighing less than 2500 gr (Yerushalmy, Van den Berg, Erhardt, & Jacobziner, 1965). McClung (1969) reports, and the recent vital statistics for the state of Colorado (1971, 1972, 1973) confirm, that populations living above 3000 m have two to three times more low-birthweight infants than low-altitude populations. It is essential that these infants be adequately classified as "small-for-date" or "premature," a classification which requires the knowledge of gestational age as well as birthweight. Subsequent postnatal morbidity and mortality risk are clearly different depending on whether the low-birthweight infant is full term but small for gestational age, or preterm and normal for gestational age, or preterm and small for gestational age (Hoffman, Stark, Lundin, & Ashbrook, 1974; Yerushalmy *et al.*, 1965).

Although birthweight is used as a general indicator of neonatal maturity, it may not be adequate to permit the assessment of maturity in the low-birthweight infant. It is a rather crude measure of the end product of fetal growth. Any environmental insult that affects the fetus will be reflected in its birthweight, even though the insult may have little effect on the overall physiological or neurological maturity of the newborn (Amiel-Tison, 1968; Dubowitz, 1974). If natural selection is operating on the newborn, it is probably operating to select against physiological immaturity and not against low birthweight per se, since immaturity could lead to failure to adapt to the extrauterine environment. However, there is some evidence that size at birth, in terms of the relationship between surface area and weight, may have adaptive significance in cold environments (Little & Hochner, 1973). This may be one example of direct selection for a certain range of birthweights under a particular environmental stress.

It is likely that variation in fetal growth at high altitude in the Andes is due in part to maternal phenotypic variation, which is a consequence of each woman's individual adaptation to hypoxic and nutritional stress during her period of growth. Variation in the potential for this type of developmental adaptation for future childbearing may even have a genetic component. Selection could have operated through the differential reproductive success of women who were better able to respond to high-altitude stress during their period of growth by developing an adult phenotype capable of producing relatively more *viable* offspring. The birthweight, the physiological, neurological, and morphological maturity of the neonate, the perinatal and infant morbidity and mortality of the offspring, as well as the placental structures and fertility of the mothers should provide good indications of the relative reproductive capacity of the female at high altitude. Furthermore, these measures of reproductive capacity should vary with the level of maternal adaptation to the high-altitude environment.

## RESEARCH OBJECTIVES

In order to assess the role of maternal adaptation to pregnancy outcome at high altitude, we have been conducting a prospective study of mothers and infants in Bolivia. The major objectives of this study are:

1. To assess whether variations in short-term adult acclimatization, long-term adult acclimatization, developmental acclimatization, and intergenerational or genetic adaptation affect female reproductive success at high altitude

2. To determine the relationship between maternal phenotypic variation and neonatal phenotypic variation associated with maturity and adaptability of infants at high altitude
3. To determine the relationship between birthweight, gestational age, and physiological, neurological, and morphological maturity in the newborn infant at high altitude
4. To determine the relationship between placental structure and neonatal maturity at high altitude
5. To determine the relationship between neonatal phenotypic variation and growth, morbidity, and mortality in the first postnatal year

The major purpose of this chapter is to present the methodology employed to investigate these objectives. Preliminary data analysis has focused on objective number two. Some of these results are presented along with descriptive data in an effort to provide a brief introduction to the nature of the problem we are investigating in Bolivia.

## METHODS AND PROCEDURES

### Research Design

Human biological adaptation to specific environmental stresses has been studied rather extensively in the past 15 years. Many research strategies have been employed in this effort and the research on high-altitude adaptation has produced several original research designs. One strategy proposed by Harrison (1966) and later employed with modification by Abelson et al. (1974) and Haas (1976) has proven very useful in identifying biological responses of native and nonnative populations in contrasting environments.

Harrison's model calls for the comparison of four human populations according to their present altitude of residence and their ancestral history of high-altitude exposure. The four groups are: (a) low-altitude natives living at low altitude; (b) low-altitude natives living at high altitude; (c) high-altitude natives living at high altitude; and (d) high-altitude natives living at low altitude. The comparison of biological responses such as work capacity (maximum oxygen uptake) or other measures of functional adaptation among the four groups permits the assessment of types of responses unique to the various groups in different environments. Presumably, characteristics of high-altitude natives at high altitude that differ from low-altitude natives at high altitude should be related to adaptations of the former group that are not due solely to acclimatization and are thus potentially genetic in nature. The "reversibility" of the high-altitude characteristic can be tested by comparing highland natives at high altitude with highland natives at low altitudes. Similarly, the degree of adaptation of the highlander to a low-altitude environment can be assessed by comparing the highland native at low altitude with the lowlander in his native low-altitude environment.

This model provides a useful approximation of the degree of adaptation of various groups to high-altitude environments. However, certain characteristics of adaptation are intergenerational or developmental in nature but not necessarily related to genetic adaptation. In this regard identifying ancestry as highland or lowland does not resolve the problem of controlling for these other long-term modes of response that may be mistakenly identified as genetic by Harrison's model.

It is clear that place of birth and age of migration of the subjects in the preceding populations (b) and (c) are essential to the interpretation of Harrison's comparative research design. Frisancho and colleagues (Frisancho, 1975; Frisancho, Martinez, Velasquez, Sanchez, & Montoye, 1973a; Frisancho, Velasquez, & Sanchez, 1973b) recognized this and studied lowland residents who moved to high altitude at various ages to identify the important role of developmental adaptation to high altitude. They concluded that much of the improved functional work capacity of highland natives at high altitude was due to adaptations acquired during the period of growth and development. They demonstrated that a similar adaptive response in aerobic capacity can also be observed in lowlanders exposed to high-altitude environments at an early age.

In an attempt to ascertain the importance of developmental adaptations in terms of reproductive success of women at high altitude, Weinstein and Haas (1977) applied Frisancho's research strategy to the study of maternal adaptation and offspring birthweight in Leadville, Colorado. The results of this study, presented in Table 11.1, indicate that lifelong exposure to high altitude does not confer an advantage to the mother when birthweight is used as an indicator of her pregnancy outcome. It should be noted that the "native" women have a maximum of two generations ancestry in Leadville, and that all three groups are representative of the middle socioeconomic class. The best adaptive strategy for maximizing birthweight is for the mother to have been born and to have spent part of her childhood at low altitude before moving to high altitude prior to puberty. Puberty appears to be a sensitive period of exposure to high altitude, but only if a good part of prepubetal growth occurred at low altitude so that the growth-retarding effects of high altitude were avoided. Short- or long-term adult acclimatization does not appear to be important, since no relationship was observed between birthweight of the infant and the mother's length of residence at high altitude. These conclusions about female reproductive success did not agree with Frisancho's conclusions about aerobic capacity in males. It is suspected that growth-retarding intergenerational factors and genetic dif-

TABLE 11.1

Birthweights of Infants Born to Three Groups of Mothers at High Altitude in Leadville, Colorado (3200 m)

| | Birthweight (gm) | Covariance adjusted[a] birthweight (gm) | |
|---|---|---|---|
| | Mean ± SD | Mean | N |
| High-altitude born and raised "native" | 3183 ± 522 | 3174[b] | 83 |
| Low-altitude born–high-altitude raised "child migrant" | 3388 ± 439 | 3419 | 80 |
| Low-altitude born and raised "adult migrant" | 3241 ± 494 | 3242 | 86 |

[a] Adjusted for mother's age, stature, parity, number cigarettes smoked, gestational age, and sex.
[b] Significantly different from "child migrant," $p < .001$, $F = 13.57$.

ferences between European and Andean Indian women contributed to the difference in conclusions.

Therefore, the resolution of the major objective of this research relating maternal adaptation to pregnancy outcome may be achieved through the use of a modified version of Harrison's model, employing characteristics of the research designs of Frisancho and colleagues (Frisancho *et al.*, 1973a, 1973b) and Weinstein and Haas (1977).

The principal characteristic of this research design is that it compares the four populations described by Harrison (1966), but adds the necessary control of different length and age of exposure to high altitude for the lowland native group and different length and age of exposure to low altitude for the high-altitude native group. This permits assessment of the degree of acclimatization to high altitude that results from short-term adult exposure to the new environment, long-term exposure as adults, and long-term exposure of children who are raised, or born and raised, at high altitude. Analysis of this continuum of exposure should permit identification of the maternal adaptive strategy that best ensures the birth of a mature and viable infant at high altitude. The infants born to the group of "best adapted" nonnative mothers would then be compared to the infants born to the native Indian population in order to assess the potential role of genetic adaptation in the Indian population.

For this research design to fulfill the research objectives, it is essential that the study population have certain characteristics:

1. A population living at an altitude high enough (above 3000 m) to impose significant chronic hypoxic stress

2. A population sufficiently heterogeneous in its genetic composition so that samples with long-term (many generations) and short-term (several years) exposure to the high-altitude stress of hypoxia can be identified
3. A long-term resident population that has resided at high altitude for a period of time sufficient for genetic adaptation to have occurred
4. A short-term resident population that varies in length of exposure from several months to several generations, and ages of migration for first generation migrants to high altitude that vary from infancy to 30 years of age
5. A population sufficiently large so that statistically valid analysis of vital statistical data on natality and mortality can be made for a 3- to 5-year birth cohort
6. Accurate civil records of births and infant deaths
7. A population of which a substantial portion of both short-term and long-term ancestry of high-altitude residence, utilizes medical facilities for prenatal care and deliveries.

The population of La Paz, Bolivia meets all of the preceding requirements. In addition, there are available control groups with similar ethnic, socioeconomic, and migration backgrounds living at low altitude in Santa Cruz, Bolivia.

## The Population

The city of La Paz, Bolivia, is located at a mean altitude of 3600 m on the Central Andean Plateau, south of Lake Titicaca (16° 30' S, 68° 15' W). According to preliminary estimates from the 1976 census, the population of La Paz was 750,000. It is the commercial center of Bolivia, and serves as the unofficial seat of government for the country. Its population is heterogeneous in that approximately 75% of the inhabitants are Aymara or Quechua Indians, 15% are *mestizo* or of mixed European and Indian ancestry, and 10% are of European ancestry. Several major hospitals and clinics in the city serve various socioeconomic and ethnic groups and approximately 8000 infants are delivered in these each year. This accounts for approximately 15–30% of all births in the city; the remaining infants are delivered at home, primarily to the poorest segment of the population.

As a result of recent heavy migration from the highlands to the eastern lowlands, there is now a substantial Quechua and Aymara population in the City of Santa Cruz de la Sierra. These Indian populations along with the descendants of the original Spanish settlers and the many recent Argentine, Brazilian, Chilean, and European immigrants to Santa Cruz provide a suitable control population for comparison with the La Paz population. Santa Cruz is located at 400 m above sea level on a semitropical agricultural and cattle herding plain. The city has grown from approximately 40,000 inhabitants in 1950 to over 200,000 (1976 census preliminary estimates) primarily as a result of this massive migration. Public and private hospitals and clinics, similar to those found in La Paz, also exist in Santa Cruz. Approximately 65% of the estimated 15,000 births in the city are delivered in three medical facilities. Two of these hospitals and clinics served as the primary sampling units for the study.

Since the study focused on the effects of high-altitude hypoxia on pregnancy, it was necessary to select subjects whose pregnancies were not complicated by malnutrition or acute infection. These confounding factors could be eliminated or at least controlled in women who attended prenatal clinics and delivered in hospitals or clinics. Since Indian and non-Indian women both utilized these maternity services, it was possible to sample the general obstetric population in both cities to obtain women of different ethnic groups who had comparable prenatal and obstetric care and who were generally free of the severe pregnancy complications that might confound the results of the analysis.

### The Samples

Considering the ethnic and altitude differences and the migration patterns of the Bolivian population, it is possible to identify eight samples of women that would fulfill the previously listed objectives.

The various relationships between all of the samples are presented in Table 11.2. The major divisions of the population are between Indian and European ancestry, altitude of residence, length of altitude exposure, and age of migration to or from high altitude. These criteria are the major ones of concern. The length of residence at high altitude for the European ancestry samples varies from short-term to long-term exposure as an adult (sample 3), to exposure as a child (sample 2), to lifelong exposure (sample 1). Presumably, if acclimatization to high altitude is important to eventual female reproductive success, the mode of adaptation that is most effective (short-term or long-term acclimatization as adults, developmental acclimatization, and exposure at a critical age for children) should be identifiable from measures of pregnancy outcome for each of the three samples.

Genetic differences in reproductive success should be expressed in the comparison of sample 4 with samples 1, 2, or 3, depending on which one of the three represents the "best" acclimatization strategy in terms of reproductive success for the European population. Sample 4 should represent a well-adapted Indian population, which may have benefited from several millennia of natural selection at high altitude and which currently enjoys relatively good prenatal care and a generally improved standard of living when com-

**TABLE 11.2**

Summary of Sample Descriptions

|  | European ancestry (no high-altitude ancestry) | High-altitude Indian ancestry |
|---|---|---|
| High altitude: La Paz (3600 m) | 1. Born and raised at high altitude (lifelong high-altitude exposure) <br> 2. Born at low altitude and migrated to high altitude as a child (variable childhood exposure to high altitude) <br> 3. Born and raised at low altitude and migrated to high altitude as an adult (variable adult exposure to high altitude) | 4. Born and raised at high altitude (lifelong high-altitude exposure) |
| Low altitude: Santa Cruz (400 m) | 5. Born and raised at low altitude (lifelong low-altitude resident) | 6. Born and raised at high altitude and migrated to low altitude as an adult (variable adult exposure to low altitude) <br> 7. Born at high altitude, migrated to low altitude as a child <br> 8. Born and raised at low altitude (lifelong low-altitude resident) |

pared to rural or ancestral populations of the *altiplano*. To complete the research design it was necessary to obtain information on highland women who migrated to lower altitudes at various stages of their life cycle. This would expand the research design by permitting an analysis of a high-altitude phenotype in a low-altitude environment. Samples 5–8 represent these control groups obtained in Santa Cruz.

These four low-altitude samples duplicate to some degree the criteria used to select the high-altitude samples, that is, age at migration to a new environment. However, in this case, the new environment for samples 6, 7, and 8 is a low altitude one that should permit assessment of the reversibility of certain characteristics acquired through genetic adaptation or developmental acclimatization to high altitude. These characteristics will be those which are associated with reproductive success and fetal growth. Analysis of background data from samples 2 and 3 compared to sample 5, and samples 6 and 7 compared to sample 4 may offer some resolution of the question "Are migrants different biologically and socially from the nonmigrants that are left behind?"

## Data Collection

In addition to the sampling format presented in Table 11.2, data were also collected according to a conceptual scheme presented in Figure 11.1. This scheme represents probable causal paths leading to infant survival or reproductive performance which should be optimized under conditions of successful adaptation.

The first level of explanation of reproductive performance is the mother's own ancestry, growth, and current health and nutritional status. These genetic and environmental factors are important, as they interact to produce the maternal phenotype for the particular pregnancy under study.

The maternal phenotype is assessed during the eighth prenatal month when significant stress is placed on the mother to provide an optimal intrauterine environment for fetal growth. During this stage of pregnancy the fetus is growing rapidly and there is great demand on the mother to provide the fetus with nutrients and oxygen. Gruenwald (1975) refers to this stage as a time when the fetus outgrows its maternal supply line so that maternal constraints may alter fetal growth. Maternal phenotypic characteristics which might be related to maternal constraint on fetal growth at this time are divided into three groups: measures of past growth achievement, measures of present level of high-altitude adaptation, and measures of current health and nutritional status. These are not mutually exclusive categories but do represent major areas of maternal effect on pregnancy outcome. The key issue in this research is the importance of phenotypic variation in maternal adaptation to high altitude. It should be recognized that previous growth experience and current health and nutritional status may in part determine the adaptability of the mother to pregnancy at high altitude. Moreover, all three areas of maternal phenotypic variation are probably influenced by genotypic, and past and present environmental variation. Thus, we have a complex, interacting, system which accounts for individual differences in adaptation to pregnancy and population differences in adaptation to high altitude over time.

Placental structure and function play an important role in the interpretation of pregnancy outcome at high altitude. The placenta may be able to compensate for inadequate adaptation on the part of the maternal organism and thus serve as an important mechanism of adaptation for the fetus. On the other hand, maternal maladaptation at high altitude may result in placental pathology which may further compromise fetal growth and newborn viability.

Body size, composition, and maturity are three of the most important predictors of infant growth, morbidity, and mortality, particularly in the neonatal period. These measures also indicate the ability of the mother to

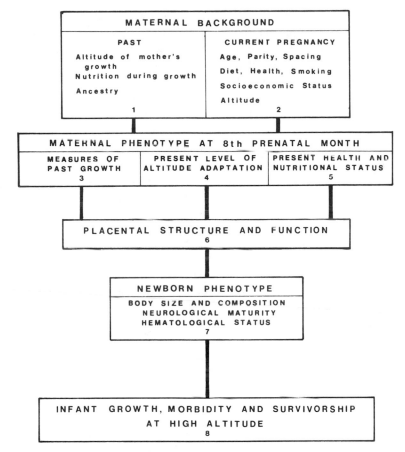

**Figure 11.1** Scheme for interpreting maternal adaptation to high altitude and its role in newborn adaptability.

adapt to that particular high-altitude pregnancy. Variation in the newborn phenotype is therefore an important indicator of population adaptation to high altitude in that it reflects success of fetal growth and predicts potential limitations to growth and survival during the immediate postnatal period.

Considering the sampling design and conceptual scheme previously presented and the framework for data collection and analysis, we now turn to a description of the data-collection procedures that provide the basis for evaluation of the research objectives. The data were collected within the specified sampling format. The high-altitude women chosen delivered their infants in the city of La Paz from September to December 1976, and the low-altitude women in Santa Cruz from July to September 1977. Data were collected longitudinally beginning with the selection of women who attended four prenatal clinics in La Paz and two clinics in Santa Cruz. Pregnant women who were between the thirty-second and thirty-sixth postmenstrual weeks were selected; nearly 70% of all women attending the clinics in La Paz and 55% in Santa Cruz, who were of the appropriate stage of gestation and had received prenatal care since the seventh month, were included in the sample. Since more eligible women attended these clinics than could be examined by our staff, approximately 25% of the total sampling pool in La Paz and 40% in Santa Cruz were excluded on a random basis. The remaining 5% in each population were excluded for reasons such as positive VDRL, severe malnutrition, infections, and hypertension. All of these complications were unrelated to high altitude, but could compromise the mother's participation and the infant's state at birth. Each woman was examined by an obstetrician, measured by one of two trained anthropometrists, and interviewed by a physician. Different medical personnel but the same anthropometrists were employed in the two cities. Table 11.3 presents an outline of the data obtained from this prenatal examination.

These data provide the information needed to evaluate part of the scheme presented in Figure 11.1 dealing with maternal background and maternal phenotypic variation. The numbers in parentheses after items in Table 11.3 refer to the boxes in Figure 11.1 representing: past (1) and current (2) maternal background, past maternal growth (3), present adaptation to high altitude (4), and present health and nutritional status (5). These data are not inclusive of all possible indicators of maternal background and phenotype which might affect pregnancy outcome. We do believe that the major factors are included with the exception perhaps of measures of present altitude adaptation. Ideally, we should have measures of oxygen transport capacity such as oxygen-hemoglobin saturation or oxygen uptake and delivery to the uterine tissues. However, logistic limitations restricted the collection of this type of data in La Paz. We believe that these limitations do not detract from our ability to fulfill the research objectives, but they may restrict our search for mechanisms by which Indian women may have adapted differently than European women to pregnancy at high altitude.

When a woman returned to the clinic for labor and delivery, she was identified as a subject in the study and immediately after delivery a sample of mixed cord blood was collected, and the placenta was saved. The infant was examined by one of three trained individuals between 12 and 30 hr after birth. Table 11.4 presents data collected on the newborn infants. All blood samples (maternal and cord) were transported on ice from the collection sites and either prepared for immediate typing and hematological analysis or frozen for transport back to Cornell University for clinical chemical analysis.

Mothers were given instructions concerning the procedures for postnatal follow-up of their infants. Women who wished to cooperate further were given appointments to bring their child to our examination sites in La Paz and Santa Cruz when the child was 1, 3, 6, 9, and 12 months of age. Infants were examined by four Bolivian pediatricians trained specifically for this project in anthropometry, psychomotor testing, and interviewing. Information listed in Table 11.5 outlines the data collected during these postnatal examinations. These data provide an extensive base for prospective analysis of the correlates of maternal phenotypic variation, fetal growth, and postnatal development. Specific objectives of the research were achieved by applying various methods of analysis to these and complementary data. The following section describes some of this analysis.

## Data Analysis

It is possible to analyze data on maternal adaptation and pregnancy outcome by identifying the eight samples of pregnant women required by the research design. There are at least 28 two-way or paired comparisons of specific samples, at least half of which may be directly applicable to the objectives of this research project. Specifically, sample comparisons answer questions concerning (a) acclimatization strategies for high- and low-altitude migrants, (b) genetic differences in reproductive success, (c) direct effects of altitude on neonatal maturity, and (d) to a lesser extent, direct effects of altitude on assessment of the biological and socioeconomic characteristics of migrants. The first three are of direct importance to the research aims of this project.

Assessment of acclimatization strategies of Europeans in the high-altitude environment (samples 1, 2, 3) and Indians in the low-altitude environment (samples 6, 7, 8) can be made. The two and three sample comparisons are designed to assess the relative importance of duration of exposure, age of migration, and place of birth in predicting pregnancy outcome in a population in a new environment. Identification of the role of these variables as well as the role of prenatal care, smoking, parity, maternal age, weight, stature, and other background information should help in predicting which women are prone to high risk pregnancies.

Levels of maternal acclimatization are assessed indirectly by length of exposure to the environment and directly by the product of her pregnancy, the newborn infant. Maternal adaptation should be linked to history of high-altitude exposure (or low-altitude exposure for the Indian Population) and may be measured in terms of specific clinical and hematological characteristics and anthropometry. Relative neonatal maturity as a measure of the success of maternal adaptation was assessed through specific anthropometry, clinical biochemistry, and neurological and physical indicators. Placental

**TABLE 11.3**

**Data Collected during Eighth Prenatal Month**

---

*Maternal Background*

| | |
|---|---|
| Migration history | Place of birth (1)[a] |
| | Altitude of previous and present residence (1) |
| | Age of migration (1) |
| Socioeconomic status | Family income (2) |
| | Family size (2) |
| | Education (2) |
| | Occupation (2) |
| Health history (1, 2, 5) | |
| Reproductive history | Menarcheal age (2) |
| | Previous pregnancies (2) |
| | Fetal loss (2) |
| | Offspring mortality (2) |
| Ethnic affinities | Languages spoken (1, 2) |
| | Type of clothing (1, 2) |
| | Family names (1) |
| Genetic affinities | Blood groups (1) |
| | Dermatoglyphics (1) |
| Anthropometry | Height (3) |
| | Sitting height (3) |
| | Head circumference (3) |
| | Biacromial diameter (3) |

*Maternal Health and Nutritional Status (current)*

| | |
|---|---|
| Nutritional anthropometry | Triceps skinfold (5) |
| | Mid-upper arm circumferences (3, 5) |
| | Weight (5) |
| Physical examination | Blood pressure (5) |
| | Edema (5) |
| | Fetal position (5) |
| 24-hr dietary recall (2) | |
| Medications and vitamins/mineral supplements noted (2) | |
| Hematology examination | Erythrocyte count (4, 5) |
| | White cell count (5) |
| | Differential count (5) |
| | Reticulocyte count (4, 5) |
| | Hematocrit (4, 5) |
| | Hemoglobin concentration (4, 5) |
| | Corpuscular volumes and concentrations (4, 5) |

---

TABLE 11.3—*Continued*

| *Maternal Health and Nutritional Status (current)* | |
| --- | --- |
| Clinical chemistry | Serum total protein (5) |
| | Serum albumin (5) |
| | Blood urea nitrogen (5) |
| | Transferrin saturation (4, 5) |
| | Free erythrocyte porphorin (4, 5) |
| | Serum ferritin (4, 5) |
| | Serum and red cell folacin (5) |

[a] Numbers in parentheses refer to boxes in Figure 11.1.

analysis also permits some assessment of maternal adaptability to hypoxia for the high-altitude samples.

Weinstein and Haas (1977) utilized a similar version of this research design to assess the importance of developmental adaptation to pregnancy at high

TABLE 11.4

**Data Collected at Delivery**

*Background Data on Labor and Delivery* (5)[a]
Type of delivery
Duration of labor and delivery
Medications
Complications

*Placental Examination* (6)
Morphometry
Macroscopic pathology and structure
Microscopic pathology and structure
Biochemical (DNA, RNA, protein)

*Cord Blood Analysis* (7)
Hematology (including percentage fetal hemoglobin)
Clinical chemistry (glucose, free erythrocyte porphorin)
Blood typing

*Newborn Infant* (7)
Anthropometry
Neurological maturation
Physical development
Body composition
Clinical evaluation
Gestational age estimate (Dubowitz)

[a] Numbers in parentheses refer to boxes in Figure 11.1

**TABLE 11.5**

Data Collected during Postnatal Visits in the First Year (at 1, 3, 6, 9, and 12 Months)

---

*Maternal Health and Nutritional Status* (8)
Nutritional anthropometry (see Table 11.1)
Medications and vitamin–mineral supplements
24-hr dietary recall
Lactation information
Hematology—at 12 month examination only (see Table 11.1)
Clinical chemistry—at 12 month examination only (see Table 11.1)

*Infant Health and Nutrition* (8)
Feeding patterns
Weaning
24-hr dietary recall
Medication and vitamin–mineral supplements
Vaccination history
Health history
Physical examination
Mortality when applicable
Blood analysis—9 and 12 months only
   Hematocrit
   Free erythrocyte porphorin
   Differential counts
Stool analysis for parasites—9 and 12 months only

*Infant Growth and Development* (8)
Anthropometry for achieved growth
Nutritional anthropometry
Dental eruption
Motor development (Bayley)

---

[a] Numbers in parentheses refer to boxes in Figure 11.1.

altitude in Leadville, Colorado (see Table 11.1). Duplication of this research design for the non-Indian women in La Paz should validate those results and provide an analysis of maternal and infant phenotype that is more detailed than was possible in the Leadville retrospective study. In addition, the native non-Indian group in La Paz includes individuals with high-altitude ancestry dating back six or seven generations. Analysis of this group will permit assessment of the role of intergenerational factors which have been hypothesized as an explanation for the smaller infants delivered to "native" Leadville mothers.

The assessment of the role played by genetic differences in reproductive success is the major goal stated in objective 1. After the three groups of European women in La Paz have been identified and the best strategy for acclimatization has been determined, women in the "best acclimatized" group will be compared with the presumably genetically adapted Aymara and Quechua Indian sample in La Paz. For example, comparison of samples 1 and 4 would match women who were all born and raised at high altitude, but belong to genetically different populations. Both groups should have had approximately equal opportunity for developmental adaptation to operate provided there is limited genetic difference in the ability of the two groups to adapt during the developmental period.

The persistence of Indian versus non-Indian differences can also be assessed at low altitude when samples 5 and 6 are compared. Non-Indian women born and raised in Santa Cruz will be compared to Indian women who were born and raised at high altitudes and migrated down to Santa Cruz after puberty. Thus the Indian women would have had an opportunity for developmental acclimatization to high altitude similar to sample 4, but would have experienced none of the ambient hypoxic stress associated with the high-altitude environment during their pregnancy in Santa Cruz. This comparison will permit an evaluation of certain indigenous maternal phenotypic characteristics not lost upon downward migration and therefore considered to be permanent either as a result of genetic or developmental differences (or both) between the highland and lowland populations.

A comparison in Santa Cruz of Indian women who have been born and raised at high altitude (sample 6) and those born and raised at low altitude (sample 8) should help differentiate those maternal phenotypic characteristics that are developmentally molded by the high-altitude environment and those that are more a genetic expression of the highland population.

The following preliminary results will deal with comparisons of maternal and newborn characteristics of samples 1, 4, 5, 6, and 8 in order to evaluate the population-specific maternal phenotypic variation related to fetal growth at high and low altitude.

## Results

Preliminary analysis of the data for these comparisons is presented in Tables 11.6, 11.7, and 11.8. Maternal background data presented in Table 11.6 reflect intersample variation in biological, socioeconomic, and physical environmental factors which are known to be related to fetal growth and pregnancy outcome. In general, the high-altitude women are slightly older and report a higher frequency of spontaneous abortions while the low-altitude groups have a greater range in the frequency of primiparous women. Socioeconomic characteristics of income and education clearly favor the non-Indian samples with the highland non-Indian sample favored over all others. Cigarette smoking during pregnancy was rarely reported by any of the groups.

**TABLE 11.6**

**Maternal Background Information**

| | Santa Cruz (400 m) | | | La Paz (3600 m) | |
| | Non-Indian | Indian | | Non-Indian | Indian |
| | | Low-altitude born | High-altitude born | | |
|---|---|---|---|---|---|
| Sample number[a] | (5) | (8) | (6) | (1) | (4) |
| N | 48 | 35 | 31 | 50 | 41 |
| Altitude of birthplace[b] (m) | 494 ± 483 | 663 ± 637 | 3184 ± 602 | 2650 ± 260 | 3480 ± 410 |
| Altitude of residence[b] (m) | 400 | 400 | 400 | 3661 ± 179 | 3692 ± 180 |
| Age at delivery[b] (years) | 23.8 ± 5.3 | 22.4 ± 4.7 | 23.5 ± 5.5 | 26.2 ± 5.6 | 25.8 ± 5.0 |
| Week of prenatal exam[b] | 35.0 ± 1.8 | 35.2 ± 1.8 | 36.3 ± 1.5 | 33.7 ± 1.7 | 34.2 ± 1.9 |
| Primipara (%) | 33.3 | 22.9 | 48.4 | 38.0 | 36.6 |
| With one or more spontaneous abortions (%) | 20.8 | 20.0 | 12.9 | 34.0 | 24.4 |
| Median monthly income[c] (pesos) | 2275 | 2043 | 2018 | 2700 | 1832 |
| Monthly income above 2800 pesos (%) | 37.5 | 34.3 | 19.7 | 48.0 | 21.9 |
| 9+ years of education (%) | 40.0 | 17.1 | 19.4 | 76.0 | 56.1 |
| Husbands 9+ years of education (%) | 40.0 | 28.6 | 32.1 | 98.0 | 65.9 |
| Smoking over five cigarettes/day (%) | 4.2 | 5.7 | 6.5 | 4.0 | 2.4 |

[a] Sample number refers to samples described in Table 11.2.
[b] Means ± 1 SD.
[c] One U.S. dollar = 20 pesos.

**TABLE 11.7**

**Selected Anthropometric, Hematologic, Biochemical, and Clinical Characteristics of La Paz and Santa Cruz Women during the Eighth Prenatal Month**

| | Santa Cruz (400 m) | | | La Faz (3600 m) | |
| | Non-Indian | Indian Low-altitude born | Indian High-altitude born | Non-Indian | Indian |
| Sample number[a] | (5) | (8) | (6) | (1) | (4) |
|---|---|---|---|---|---|
| Anthropometry | | | | | |
| Stature (cm) | 155.0 ± 4.5 | 152.8 ± 5.4[d] | 150.8 ± 5.2[e] | 153.0 ± 6.0 | 149.8 ± 5.1[f] |
| Biacromial diameter (cm) | 34.7 ± 1.4 | 34.9 ± 1.6 | 34.9 ± 1.7 | 34.5 ± 1.7 | 34.2 ± 1.5 |
| Head circumference (cm) | 53.9 ± 1.3 | 53.8 ± 1.5 | 54.2 ± 1.6 | 53.7 ± 1.6 | 53.9 ± 1.4 |
| Nutritional anthropometry | | | | | |
| Weight = eighth month (kg) | 64.9 ± 7.9[b] | 63.2 ± 8.4 | 63.1 ± 6.5 | 61.1 ± 8.1 | 61.4 ± 7.2 |
| Muscle cross-sectional area (cm²) | 34.9 ± 6.5 | 39.1 ± 6.7[d] | 38.0 ± 12.4 | 34.9 ± 6.5 | 35.3 ± 5.1 |
| Fat cross-sectional area (cm²) | 21.8 ± 7.7 | 20.4 ± 8.9 | 19.3 ± 5.7 | 19.7 ± 6.2 | 19.3 ± 6.4 |
| Triceps skinfold (mm) | 17.8 ± 5.5 | 17.0 ± 5.8 | 16.9 ± 4.9 | 16.7 ± 4.6 | 16.2 ± 4.9 |
| Maternal hematology | | | | | |
| Hematocrit (% PCV) | 36.6 ± 3.2[b] | 37.7 ± 5.2[d] | 35.4 ± 3.2[c] | 43.1 ± 5.7 | 41.2 ± 4.1 |
| Hemoglobin (gm/dl) | 12.0 ± 1.5[b] | 12.0 ± 1.7[d] | 11.4 ± 1.4[c] | 14.1 ± 1.7 | 13.7 ± 1.6 |
| Clinical examination | | | | | |
| Serum total protein (gm/dl) | 6.63 ± .80 | 6.79 ± .45 | 6.57 ± .40 | 6.76 ± .90 | 6.73 ± .78 |
| Serum albumin (gm/dl) | 3.82 ± .22 | 3.73 ± .21 | 3.73 ± .19 | 3.75 ± .47 | 3.82 ± .39 |

[a] Refers to Table 11.2.
[b] Significant altitude differences between samples 1 and 5, $p < .05$.
[c] Significant altitude differences between samples 4 and 6, $p < .05$.
[d] Significant altitude differences between samples 4 and 8, $p < .05$.
[e] Significant ethnic differences between samples 5 and 6, $p < .05$.
[f] Significant ethnic differences between samples 1 and 4, $p < .05$.

**TABLE 11.8**

**Selected Anthropometric, Clinical, and Biochemical Characteristics for La Paz and Santa Cruz Newborns**

| | Santa Cruz (400 m) | | | La Paz (3600 m) | |
| | | Indian | | | Indian |
| | Non-Indian | Low-altitude born | High-altitude born | Non-Indian | Indian |
| | (5) | (8) | (6) | (1) | (4) |
|---|---|---|---|---|---|
| Sample number[a] | | | | | |
| **Anthropometry** | | | | | |
| Weight (gm) | 3330 ± 488[b] | 3427 ± 427[d] | 3507 ± 319[c] | 3056 ± 372 | 3165 ± 428 |
| Crown–heel length (cm) | 49.4 ± 2.1[f] | 50.1 ± 1.7[d] | 50.2 ± 2.1[c] | 48.9 ± 1.7 | 48.9 ± 1.8 |
| Crown–rump length (cm) | 33.3 ± 1.4 | 33.4 ± 1.6 | 33.3 ± .8[c] | 32.8 ± 1.4 | 32.7 ± 1.6 |
| Head circumference (cm) | 34.5 ± 1.2 | 34.6 ± 1.2 | 34.9 ± .9[c] | 34.0 ± 1.1 | 34.2 ± 1.3 |
| Thigh circumference (cm) | 15.7 ± 1.4[b] | 15.8 ± 1.3 | 15.9 ± 1.1 | 15.1 ± 1.3 | 15.5 ± 1.3 |
| Upper arm circumference (cm) | 10.3 ± .8 | 10.3 ± .8 | 10.4 ± .6 | 10.3 ± .7 | 10.4 ± .9 |
| Triceps skinfold (mm) | 3.8 ± 1.2[b] | 4.6 ± 1.5[f] | 4.6 ± 1.2[e] | 4.3 ± .9 | 4.5 ± 1.4 |
| Subscapular skinfold (mm) | 3.9 ± 1.5 | 4.8 ± 1.3[f] | 4.4 ± 1.1 | 4.0 ± 1.1 | 4.4 ± 1.1 |

| | | | | | |
|---|---|---|---|---|---|
| Clinical examination | | | | | |
| Estimated gestation age (days) | 276 ± 4.2 | 273 ± 4.9 | 276 ± 3.5[c] | 275 ± 5.0 | 273 ± 4.6 |
| Dubowitz neurological score | 27.7 ± 2.7 | 26.4 ± 2.9[f] | 28.0 ± 3.0[c] | 27.3 ± 3.0 | 26.4 ± 2.8 |
| Dubowitz clinical score | 26.6 ± 3.0 | 25.5 ± 3.4 | 26.3 ± 2.7 | 26.5 ± 2.9 | 25.8 ± 3.1 |
| Hematology | | | | | |
| Hematocrit (% PCV) | 49.6 ± 5.8[b] | 50.1 ± 7.7 | 51.3 ± 7.3 | 54.2 ± 6.5 | 53.9 ± 6.4 |
| Hemoglobin (gm/dl) | 15.3 ± 1.8[b] | 15.4 ± 1.8[b] | 15.7 ± 1.9[c] | 17.4 ± 2.1 | 17.1 ± 1.7 |
| Fetal hemoglobin (%) | 58.0 ± 11.6[b] | 54.2 ± 11.3[d] | 58.1 ± 11.9 | 66.9 ± 14.0 | 62.6 ± 13.6 |
| Males | 28 | 17 | 19 | 23 | 13 |
| Females | 20 | 18 | 12 | 27 | 28 |

[a] Refers to Table 11.2.
[b] Significant altitude differences between samples 1 and 5, $p < .05$.
[c] Significant altitude differences between samples 4 and 6, $p < .05$.
[d] Significant altitude differences between samples 4 and 8, $p < .05$.
[e] Significant ethnic differences between samples 5 and 6, $p < .05$.
[f] Significant ethnic differences between samples 5 and 8, $p < .05$.

Altitudes of mother's birth and residence vary according to the research sampling criteria. The lower altitude of maternal birthplace for sample 6 compared to samples 1 and 4 reflects the broader altitude range of place of origin for the Indian migrants to Santa Cruz, many of whom come from the high valleys (2600–3500 m) as well as the *altiplano* (3500–4000 m).

Intergroup variation in maternal biological characteristics reported in Table 11.7 is primarily associated with altitude differences, although ethnic differences in stature are apparent. Women who are born and raised at high altitude are shorter than their low-altitude counterparts and Indian women are shorter than non-Indian women. Other measures of past growth such as head circumference and biacromial diameter do not differ among the five groups.

Anthropometric characteristics that reflect current nutritional status indicate a fairly homogeneous pattern. Low-altitude women, especially the non-Indian women, weigh more than their high-altitude counterparts; however, this may be due to the fact that the Santa Cruz prenatal examinations were about 1 to 2 weeks later in the pregnancy than the La Paz exams. Also, the lowland women are taller and have slightly although not significantly more fat and muscle. The lowest values for fat and muscle area observed for these samples are above the value considered as indicative of energy–protein malnutrition reported by Frisancho (1974).

Serum total protein and albumin levels also reflect adequate protein nutritional status. Hemoglobin and hematocrit values reflect the altitude differences reported elsewhere (ICNND, 1964; Sauberlich, Dowdy, & Skala, 1974). These values when compared to published standards indicate that none of the women suffer from anemia.

Altitude differences in infant birthweight as seen in Table 11.8 are of the magnitude reported for other Andean populations (Haas *et al.*, 1977; McClung, 1969; Sobrevilla, 1971). When samples of similar ethnic and socioeconomic compositions are compared, the high-altitude birthweights are from 174 to 342 gr less than their low-altitude counterparts. These altitude differences are statistically significant for all pairwise comparisons. Crown–heel length, crown–rump length, and head circumference also differ significantly between high- and low-altitude Indians. The non-Indian infants at low altitude are significantly smaller in comparison to their highland counterparts on thigh circumference and triceps skinfold. The only other characteristics distinguishing the high- and low-altitude infants are certain hematological measures determined from cord blood samples. Hemoglobin concentration is significantly greater at high altitude for all altitude comparisons, while a significant altitude difference in hematocrit is observed only in the non-Indians. Fetal hemoglobin as a percentage of total hemoglobin is also greater at high altitude.

In order to verify gestational ages calculated from last menstrual period, the Dubowitz examination (Dubowitz, Dubowitz, & Goldberg, 1970) was administered to all infants within 24 hr of delivery. The estimated gestational ages reported in Table 11.7 suggest homogeneity among all groups. No infants were included for data analysis who had an estimated gestation of less than 37 weeks or more than 42 weeks.

Since several factors known to influence birthweight covary among the five groups, it is difficult to determine precisely what influence altitude or ethnic group has on fetal growth. While it is possible to attribute part of the large altitude differences in birthweight reported here to the confounding effects of maternal stature (which is in itself altitude related), most of the other common influences run counter to observed patterns. The altitude trends in mother's age, socioeconomic status, and infants' sex ratio would suggest heavier infants in La Paz, if all other factors, such as altitude, were equal.

The influences of these intervening factors are less clear when one tries to evaluate the smaller ethnic differences in birthweight. Since the assessment of ethnic differences in maternal adaptability to high altitude is one of the primary objectives of this research project, it was necessary to explore this potential ethnic difference more thoroughly through the use of multiple regression analysis. The results of this analysis are presented for birthweight in Table 11.9 and crown–heel length in Table 11.10. The prediction

**TABLE 11.9**

Prediction Equations for Birthweight in La Paz and Santa Cruz

|  | Santa Cruz | | La Paz | |
| --- | --- | --- | --- | --- |
|  | Regression coefficient | $F$ ratio | Regression coefficient | $F$ ratio |
| Gestation age (days) | 35.79 | $19.29^a$ | 36.25 | $19.25^a$ |
| Sex (0 = F, 1 = M) | 152.46 | $4.55^a$ | —$^c$ | —$^c$ |
| Ethnic group (0 = Non-Indian, 1 = Indian) | 184.29 | $5.29^a$ | 154.56 | $4.05^b$ |
| Parity (0 = primiparous, 1 = multiparous) | 96.81 | 1.71 | 107.43 | 1.69 |
| Mother's stature (cm) | 9.70 | 1.58 | —$^c$ | —$^c$ |
| Triceps skinfold (mm) | —$^c$ | —$^c$ | 11.33 | 1.85 |
| Maternal hemoglobin (gm/dl) | —$^c$ | —$^c$ | −44.85 | $3.40^b$ |
| Y intercept | −8101.68 | | −6535.38 | |
| R | .465 | | .493 | |
| df | 5, 107 | | 5, 85 | |
| Uncorrected birthweight (gm) | | | | |
| $\bar{X} \pm SD$ | 3479 ± 413 | | 3105 ± 400 | |

$^a$ Significance, $p < .001$.

$^b$ Significance, $p < .01$.

$^c$ Variables that did not contribute significantly to the regression equation as judged by an $F$ ratio of less than 1.0 when entering the analysis in a stepwise fashion.

**TABLE 11.10**

Prediction Equations for Newborn Crown–Heel Length in Santa Cruz and La Paz

| | Santa Cruz | | La Paz | |
|---|---|---|---|---|
| | Regression coefficient | $F$ ratio | Regression coefficient | $F$ ratio |
| Gestation age (days) | 0.115 | 9.83[a] | .150 | 18.03[a] |
| Sex (0 = F, 1 = M) | 1.240 | 14.86[a] | .428 | 1.40 |
| Ethnic group (0 = Non-Indian, 1 = Indian) | 1.177 | 10.58[a] | .342 | 1.00 |
| Parity (0 = primiparous, 1 = multiparous) | —[c] | —[c] | .508 | 2.14 |
| Mother's stature (cm) | .066 | 3.74[b] | —[c] | —[c] |
| Triceps skinfold (mm) | .044 | 1.95 | —[c] | —[c] |
| Hemoglobin (gm/dl) | —[c] | —[c] | —[c] | —[c] |
| Y intercept | 6.125 | | 7.002 | |
| R | .498 | | .435 | |
| df | 4, 108 | | 4, 86 | |
| Corrected crown–heel length (cm) | | | | |
| $\bar{X} \pm SD$ | 49.97 ± 1.89 | | 48.87 ± 1.71 | |

[a] Significance, $p < .001$.
[b] Significance, $p < .01$.
[c] Variables that did not contribute significantly to the regression equations as judged by an $F$ ratio of less than 1.0 when entering the analysis in a stepwise fashion.

equations generated from this analysis are presented separately for high- and low-altitude samples while the same independent variables were used in the analysis of both altitude groups. The independent variables selected represent the broad range of factors known to affect fetal growth and also shown in Tables 11.6, 11.7, and 11.8 to vary between ethnic groups in each city. Dummy variables were used to permit the inclusion of binary (sex, ethnic group) or nonnormally distributed (parity) variables into the regression model. A stepwise mode for entry of independent variables was employed; the best regression model was considered to have been presented when the maximum $R^2$ was reached after adjustment for degrees of freedom.

Gestation age is the primary predictor of birthweight in both La Paz and Santa Cruz with approximately a 36-gm increase in weight accounted for by each daily increase in gestation between 37 and 42 weeks. Ethnic group is the second most important predictor of weight in both cities. Infants born to indigenous mothers are 184 gm heavier in Santa Cruz and 155 gm heavier in La Paz than infants born to nonindigenous women from the same city. These differences are adjusted for covariation in gestation age, parity, and all other significant independent variables presented for the respective regression equations in Table 11.9.

The importance of maternal hemoglobin concentration in predicting birthweight is much greater in La Paz than in Santa Cruz. In La Paz, one can predict a 45-gm *decrease* in birthweight with each gram *increase* in maternal hemoglobin concentration.

The only other factor significantly contributing to birthweight variation in these equations is sex in the low-altitude sample. Male infants are 152 gm heavier than female infants in Santa Cruz; sex differences in La Paz are not significant.

The regression models predicting crown–heel length differ somewhat from those for weight. In La Paz gestation age is the only significant predictor, while gestation age, sex, ethnic group, and mother's stature are significant predictors in the regression model for Santa Cruz.

## DISCUSSION

This analysis confirms previously reported observations of altitude differences in maternal and newborn phenotype (Haas *et al.*, 1977; McClung, 1969). However, the analysis of extensive data on maternal phenotypic variation in relation to fetal growth at high altitude has not been reported in these earlier studies. One of the most significant findings is the ethnic differences in birthweight observed in both Santa Cruz and La Paz. Considering the poor socioeconomic situation (SES) under which the Indian women live, the fact that their infants are larger than infants born to the higher SES non-Indian women requires further explanation. Such factors as gestation age, parity, sex, and mother's stature and upper arm soft tissue composition have been controlled in this analysis, but the significant ethnic differences in birthweight persist. If birthweight variation in a population can be inferred to be related to the quality of the intrauterine environment and the mother's supply line to the growing fetus (Gruenwald, 1975), then the analysis of variation in birthweight reported here would suggest a more favorable maternal–fetal supply line among the Indian population compared to the non-Indian population in Santa Cruz and La Paz.

This ethnic difference in La Paz may reflect a better state of adaptation to the high-altitude environment by the Indian women who have had an extensive history of exposure to the high Andean *altiplano* environment. In contrast, the non-Indian mothers in La Paz had similar opportunities as the Indian mothers to adapt to the environment during their own lifetime, but lacked the extensive high-altitude ancestry. As a consequence, the capacity to adapt to the high-altitude environment during either the developmental or adult period may be quite different for the two populations, especially if the Indian women represent a population that has been selected over several hundred generations for their adaptability to this stressful environment.

It is interesting that larger babies continue to be delivered to Indian women at low altitude where such high altitude stresses as hypobaric hypoxia are removed. If the ethnic differences are due to the Indian women being better adapted to the high-altitude environment, why should the differences persist when the stress is removed upon migration to low altitude? One explanation may lie in the fact that even at low altitude, variation in fetal growth should be related to the ability of the mother to adapt to the demands of pregnancy. The superior oxygen transport in the Indian mothers, which we hypothesize to be the result of natural selection and lifelong altitude exposure, may confer an advantage to these highland women even after they migrate to low altitude. This adaptability may be particularly apparent when the oxygen transport system and fetal supply line are stressed during the last months of gestation.

If this ethnic difference in fetal growth at low altitude is attributable to a greater adaptability for the Indian women, the adaptability is probably not totally a genetic characteristic of the population. Since Indian women who are born and raised at high altitude deliver slightly heavier infants than Indian women who are born and raised at low altitude, it is likely that developmental adaptations to high altitude play an important role in this cross-adaptation to pregnancy at low altitude.

If we turn our attention to the prediction of birthweight and newborn recumbent length at high and low altitude, there are several additional observations to be made beyond the role of ethnic variation. First, sex differences in fetal growth are more important predictors of birthweight at low altitude than at high altitude. This supports the observations made by several investigators (Haas, 1974; Haas et al., 1977; Stini, 1969) that females growing under poor conditions of malnutrition or high altitude may be better buffered against biological stress than males. Male infants are normally larger than female infants at birth. However, at high altitude the lack of sex difference may reflect a more "canalized" fetal growth pattern for female infants whose development is not affected by intrauterine stress as much as the male infant.

Second, gestation length (age) appears to have similar effects on fetal growth in both altitude groups. This appears to contradict earlier findings that altitude differences in birthweight in Peru (Haas et al., 1977) and the United States (McCullough, Reeves, & Liljergren, 1977; Weinstein & Haas, 1977) are primarily due to a slowing of fetal growth in the last few weeks of gestation. If one can infer fetal growth rates from these cross-sectional data, it is interesting that the La Paz and Santa Cruz fetuses grow at a rate of about 245 g/week during the last 3 weeks of gestation. This is a growth rate that is comparable to or exceeds the rates computed from other cross-sectional samples of newborns in more developed countries (Gruenwald, 1975). This apparent maintenance of a substantial fetal growth rate at high altitude is further supported by the lack of significant altitude differences in skinfold thickness. Haas *et al.* (1977) and McClung (1969) report lesser adipose deposition at high altitude in Peru, and attribute the lower birthweights, in part, to reduced fat accumulation which normally occurs during late gestation. The fact that the La Paz infants are shorter in crown–heel length as well as lighter in weight than the Santa Cruz infants suggest a more chronic suppression of fetal growth at high altitude which may extend back to the second trimester of gestation. Further interpretation of these data must await the analysis of gestation age variation in a regression model that combines high- and low-altitude samples, as well as analysis of the interrelationships of various fetal growth measures.

A third observation relates to the altitude differences in several maternal and fetal hematological characteristics. As a result of hematological studies on sheep (Barron, Metcalf, Meschia, Huckebee, Hellegers, & Prystowsky, 1964) and humans (Howard, Bruns, & Lichty, 1957) and a study of human newborn blood gases (Sobrevilla, 1971), it has been suggested that the high-altitude fetus may not be any more hypoxic at high altitude than at low altitude. The data reported here showing elevated hemoglobin concentrations and percentage fetal hemoglobin in the cord blood of La Paz infants would suggest that a significant degree of fetal hypoxia exists in late gestation at high altitude. This hematological pattern in La Paz suggests that hematopoiesis and maintenance of the strong oxygen-binding fetal hemoglobin may be compensation for reduced oxygen tension at the placenta.

The inverse relationship between maternal hemoglobin concentration and birthweight in La Paz also requires further examination. If increased maternal hematopoiesis is an adaptive response to high altitude, as is commonly believed, then why would women with higher hemoglobin concentrations deliver smaller infants? One explanation for this observation requires a reevaluation of the role of hematological responses to hypoxia. Better adapted women should be able to transport more oxygen to the uterine arteries with greater physiological efficiency, that is with less physiological strain to any one link in the complex chain of oxygen delivery. One link in that chain is hematopoiesis, and reduced demand on erythrocyte formation would reflect a more adaptive state, especially if iron or folic acid is limited in the diet. It could be hypothesized that better adapted women at high altitude, who are not anemic, deliver larger infants at a lesser physiological strain to hematopoiesis than poorly adapted women. Support for this hypothesis comes from a more complete analysis of maternal iron status and hematological relationships to birthweight in Indian and non-Indian samples in La Paz (Haas, Small, Beard, & Hurtado, 1980) where regression equations predicting birthweight from maternal hemoglobin are compared for the two ethnic groups. After controlling for transferrin saturation, there is no relationship between hemoglobin and birthweight in the Indian sample, however, a significant negative regression is shown for the non-Indian sample. This negative relationship is interpreted as an 80-g decrease in birthweight for each gram per deciliter increase in hemoglobin concentration. It appears as if the Indian sample is more homogeneous in its hematological response to hypoxia during pregnancy while there is a great deal of variation in this response among the non-Indians. Moreover, the hemoglobin-to-birthweight relationship in the non-Indian sample suggests that there are both well-adapted and poorly adapted women who represent the opposite extremes of the birthweight and hemoglobin distributions.

## CONCLUSIONS

While many of these results are preliminary, we are able to see clear trends in the data that indicate some potential application to expanding our understanding of human adaptation and to the identification of high-risk pregnancies at high altitude. Practical application of the results of this study may serve to alleviate a major health problem, affecting a population estimated at 25 million residing at altitudes above 3000 m (DeJong, 1970). Nearly all of these 25 million persons reside in less developed countries in which undernutrition and chronic infectious disease prevent the achievement of even a modest standard of living. The combined effects of these stresses create particular risk for the pregnant woman and the young infant. We are hopeful that the identification of the role of one of these stresses, hypoxia, as it affects reproductive performance and infant growth will contribute to our identification of high-risk mothers and infants at high altitude.

The classic studies of human adaptation to environmental stress among non-Western societies deal primarily with adaptive responses that maintain "functional capacity." "Functional capacity" usually pertains to work capacity and production or acquisition of food by the male segment of the society. The present research adds to the anthropological study of adaptation by expanding the view of "functional capacity" to include the "reproductive capacity" of the female segment of the population. In this context, one can propose an adaptive strategy that could have operated in the high Andes over the past 6000–8000 years. This strategy may have operated through maternal adaptation to her environment during growth, conferring a reproductive advantage in terms of increased fecundity, fertility, and the delivery of a more physically mature newborn who is less likely to die in the first postnatal year. A demonstration of the unique utilization of this strategy by the high-altitude Aymara and Quechua of Bolivia when compared to a European population exposed for a lifetime to the same high-altitude stress would be a strong indicator of genetic adaptation on the part of the indigenous population.

## ACKNOWLEDGMENTS

I would like to thank Dr. Luis Hurtado Gomez for his help and advice in conducting this research. Special acknowledgement goes to the field research team who assisted in data collection and analysis. They include: Cipriana Apaza, Stephen Bailey, John Beard, Ed Frongillo, Susan Gregg, Sharon Haas, Norma de Hurtado, Jose Muñoz, Victor Ortuño, Javier Pabon, Fanny Parada, Gerardo Pareja, Wilma Sandoval, Dan Small, Carol Stepick, Olga Suarez, and Jorge Ybarnegaray. I am grateful to the Bolivia Ministry of Health, Instituto Nacional de Laboratorios de Salud, Instituto Boliviano de Biologia de la Altura, Centro Nacional de Enfermedades Tropicales and the hospitals in La Paz and Santa Cruz for their invaluable help during the collection of data. This material is based upon work supported by the National Science Foundation under Grant BNS 76-12312. Any opinions, findings, conclusions or recommendations expressed in this publication are those of the author and do not necessarily reflect the views of the National Science Foundation. This is a report of research of the Cornell University Agricultural Experiment Station, Division of Nutritional Sciences.

## REFERENCES

Abelson, A. E., Baker, T. S., & Baker, P. T. Altitude, migration and fertility. *Social Biology*, 1974, *21*, 12–27.

Amiel-Tison, C. Neurological evaluation of the maturity of newborn infants. *Archives of Diseases of Childhood*, 1968, *43*, 89–93.

Baird, D. Epidemiology of congenital malformations of the central nervous system in (a) Aberdeen and (b) Scotland. *Journal of Biosocial Science*, 1974, *6*, 113–137.

Baker, P. T., & Dutt, J. S. Demographic variables as measures of biological adaptation: A case study of high altitude human populations. In G. A. Harrison & A. Boyce (Eds.), *The structure of human populations*. Oxford: Clarendon Press, 1972. Pp. 352–378.

Baker, P. T., & Little, M. A. (Eds.). *Man in the Andes: A multidisciplinary study of high altitude Quechua*. Stroudsberg, Pa.: Dowden, Hutchinson & Ross, 1976.

Barron, D. H., Metcalf, J., Meschia, G., Huckebee, W., Hillegers, A., & Prystowsky, H. Adaptation of pregnant ewes and their fetuses to high altitudes. In W. H. Weihe (Ed.), *The physiological effects of high altitude*. New York: Pergamon Press, 1964.

Beall, C. M. *The effects of high altitude on growth, morbidity and mortality of Peruvean infants*. Unpublished doctoral dissertation, The Pennsylvania State University, 1976.

Beall, C. M., Baker, P. T., Baker, S. T., & Haas, J. D. The effects of high altitude on adolescent growth in southern Peruvian Amerindians. *Human Biology*, 1977, *49*, 109–124.

Birch, H., & Gussow, D. *Disadvantaged children: Health, nutrition and school failure.* New York: Harcourt Brace, 1970.

Bouloux, C. J. Contribution a 'etude biologique des phenomenes pubertaires en tres haute altitude. *Mongraphies du Centre D'hemotypologie*, C. H. U. de Toulouse, Hermann.

Clegg, E. J., & Harrison, G. A. Reproduction in human high altitude populations. *Hormones*, 1971, *2*, 13–25.

Colorado Vital Statistics. *1971 annual report of vital statistics, Colorado.* Denver: Colorado Department of Health, Division of Administrative Services, Records and Statistics Section.

Colorado Vital Statistics. *1972 annual report of vital statistics, Colorado.* Denver: Colorado Department of Health, Division of Administrative Services, Records and Statistics Section.

Colorado Vital Statistics. *1973 annual report of vital statistics, Colorado.* Denver: Colorado Department of Health, Division of Administrative Services, Records and Statistics Section.

Cruz-Coke, R., Cristoffanini, A. P., Aspillaga, M., & Biancani, F. Evolutionary forces in human populations in an environmental gradient in Arica. *Human Biology*, 1966, *38*, 421–438.

DeJong, G. F. Demography and research with high altitude populations. *Social Biology*, 1970, *17*, 114–119.

Drillien, C. M. The social and economic factors affecting the incidence of premature birth. *Journal of Obstretrics and Gynecology of the British Empire*, 1957, *64*, 161–184.

Dubowitz, V. Infants of inappropriate size. In K. Elliott & J. Knight (Eds.), *Size at birth*. Ciba Foundation Symposium, No. 27, Association Scientific Publication, Amsterdam, 1974. Pp. 47–64.

Dubowitz, L. M. S., Dubowitz, V., & Goldberg, C. Clinical assessment of gestation age in the newborn infant. *Journal of Pediatrics*, 1970, *77*, 1–10.

Dutt, J. S. *Altitude and fertility: The Bolivian case. Unpublished doctoral dissertation*, The Pennsylvania State University, 1976.

Emanuel, I., & Sever, L. E. Questions concerning the possible association of potatoes and neural-tube defects and an alternative hypothesis relating to maternal growth and development. *Teratology*, 1974, *8*, 325–329.

Frisancho, A. R. Triceps skinfolds and upper arm muscle size norms for assessment of nutritional status. *American Journal of Clinical Nutrition*, 1974, *27*, 1052–1058.

Frisancho, A. R. Functional adaptation to high altitude hypoxia. *Science*, 1975, *187*, 313–319.

Frisancho, A. R., & Baker, P. T. Altitude and growth: A study of the patterns of physical growth of a high altitude Peruvian Quechua population. *American Journal of Physical Anthropology*, 1970, *32*, 279–292.

Frisancho, A. R., Martinez, C., Velasquez, T., Sanchez, J., & Montoye, H. Influence of developmental adaptation on aerobic capacity at high altitude. *Journal of Applied Physiology*, 1973, *34*, 176–190. (a)

Frisancho, A. R., Velasquez, T., & Sanchez, J. Influences of developmental adaptation on lung function at high altitude. *Human Biology*, 1973, *44*, 583–594. (b)

Grahn, D., & Kratchman, J. Variation in neonatal death rate and birth weight in the United States and possible relations to environmental radiation, geology and altitude. *American Journal of Human Genetics*, 1963, *15*, 329–352.

Gruenwald, P. Pathology of the deprived fetus and its supply line. In K. Elliott & J. Knight (Eds.), *Size at birth*. Ciba Foundation Symposium No. 27, Association of Scientific Publications, Amsterdam, 1974. Pp. 3–19.

Gruenwald, P. (Ed.). *The placenta and its maternal supply line.* Baltimore, Md.: University Park Press, 1975.

Haas, J. D. *Altitudinal variation and infant growth and development in Peru.* Unpublished doctoral dissertation, The Pennsylvania State University, 1973.

Haas, J. D. Variation in the pattern of sexual dimorphism of infants under environmental stress (abstract). *American Journal of Physical Anthropology*, 1974, *41*, 483.

Haas, J. D. Prenatal and infant growth and development. In P. T. Baker & M. A. Little (Eds.), *Man in the Andes: A multidisciplinary study of high altitude Quechua.* Stroudsburg, Pa.: Dowden Hutchinson & Ross, 1976. Pp. 161–179.

Haas, J. D. Baker, P. T., & Hunt, E. E., Jr. The effects of high altitude on body size and composition of the newborn infant in Southern Peru. *Human Biology*, 1977, *49*, 611–628.

Haas, J. D., Small, D. A., Beard, J. L., & Hurtado, L. Variacion en hemoglobina materna y peso al nacer en las grandes alturas. *Revista del Instituto Boliviano de Biologia de le Altura* (La Paz), 1980.

Habicht, J-P., Yarbrough, C., Lechtig, A., & Klein, R. E. Relation of maternal supplementary feeding during pregnancy to birth weight and other sociobiological factors. In M. Winick (Ed.), *Nutrition and fetal development.* New York: Wiley, 1974. Pp. 127–147.

Harrison, G. A. Human adaptability with reference to the IBP proposals for high altitude research. In P. T. Baker & J. S. Weiner (Eds.), *The biology of human adaptability.* Oxford: Clarendon Press, 1966. Pp. 509–520.

Hoff, C. A., Baker, P. T., Haas, J. D., Garruto, R. M., & Specter, R. Variaciones altitudinales en el crecimiento y desarrollo fisicos del Quechua Peruana. *Revista del Instituto Boliviano de Biologia de la Altura* (La Paz), 1974, *4*, 5–20.

Hoffman, H. J., Stark, C. R., Lundin, F. E., & Ashbrook, J. D. Analysis of birth weight, gestational age, and fetal viability. U.S. Births, 1968. *Obstretics and Gynecology Survey*, 1974, *29*, 651–681.

Howard, R. C., Bruns, P. D., & Lichty, J. A. Studies of babies born at high altitude. III. Arterial oxygen saturation and hematocrit values at birth. *American Journal of Diseases of Children*, 1957, *93*, 674–677.

ICNND. *Bolivia: Nutrition survey.* Washington, D.C.: Interdepartmental Committee for Nutrition and National Defense, U.S. Department of Defense, 1964.

Lichty, J. A., Ting, T. Y., Bruns, P. D., & Dyar, E. Studies of babies born at high altitude. I. Relation of altitude to birth weight. *American Journal of Diseases of Children*, 1957, *93*, 666–669.

Little, M. A., & Hochner, D. H. Human thermoregulation, growth and evolution. *Addison-Wesley Module in Anthropology No. 36.* Reading, Ma.: Addison-Wesley Publishing, 1973.

Lubchenco, L. O., Searls, D. T., & Brazie, J. V. Neonatal mortality rate: Relationship to birth weight and gestational age. *Journal of Pediatrics*, 1972, *81*, 814–822.

Mazess, R. B. Human adaptation to high altitude. In A. Damon (Ed.), *Physiological anthropology.* New York: Oxford University Press, 1975. Pp. 167–209.

McClung, J. *Effects of high altitude on human birth.* Cambridge, Ma.: Harvard University Press, 1969.

McCullough, R. E., Reeves, J. T., & Liljergren, R. L. Fetal growth retardation and increased infant mortality at high altitude. *Obstetric and Gynecology Survey*, 1977, *32*, 596–598.

NAS. *Maternal nutrition and the course of pregnancy.* Washington, D.C.: National Academy of Sciences, 1970.

Peñaloza, J. B. *Crecimiento y desarrollo sexual del adolescente andino.* Unpublished doctoral dissertation. Lima, Peru: Universidad Nacional Mayor de San Marcos, 1971.

Sauberlich, H. E., Dowdy, R. P., & Skala, J. H. *Laboratory tests for the assessment of nutritional status.* Cleveland: C.R.C. Press, 1974.

Sobrevilla, L. A. *Nacer en los Andes: Estudios fisiologicos sobre el embarzo y parto in la altura.* Unpublished doctoral thesis, Universidad Peruana Cayetano Heredia, Instituto de Investigaciones de la Altura, Lima, Peru, 1971.

Stini, W. A. Nutritional stress and growth: Sex differences in adaptive response. *American Journal of Physical Anthropology,* 1969, *31,* 417–426.

Tanner, J. M. Growth and physique in different populations of mankind. In P. T. Baker & J. S. Weiner (Eds.), *The biology of human adaptability.* Oxford: Clarendon Press, 1966. Pp. 45–66.

Weinstein, R. S., & Haas, J. D. Early stress and later reproductive performance under conditions of malnutrition and high altitude hypoxia. *Medical Anthropology,* 1977, *1,* 25–54.

Weitz, C. A., Pawson, I. G., Weitz, M. V., Lang, S. D. R., & Lang, A. Cultural factors affecting the demographic structure of a high altitude Nepalese population. *Social Biology,* 1979, *25,* 179–195.

Yerushalmy, J. The classification of newborn infants by birth weight and gestation age. *Journal of Pediatrics,* 1967, *71,* 164–172.

Yerushalmy, J., Van den Berg, B. J., Erhardt, C. L., & Jacobziner, H. Birth weight and gestation as indices of "immaturity." *American Journal of Diseases of Children,* 1965, *109,* 43–57.

# 12

# A Factor Analysis of Correlates of Nutritional Status in Mexican Children, Birth to 3 Years[1]

FRANCIS E. JOHNSTON, BRUCE NEWMAN,
JOAQUIN CRAVIOTO, ELSA DELICARDIE, AND
THERESA SCHOLL

## INTRODUCTION

Human nutritional ecosystems consist of complex clusters of interacting variables. Some of these variables influence nutritional status directly, acting upon an individual in a straightforward manner. Others, however, exert their influence indirectly, acting through the web of interrelationships which exist. One of the primary problems confounding the interpretation of research is difficulty in determining the extent to which a given correlate of nutritional status acts, within the ecosystem, directly or indirectly (see e.g., the discussion in Cravioto, Birch, & DeLicardie, 1967).

A related problem is the development of predictors of disturbed nutritional status in human populations. Many investigators have described the patterns of physical growth and maturation of children from communities exhibiting nutritional deficiencies (Blanco, Acheson, Canosa, & Salomon, 1972; Burgess & Burgess, 1964; Frisancho & Garn, 1971). Others have

[1]Supported in part by the Nutrition Foundation, the Foundation for Child Development, the Van Amergin Foundation, Carnation de Mexico, S.A., and USPHS Grant HD-AM 08939.

**291**

identified correlates of these patterns from the socioeconomic, demographic, and health-related variables that were measured. For example, Kanawati and McLaren (1973) compared Lebanese children diagnosed as failing-to-thrive to the other children in a community. Environmental correlates of failure to thrive were identified from a long list of observations by means of a $\chi^2$ analysis. Although such an analysis detected specific variables associated with this condition, it could not provide any information on causation, or on which were directly related and which were merely statistically significant correlates. Univariate statistics will never provide such information when applied to complex and interacting data sets.

There have been virtually no attempts to reduce the mass of data collected by investigators studying nutritional ecosystems to a simplified data set which would reflect some underlying structure. Not only would this simpler set provide us with a more parsimonious group of indicators, it could also help to understand better the structure of a nutritional ecosystem and the ways in which the components act in determining nutritional status.

In this chapter, we present one approach to data reduction growing out of a study of a single community exhibiting signs of nutritional stress. Our purpose is to produce a more realistic set of correlates of nutritional status as well as a set that reflects the operation of underlying factors in a more meaningful way than by employing univariate statistical procedures, or even simple bivariate techniques. To a large extent, the approach is still exploratory, so that the results are suggestive more than they are conclusive. Nonetheless, it is hoped that the methodology, as well as the results of the analysis, will help to shed light upon those factors that determine nutritional status in human communities and the interactions that exist among them, as well as to stimulate other investigators to employ more sophisticated and promising methods than have generally characterized previous efforts.


## STUDY DESIGN


### Study Population

The data presented here come from a large and comprehensive longitudinal study of a community in the state of Morelos, south of Mexico City, referred to as the 'Land of the White Dust' (*El Lugar de la Tierra Blanca*). The community is located in the *tierra caliente* zone at an altitude of 950 m above mean sea level; the climate permits an almost continual agricultural cycle. Sixty-five percent of the adult male population is engaged in agriculture, the majority as *jornaleros*, or 'day laborers', who neither own nor rent land.

The study was initiated by one of us (J.C.) and the design and general methodology have been described elsewhere (Cravioto, Birch, de Licardie, Rosales, & Vega, 1969; Cravioto, DeLicardie, & Birch, 1966). The study focuses on a cohort of children. Every child born in the village between February 1966 and February 1967 was enrolled; this amounted to 324 subjects. Twelve children, whose parents moved into the community during the child's infancy, were added to the group. Sixty of the cohort are not included in the study because their parents declined to participate or because they moved away. The final sample size was therefore 276.

The demographic and socioeconomic profiles, as well as the patterns of physical growth, have been described by Cravioto et al. (1969) and Scholl (1975). The profiles of the study cohort do not differ to any significant extent from those of the entire community. Family incomes are minimal and, in 1966, the great majority of families earned between 450 and 8500 pesos per year. The median daily income was equivalent to 35¢ (U.S.). Much of this income is spent for food and, in the late 1960s, the median family expenditure for food was 44% of total income. Literacy and educational levels were low, with over 40% of the mothers and 25% of the fathers classed as illiterate.

Infant mortality had been high. In 1965 the infant mortality rate in the community was 96.5/1000. Mortality among cohort infants occurred at a rate of 63.0/1000, the lower figure probably a consequence of the extensive medical and social care introduced along with the study.

None of the above figures differ remarkably from those of rural Mexico as a whole during this period. This suggests that the "Land of the White Dust" is representative of the bulk of the small preindustrial communities located throughout the country.

## Measurements

All infants were measured at birth and then monthly for the first 3 years of life; from 4 through 6 years of age they were measured six times per year. The measurements taken included length, weight, head and chest circumference, upper arm circumference, and the thickness of the triceps skinfold. Morbidity histories were obtained every 2 weeks. The heights and weights of the parents were measured shortly after the birth of the cohort infant. In 1974, one of us (T.S.) measured parental triceps and subscapular skinfolds, arm circumferences, and biacromial and bicristal diatemeters. Upper arm muscle circumference was calculated from arm circumference and triceps skinfold: circumference $-\pi$(triceps).

A battery of socioeconomic and demographic data was collected at the onset of the study. Included is information on family income, demography, exposure to mass media, household inventory and sanitation, parental education and personal hygiene, and the reproductive history of the mother. Finally, there are cognitive and other psychometric data, hand-wrist radiographs, taken at 4, 5, and 6 years of age, and a record of the child's dietary intake on his or her second birthday.

## DATA ANALYSIS

All data have been put onto magnetic tape for high-speed multivariate analysis. However, the results presented here cover only the growth of the children in their first 3 years of life. The descriptive statistics of the growth parameters may be found in Scholl (1975), along with an analysis of their correlation with environmental variables. In general, the mean lengths and weights of the children fall below the tenth percentiles of the familiar North American reference standards, especially after the first year of life (Figures 12.1 and 12.2).

In the present analysis we have selected 40 variables to be related to nutritional status. Nutritional status is here represented by the individual's physical growth from birth until 1080 days (i.e., 3 years). These variables are

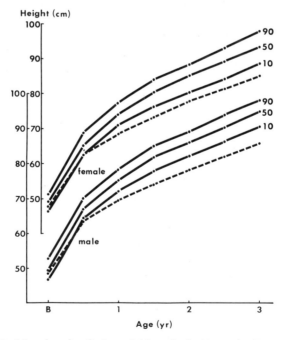

Figure 12.1    Mean lengths of cohort children, birth–36 months (Denver standards).

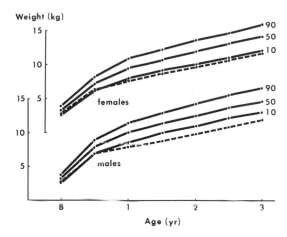

**Weight (kg)**

Figure 12.2   Mean weights of cohort children, birth–36 months (Denver standards).

listed in Table 12.1; they include information on the parent's socioeconomic status, demography, body size, and on the mother's reproductive history. We have also included various data on the number of days a child was reported to be ill with particular symptoms (Condon-Paoloni, Cravioto, Johnston, de Licardie, & Scholl, 1977), as well as the estimated energy intake, in calories, at 24 months of age.

We performed a principal component analysis of the intercorrelation matrix of these 40 variables, using the program package provided by the Statistical Analysis System, SAS-76 (Barr, Goodnight, Sall, & Helwig, 1976). The analysis was taken through one Varimax rotation and the first five factors, presented in Table 12.2, were retained for analysis. These factors collectively accounted for 44.8% of the variance among the 40-variable matrix.

Those variables that loaded the highest on each factor were utilized in the subsequent analysis. They are given in Table 12.3. The proportion of the variance of each factor explained by the variables retained ranged from 82% for Factor 5 to almost 94% for Factor 3.

## RESULTS

The interpretation of each of the five factors retained is straightforward. Factor 1 is a general socioeconomic (SES) factor, with variables such as family income, income spent on food, and parental education and hygiene loading high upon it. Factor 2 loads highest on variables reflecting the mother's reproductive history and the mortality experience of all of her offspring. Factors 3 and 4 indicate the body size of the mother and the father,

**TABLE 12.1**

**Variables Utilized in Factor Analysis**

Annual expenditure on food
Annual expenditure on nonfood items
Percentage of income spent on food
Father's education
Mother's education
Father's hygiene score
Mother's hygiene score
Sanitation score of household
Mother's age at marriage
Years in marital union
Number of live births
Total abortions and stillbirths
Number of children dying, 3–15 years
Number of infants dying, birth–1 month
Number of infants dying, 1–36 months
Family size
Caloric intake of child at 24 months
Days ill, diarrhea, birth–12 months
Days ill, diarrhea, 12–24 months
Days ill, diarrhea, 24–36 months
Days ill, upper respiratory, birth–12 months
Days ill, upper respiratory, 12–24 months
Days ill, upper respiratory, 24–36 months
Days ill, lower respiratory, birth–12 months
Days ill, lower respiratory, 12–24 months
Days ill, lower respiratory, 24–36 months
Mother's height
Mother's weight
Mother's biacromial diameter
Mother's bicristal diameter
Mother's triceps skinfold
Mother's subscapular skinfold
Mother's upper arm circumference
Father's height
Father's weight
Father's biacromial diameter
Father's bicristal diameter
Father's triceps skinfold
Father's subscapular skinfold
Father's upper arm circumference

**TABLE 12.2**

Results of Principal Component Analysis

| | Factor 1 | Factor 2 | Factor 3 | Factor 4 | Factor 5 |
|---|---|---|---|---|---|
| Nonfood expenditure | .775 | −.063 | .143 | .035 | −.024 |
| Food expenditure | .746 | −.097 | .128 | .071 | −.011 |
| Father's education | .713 | .008 | −.176 | −.074 | −.064 |
| Mother's education | .693 | −.075 | −.219 | −.217 | −.009 |
| Father's hygiene | .576 | −.067 | −.176 | −.049 | −.075 |
| Sanitation score | .565 | −.091 | −.038 | −.232 | −.060 |
| Mother's hygiene | .483 | .029 | .000 | −.114 | −.217 |
| Percentage income on food (−) | −.463 | .024 | −.158 | .207 | −.056 |
| Total live births | −.039 | −.056 | .926 | −.015 | .036 |
| Years married | −.104 | −.045 | .928 | −.058 | −.037 |
| Maternal age | .029 | −.026 | .904 | −.090 | .007 |
| Infant deaths, birth to 1 month | −.018 | −.089 | .342 | .155 | −.298 |
| Infant deaths, 1–36 months | −.063 | .011 | .455 | .072 | .241 |
| Child deaths, 3–15 years | −.141 | .003 | .460 | .074 | .258 |
| Abortions and stillbirths | .057 | .009 | .479 | .018 | −.041 |
| Mother's upper arm circumference | .058 | −.864 | .069 | −.120 | .005 |
| Mother's subscapular skinfold | .061 | −.803 | .018 | −.065 | .037 |
| Mother's triceps skinfold | .057 | −.845 | .014 | −.122 | −.003 |
| Mother's weight | .039 | −.790 | .140 | −.040 | .029 |
| Mother's height | .130 | −.411 | −.132 | −.071 | .003 |
| Mother's biacromial diameter | −.018 | −.498 | .043 | −.104 | −.000 |
| Mother's bicristal diameter | .141 | −.690 | .005 | .073 | .058 |
| Father's upper arm circumference | .119 | −.119 | −.005 | −.800 | −.162 |
| Father's subscapular skinfold | .114 | −.161 | .003 | −.773 | −.141 |
| Father's triceps skinfold | .188 | −.186 | −.039 | −.746 | −.136 |
| Father's weight | .236 | .003 | .116 | −.658 | −.070 |
| Father's height | .336 | −.067 | −.008 | −.474 | −.133 |
| Father's bicristal diameter | .046 | −.189 | −.014 | −.743 | .184 |
| Father's biacromial diameter | .044 | .099 | −.162 | −.555 | .134 |
| Diarrhea, birth–12 months | −.316 | −.075 | .021 | .070 | .248 |
| Lower respiratory, birth–12 months | −.120 | −.021 | .069 | −.167 | .562 |
| Upper respiratory, birth–12 months | −.083 | −.129 | .135 | .148 | .392 |
| Diarrhea, 12–24 months | −.185 | −.057 | −.012 | −.067 | .475 |
| Lower respiratory, 12–24 months | −.104 | −.109 | .019 | −.117 | .614 |
| Upper respiratory, 12–24 months | .026 | .028 | −.025 | .066 | .330 |
| Diarrhea, 24–36 months | −.215 | .063 | .082 | .116 | .155 |
| Lower respiratory, 24–36 months | .018 | .015 | −.009 | .188 | .609 |
| Upper respiratory, 24–36 months | .004 | .089 | .082 | .116 | .661 |
| Kilocalories at 24 months | .298 | −.132 | −.019 | −.066 | .009 |

TABLE 12.3

**Factor Structure Obtained by Principal Components Analysis of 40 Variables and List of**

| Factor 1 | Factor 2 | Factor 3 |
|----------|----------|----------|
| Nonfood expenditure | Live births | Mother's upper arm |
| Food expenditure | Years married | circumference |
| Father's education | Maternal age at marriage | Mother's triceps skinfold |
| Mother's education | Child deaths 3–15 years | Mother's subscapular skinfold |
| Father's hygiene | Number of abortions and stillbirths | Mother's weight |
| Sanitation score | Infant deaths 1–36 months | Mother's bicristal diameter |
| Mother's hygiene | Infant deaths birth to 1 month | Mother's biacromial diameter |
| Percentage income on | | Mother's height |
| food | | |

respectively, and Factor 5 loads highest on variables dealing with the illness history of the cohort child.

Four of the 40 variables did not load significantly enough on any of these five factors to warrant inclusion and have therefore been excluded from further analysis. These variables are the frequency of diarrhea from birth to 12 months and from 24 to 36 months of age, the caloric intake at 24 months, and the size of the family.

The principal component analysis was next used to derive a factor-scoring matrix. This allowed us to compute, for each child in the cohort, a score on each factor. In effect, this reduced the original 40 variables to 5 factors, which could be "scored" for each subject. These factor scores are standardized deviates with a zero mean and a standard deviation of 1.

The factor scores (independent variables) were correlated with the body measurements of the children (dependent variables) at 6-month intervals from birth through 36 months of age; correlations were calculated for length, weight, triceps skinfold, upper arm circumference, and the estimated cross-sectional area of muscle of the upper arm. This gave us a matrix of 175 correlations (5 factors × 5 measurements × 7 age groups). We also correlated the five factors with the 6–7 month, the annual, and the 36-month increments of each measurement. The results were by and large not significant and are not included here.

Table 12.4 presents the analysis of this matrix of intercorrelations. The number of times a particular correlation with a dependent variable was significant regardless of age or factor is summarized in the table. It can be seen that significant correlations were most often found for length and weight. The triceps skinfold yielded significant $r$s only 3 of 32 times. In view of this generally nonsignificant relationship, we have excluded it from further analysis. The upper arm circumference and upper arm muscle area

**Variables Retained in Each Factor**

| Factor 4 | Factor 5 |
|---|---|
| Father's upper arm circumference | Upper respiratory, 24–36 months |
| Father's subscapular skinfold | Lower respiratory, 24–36 months |
| Father's triceps skinfold | Lower respiratory, 12–24 months |
| Father's bicristal diameter | Lower respiratory, birth to 12 months |
| Father's weight | Diarrhea, 12–24 months |
| Father's biacromial diameter | Upper respiratory, birth to 12 months |
| Father's height | Upper respiratory, 12–24 months |

showed similar correlation patterns. This suggested that the variable of importance was the muscle area and led to us exclude the arm circumference from further analysis. Thus, we restricted our analysis, based upon the pattern of correlations, to length, weight, and arm muscle area.

Table 12.4 also summarizes the correlation pattern by factor, regardless of measurement or age. It is obvious that Factors 1, 3, and 4 are the only ones consistently related to the size of the child between birth and 36 months. These factors are SES, the mother's body size, and the father's body size, respectively. The mother's reproductive history yielded only one significant correlation while the illness factor provided no significant $rs$. We therefore restricted our analysis to Factors 1, 3, and 4.

Table 12.5 presents the correlations between each of the three factors (independent variables) and the three measures of growth at 6–7 month intervals (dependent variables). For length, the relationship to maternal size (Factor 3) is constant across age, the $rs$ clustering around .30. SES and father's size (1 and 4) show increasing correlations with length until 30 months, when they level off. All of the $rs$ are significant except for Factors 1 and 4 and the birth length.

The correlations between body weight and the factors do not differ substantially in pattern from those of length. The relationship with Factor 3 may decrease at the latter ages, though this is not clear. The correlations with Factors 1 and 4 increase through the first year, leveling off thereafter. The correlations with SES (Factor 1) are generally higher than are those with father's size (Factor 4).

The correlations of arm muscle area with these factors are much lower and little variance in muscle area is explained by the three. The size of the father is significantly related to muscle area of the child only between 12 and 24 months.

**TABLE 12.4**

**Summary of Correlations of Anthropometry with Factor Scores**

| Anthropometric variable | Significant *r*s with factor scores | Nonsignificant *r*s with factor scores | Factor | Significant *r*s with anthropometry | Nonsignificant *r*s with anthropometry |
|---|---|---|---|---|---|
| Length | 19 | 16 | 1 (SES) | 22 | 29 |
| Weight | 18 | 17 | 2 (Reproductive history) | 1 | 41 |
| Upper arm muscle area | 10 | 25 | 3 (Mother's size) | 30 | 12 |
| Triceps skinfold | 3 | 32 | 4 (Father's size) | 15 | 27 |
| Upper arm circumference | 10 | 25 | 5 (Illness) | 0 | 42 |

**TABLE 12.5**

**Correlations of Factor Scores and Anthropometric Variables at 6-Month Intervals**

| Age (months) | Factor 1 (SES) | Factor 3 (Maternal size) | Factor 4 (Paternal size) |
|---|---|---|---|
| | | *Length* | |
| Birth | .105 | .239* | .137 |
| 6 | .175* | .318* | .204* |
| 12 | .276* | .346* | .257* |
| 18 | .349* | .272* | .352* |
| 24 | .424* | .326* | .352* |
| 30 | .417* | .310* | .362* |
| 36 | .422* | .298* | .365 |
| | | *Weight* | |
| Birth | .087 | .230* | .116 |
| 6 | .158* | .324* | .110 |
| 12 | .308* | .352* | .277* |
| 18 | .356* | .347* | .269* |
| 24 | .329* | .328* | .283* |
| 30 | .289* | .297* | .284* |
| 36 | .232* | .310* | .226* |
| | | *Upper arm muscle area* | |
| Birth | .098 | .297* | .284* |
| 6 | .062 | .123 | .002 |
| 12 | .214* | .179* | .198* |
| 18 | .243* | .282* | .106 |
| 24 | .123 | .288* | .196* |
| 30 | .277* | .095 | .061 |
| 36 | .183 | .170 | .026 |

*Significant at $p < .01$.

In principle, the factors extracted by such an analysis are orthogonal so that their effects are additive. In this analysis, however, there were significant correlations among the three factors, as shown in Table 12.6. Consequently, the above correlations are distorted by the fact that they reflect not only the direct effect of each factor, but also joint effects due to multicollinearity. To adjust for this we have conducted a series of path analyses. Path analysis is a statistical technique designed to permit the analysis of a multicollinear data set (Li, 1975). It permits one to determine the proportion of the variance of a variable (for example, body length) explained by the direct effect of a causal variable (for example, sosioeconomic status), as well as the

**TABLE 12.6**

**Intercorrelations of Factors**

|   | 2 | 3 | 4 | 5 |
|---|---|---|---|---|
| 1 | −.039 | .173* | .280* | −.169 |
| 2 |  | .092 | −.004 | .033 |
| 3 |  |  | .211* | .082 |
| 4 |  |  |  | −.086 |
| Partial $rs$ |  | $13_4 = .121$ |  |  |
|  |  | $14_3 = .253*$ |  |  |

*Significant at $p < .01$.

proportion explained by the joint effects of two or more causal variables (for example, SES and father's size). In other words, a given correlation coefficient is "decomposed" into a series of values which give the direct contributions of single causal variables (in this case, factors), as well as the joint effects of two or more variables, to some dependent variable.

Table 12.7 presents the results of the path analyses of the three factors and

**TABLE 12.7**

**Path Coefficients of Factors 1, 3, and 4 with Selected Anthropometric Variables**

| Age (months) | Factor 1 | Factor 2 | Factor 3 |
|---|---|---|---|
| | | *Length* | |
| Birth | .046 | .214 | .079 |
| 12 | .186 | .283 | .146 |
| 24 | .325 | .225 | .213 |
| 36 | .323 | .194 | .234 |
| | | *Weight* | |
| Birth | .032 | .211 | .063 |
| 12 | .240 | .280 | .146 |
| 24 | .239 | .246 | .165 |
| 36 | .151 | .256 | .130 |
| | | *Upper arm muscle area* | |
| Birth | .098 | .065 | −.039 |
| 12 | .171 | .013 | .148 |
| 24 | .045 | .253 | .128 |
| 36 | .172 | .151 | −.053 |

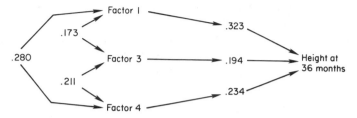

**Figure 12.3** Path diagram for body length at 36 months.

each of the three growth variables. Figure 12.3 indicates these values dia-
grammatically for length at 36 months. For example, for length at 36 months,
the path coefficient between that variable and Factor 1 is .323. This is the
direct effect of socioeconomic status upon length, independent of the other
two factors; its square gives the percentage of variance in length attributable
solely to this factor (10.4%). Other paths involving Factor 1 may be traced
and their contribution is calculated as twice the product of the two path
coefficients and the single coefficient of correlation involved. It is multiplied
by 2 because a path involving joint effects may be traced in either direction.
Thus, the percentage of variance in length accounted for by the joint effects
of Factors 1 and 3 is (2)(.323)(.173)(.194) = .022, or 2.2%. The percentage of

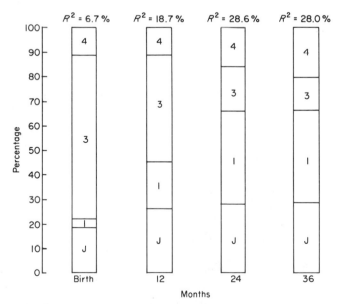

**Figure 12.4** Relative proportion of explained variance in body length explained by Factors
1, 3, and 4, and by their joint effects, of cohort children from birth through 36 months.

variance accounted for by this model is, for length, 28%, and its square root, .529, is the multiple correlation.

This model explains much less of the variance in weight and in upper arm muscle area. For weight, the percentage explained at 36 months is 14.4% while, for arm muscle area, only 5.6% is explained.

Figure 12.4 diagrams the relative proportion of explained variance in body length that is explained by each of the three factors, as well as the proportion explained by their joint effects. The proportion explained by this model, indicated at the top of each bar, increased from 6.7% at birth to 28% by 24 months. The amount that each factor contributes varies systematically with age. The influence of mother's body size (Factor 3) declines steadily, while that of the father's size increases until, by 24 months, it approximates that of the mother. The socioeconomic factor (1) also increases in importance, statistically, with age, while its joint effects increase slightly, though not substantially.

## DISCUSSION

This analysis, though preliminary, suggests a number of things about the interactions found in human nutritional ecosystems and how these interactions may be investigated. Of initial interest is the factor structure we have elicited. This structure is a function of the variables that were used in the factor analysis. A principal component analysis does not attempt to determine some underlying, hidden, structure. Rather, it is a means of reducing a large data set to a smaller group of units, or factors. While some unexpected factor may emerge, this reflects the pattern of correlations in the input matrix. Thus, the design underlying a principal component analysis is somewhat less important than that underlying a true factor analysis, which searches for some hidden structure. Such investigations should be taken with great care, as factor analyses are conceptually quite complex.

Since the factor structure which appears is a function of the data used as input, it is possible that studies of other communities, using different data bases, might find different structures. If so, this would indicate that a principal component analysis is of value primarily as a data reduction device. If, however, similar factors consistently reappear, then a principal component analysis might generate data that would be meaningful in a more general sense.

Of the five factors retained in this study, two, illness history and maternal reproductive history, showed no relationship to the growth variables studied. While the lack of relationship of illness to growth may be surprising, it is consistent with other studies of similar communities, as well as with other analyses of this particular cohort. In her 1975 analysis, Scholl found no relationship between growth and illness history in those children with no missing illness data. Condon-Paoloni *et al.* (1977) subsequently analyzed this question, comparing the growth of children in the highest and lowest quartiles of illness frequency. They found a relationship only between diarrhea and body weight. In a similar study of Guatemalan infants, Martorell (1973) found a relationship only between length and weight and the frequency of diarrheal disease.

The failure of our analysis to detect a relationship between growth and illness may be due to the outcome of the principal components analysis. The frequency of diarrhea showed low correlations with other variables in the matrix, and diarrhea appeared in the factor structure utilized only between 12 and 24 months of age (Table 12.2). The illness factor which our analysis elicited therefore reflected almost entirely respiratory disorders. Since illness was determined through interviews every 2 weeks, it may be that the inability to diagnose intensity, or to identify the responsible pathogens, might have introduced an error preventing our detection of its effects upon growth.

The failure of the triceps skinfold thickness to relate to any of the factors was surprising. Children from this community, showing signs of chronic undernutrition, displayed, as a group, smaller triceps skinfold thicknesses (Scholl, 1975; Scholl, Johnston, Craviolo, DeLicardie, & Lurie, 1979), and it was expected that this might be reflected in the correlations. Perhaps the variation in triceps skinfold thickness is too great to be related to other variables by means of correlations and significant differences appear only when groups are compared. If that is the case, then the triceps skinfold is not a reliable indicator of nutritional stress among children with chronic protein–energy malnutrition.

The value of length as an indicator of nutritional status is emphasized by these results. Correlations and path coefficients were higher with body length than with any other growth variable used in the analysis.

Of particular interest was the small proportion of variance of any growth measurement attributed to joint effects of the factors. Because of the interrelatedness of components of a nutritional ecosystem, one might suppose that joint effects would be especially strong and that it would not be possible to disentangle them. However, the results of the path analyses suggest that joint effects may be relatively rather small and that it may be possible to study the contributions of specific factors as direct causal agents.

Also of interest are the differential contributions of the factors at different ages. At birth, some 70% of the variance in body length that was explained by this model was attributed to the mother's body size, while the SES Factor contributed little. However, by 36 months of age, the mother's size contributed only 10% of the explained variance, while SES explained approximately 40%. This did not result from an absolute decrease in the influence of the maternal factor, which remained generally constant from birth through 36 months. Rather, the increase in the influence of SES and father's size, especially the former, caused a relative decrease in the maternal size contribution.

The increasing importance of Factor 1 seems to indicate the cumulative effect of socioeconomic status through the early years of childhood. It would be of interest to know if the leveling off of this factor at 24 months indicates a maximum effect, or if further increases occur after 3 years of age.

Factors 3 and 4 are attributed to the effects of maternal and paternal body size. Since this is a statistical effect, we cannot be certain to what extent it reflects genotypic influences, or if parental body size reflects the effects of parental environments upon their own development. If the joint effects of parental size and SES indicate the interaction between environment and the size of parents, then the direct effect of the parental factors upon growth may reflect largely genetic influences.

On the other hand, Scholl (1975) found that children whose growth had failed due to chronic undernutrition could be discriminated statistically from the other children primarily on the basis of parental anthropometry. The most discriminating measurements were the bicristal and biacromial breadths of the parents, which develop most markedly during adolescence. This suggests that factors in the parental environments, when they were children, which may have affected their own adolescent growth, were replicated in the environments of their children.

We must be aware that our analysis explained, at best, a maximum of 25 to 30% of the variance in any single growth parameter. Had we included more than 40 variables, or had we retained more than the first five factors, we might have increased this percentage. Although subsequent analysis will be directed at this question, it seems unlikely that we will be able to increase the percentage of variance that we can explain by a dramatic amount. There are many potential determinants of physical growth. Investigators who are undertaking an ecological approach should collect data on as broad a range of determinants as they can. Parental attitudes, the attitudes of the society, the ways in which children are treated, and the ways in which the resources of the home are used, are all examples of potentially important effects. We must go beyond the easy-to-measure traditional variables if we are to develop a model of growth which accounts for a major proportion of the variance exhibited by any sample of children.

## REFERENCES

Barr, A. J., Goodnight, J. H., Sall, J. P., & Hellwig, J. T. *A user's guide to the Statistical Analysis System 76*. Raleigh, NC: SAS Institute Inc., 1976.

Blanco, R. A., Acheson, R. M., Canosa, C., & Salomon, J. B. Retardation of ossification centers in deprived Guatemalan children. *Human Biology*, 1972, *44*, 525–536.

Burgess, A. P., & Burgess, H. L. The growth patterns of East African schoolgirls. *Human Biology*, 1964, *36*, 177–193.

Condon-Paoloni, D., Cravioto, J., Johnston, F. E., DeLicardie, E. R., & Scholl, T. O. Morbidity and growth of infants and young children in a rural Mexican village. *American Journal of Public Health*, 1977, *67*, 651–656.

Cravioto, J., Birch, H. G., & de Licardie, E. R. Influencia de la desnutricion sobre la capacidad de aprendizaje del niño escolar. *Boletin Medico del Hospital Infantil de Mexico*, 1967, *24*, 217–233.

Cravioto, J., Birch, H. G., de Licardie, E. R., Rosales, L., & Vega, L. The ecology of growth and development in a Mexican preindustrial community, Report 1: Method and findings from birth to one month of life. *Monographs of the Society for Research in Child Development*, 1969, (number 5) Serial Number 129–134.

Cravioto, J., de Licardie, E. R., & Birch, H. G. Nutrition, growth, and neurointegrative development: An experimental and ecological study. *Pediatrics*, 1966, supplement no. 2, part II, *38*.

Frisancho, A. R., & Garn, S. M. The implications of skinfold and muscle size to developmental and nutritional status of Central American children. III. Guatemala. *Tropical and Geographical Medicine*, 1971, *23*, 167–172.

Kanawati, A., & McLaren, D. S. Failure to thrive in Lebanon. *Acta Paediatrica Scandinavia*, 1973, *62*, 571–576.

Li, C. C. *Path analysis*. Pacific Grove, Calif.: Boxwood Press, 1975.

Martorell, R. *Illness and incremental growth in young Guatemalan children*. Unpublished doctoral dissertation, University of Washington, Seattle, 1973.

Scholl, T. O. *Body size in developing nations: Is bigger really better?* Unpublished doctoral dissertation, Temple University, Philadelphia, 1975.

Scholl, T. O., Johnston, F. E., Cravioto, J., DeLicardie, E. R., & Lurie, D. S. The relationship of growth failure (chronic undernutrition) to the prevalence of clinically-severe protein-energy malnutrition and to growth retardation in PEM. *American Journal of Clinical Nutrition*; 1979, *32*, 872–878.

# Part V

CONCLUSIONS

# 13

# Factors Affecting Nutritional Status, Physical Growth, and Neurological Development: Final Comments

LAWRENCE S. GREENE

## INTRODUCTION

Over the past 2 decades there has been a growing concern among nutritionists and clinicians in defining nutritional status and in describing those social and biological factors that influence nutritional status and, consequently, physical growth and neurological development in poorly nourished human subjects. At the same time there has been a parallel interest among developmental psychologists in how components of the social and familial milieux influence different aspects of child development, while biological and cultural anthropologists have been busy attempting to understand how environmental factors (physical, nutritional) and cultural factors have influenced the pattern of biological variation observed among different human populations.

The chapters in this volume represent a coming together of these disciplinary approaches to different aspects of the same problem—factors influencing human variability either directly or indirectly through their effect on nutritional status. In this discussion I will briefly review them within the context of the four main sections of the volume: (a) the anthropometric assessment of nutritional status over time; (b) the interaction between diet and infectious disease, and the relationship between breast- and bottle-

Social and Biological Predictors of
Nutritional Status, Physical Growth,
and Neurological Development

feeding and nutritional status in different environments; (c) the question of benign neglect in human populations; and (d) the empirical studies evaluating the relative importance of a variety of environmental, biological, and social factors as predictors of nutritional status, physical growth, and neurological development in human populations. The chapters cover these four areas at varying lengths and this will be reflected in my discussion.

## THE ANTHROPOMETRIC ASSESSMENT OF
## NUTRITIONAL STATUS

The chapters presented in the first section of this volume (Himes, Chapter 1; Harrison, Chapter 2; Frisancho, Chapter 3) discuss the assessment of subcutaneous fat thickness as an indicator of nutritional status and the question of a population-specific categorization of growth, and of obesity in particular. They also attempt to clarify the issue of the relative importance of energy and protein intake in affecting growth and development.

### Anthropometric Indicators of Caloric Nutriture

Himes (this volume, Chapter 1) discusses the utility of using measures of subcutaneous fat thickness as an indicator of nutritional status. He notes that *subcutaneous fat* accounts for 30 to 40% of *total body fat* and that this percentage does not appear to vary greatly with nutritional status. Subcutaneous fat thickness is thus a good indicator of *total body fat*, which represents an individual's stored caloric reserve. That subcutaneous fat thickness varies with nutritional status is demonstrated by its decrease in malnourished children and its increase in these same subjects following nutritional rehabilitation. Himes thus notes that subcutaneous fat thickness is a good indicator of short-term caloric nutriture in contrast to stature, which reflects the total accumulated nutritive experience of the individual.

The measurement of subcutaneous fat thickness is particularly useful in that it reflects the mass of a specific tissue (adipose tissue) rather than a heterogeneous complex such as body weight. While adipose tissue mass represents short-term caloric nutriture, body weight is influenced by the long-term effects of nutrition on statural growth (length and thickness of the bony skeleton). Additionally, body weight does not distinguish between the weight of muscle and fat stores. The utility of weight as a measure of current nutritional status can be increased by considering weight-for-height; however, this measure still does not tell us anything about the relative contributions of fat and muscle mass to a given weight.

Himes also presents a useful discussion of the comparability between subcutaneous fat thickness as measured by skinfold calipers, soft tissue radiography, and ultrasound. It is clear that the measurement of skinfold thickness is the method of choice under the conditions of most nutrition surveys. It is a valid indicator of total body fat, has a high degree of replicability in the hands of trained individuals, is noninvasive, and is inexpensive. The light weight and easy portability of the standard skinfold calipers make them especially suited for field studies.

However, there are some difficulties with this measure. Himes notes that a certain amount of compression normally takes place in the determination of skinfold thickness, and that the degree of compression may vary between individuals according to age and sex, and according to the site of measurement. If skinfold compression is significant, there will be an underestimation of fat thickness and a consequent overestimation of muscle area when upper arm muscle area is derived from measures of upper arm circumference and triceps skinfold thickness. Since subcutaneous fat thickness and upper arm muscle mass are taken to be indicators of caloric and protein reserves, respectively (see following), then any measurement error in the determination of these reserves will weaken the precision of these measures, and limit their utility as indicators of nutritional status (see following).

Furthermore Himes' warning about individual differences in the patterning of subcutaneous skinfold thickness across sites should alert us to the importance of skinfold determinations at multiple sites and the probable advantage of using a measure of summed skinfold thickness in data analysis.

## Population-Specific or Reference Standards

Both Himes (this volume, Chapter 1) and Harrison (this volume, Chapter 2) have addressed themselves to the difficult problem of defining obesity in a biologically meaningful manner. Himes (this volume, p. 13) notes that the precise degree of fatness that defines the obese state is entirely arbitrary. The criterion most frequently employed is a skinfold thickness greater than the eighty-fifth age and sex-specific percentile for the population being measured, or, beyond the eighty-fourth percentile of a particular reference standard (Seltzer & Mayer, 1965).

The problem with these criteria is that they are population specific, thus, individuals with equivalent degrees of fatness may be classified either as obese or nonobese depending on their population of origin. Under such circumstances, a Bundi boy with only moderate skinfold thickness could be classified as being obese in his own population and nonobese in the United States population (see Himes, this volume, p. 14, Fig. 1.1). However, when there is a single reference standard, the prevalence of obesity may vary enormously from population to population (see Harrison, this volume, Chapter 2). The question ultimately revolves around the issue of whether the determinants of degree of fatness are primarily genetic or nutritional, and the further question of whether there are specific health-related criteria that can be utilized to classify degree of fatness functionally in terms of relative health risk.

Harrison (this volume, Chapter 2) discusses the use of reference standards in assessing growth and how the choice of reference standard has a significant effect on the anthropometric assessment of nutritional status. She cites data comparing American Black and White children and data comparing Asian (India), North European, and Black children which suggest that these racial groups have different patterns of growth even when a number of immediate environmental factors are controlled. These findings, among others, suggest genetic differences in the patterning of growth among different human populations which may require population-specific growth-reference standards for a more precise assessment of growth and of nutritional status.

Harrison's own work with Arizona infants of White, Mexican–American, and American–Indian ethnic background indicates that weight-for-length during the second year of life is significantly related to both ethnic group and to size at birth. Thus, Anglo infants are lightest for length at all ages, while Mexican–American infants are intermediate and American–Indian infants are heaviest. On the basis of these data it would appear that American–Indian children are much more likely to be classified as obese during the second year of life on the National Center for Health Statistics reference standards than are White children, and that children of high birthweight are more likely to be classified as obese during this period than are children of low birthweight.

If the observed population differences in weight-for-length among the White, Mexican–American, and American–Indian subpopulations are a consequence of genetic factors, and the expression of the genetic factors show no interaction with the environment (nutritional history), and there is no health risk associated with these degrees of fatness, then population-specific reference standards may be appropriate. However, if the observed differences in weight-for-length among the three Arizona ethnic subpopulations are a consequence of differences in diet or of genetic factors that interact with nutritional history and which place the heavier-for-length children at greater health risk, then population-specific standards may be as entirely inappropriate for these groups as would be Bundi-specific standards that operationally define everyone as well nourished except those children below the tenth percentile for weight-for-height.

The choice of population-specific or reference standards depends upon the particular question at hand. Population-specific standards are useful in comparing a child to his/her genetic peers living under similar circumstances; reference standards provide as a universal reference a well-defined sample, even though it may be drawn from a genetically different population. The choice of population-specific or reference standards for the three Arizona ethnic groups should then rest on the question of the causes of the observed differences (genetic versus nutritional) and the likely health risk of the condition to the child. It would be unfortunate indeed to misclassify children as nonobese merely because they are part of a population whose genetic endowment and present dietary patterns predispose them to obesity.

## The Relative Effects of Protein and Calories on Growth

The relative role of calories and protein in influencing growth is a question that has generated a significant amount of controversy in recent years (Beaton & Swiss, 1974; Calloway, 1975; Dugdale, Chen, & Hewitt, 1970; Gopalan, Swamminathan, Kumari, Rao, & Vijayaraghavan, 1973; Lechtig, Yarbrough, Delgado, Habicht, Martorell, & Klein, 1975; Malcolm, 1970; Martorell, Lechtig, Yarbrough, Delgado, & Klein, 1978; McLaren, 1974; Payne, 1975; Waterlow & Payne, 1975). Thus, the INCAP group (Habicht, Lechtig, Yarbrough, & Klein, 1974; Lechtig *et al.*, 1975) has presented data indicating that, in the villages they are studying in Guatemala, caloric supplementation of pregnant mothers has a significant effect on infant birthweight, while the effect of protein supplementation is negligible. Lechtig *et al.* (1975) argue that the availability of maternal protein stores and a preferential placental transfer of amino acids tends to buffer the fetus against protein deficits, and suggest that the consistently lower blood glucose levels observed in the fetal circulation indicate that the fetus is more vulnerable to insufficient energy intake. Furthermore, Martorell *et al.* (1978) have shown that the effect of calorie supplements on growth rates was the same as protein and calorie supplements among preschool children in the same Guatemalan populations.

There is also widespread recognition of the influence of energy deficits on protein (amino acid) availability. Studies by Gopalan *et al.* (1973), Calloway (1975), Beaton and Swiss (1974), and Payne (1975) lend support to the view emphasizing the primacy of energy deficiency in affecting nutritional status, while work by Malcolm (1970), and Lampl, Johnston, and Malcolm (1978) stress the importance of protein nutriture in supporting growth.

Frisancho's contribution (this volume, Chapter 3) deals with these important issues by evaluating the relationship between calorie and protein reserves (as estimated from measurements of subcutaneous skinfold thickness and upper arm muscle area) and height among Peruvian children. He finds that greater protein and calorie reserves are consistently associated with increased growth in all sex and age-adjusted groups, and that greater protein reserves have a significantly larger effect on growth in height than do increased calorie reserves. This study thus supports the findings of Malcolm (1970) and Lampl et al. (1978) on the superior growth-supporting effect of protein supplementation and is contrary to the findings of Gopalan et al. (1973) and Martorell et al. (1978) which indicated that an energy deficit was of primary importance. These disparate findings have enormous policy implications as the expense of improving protein nutriture is considerable, while a strategy to increase total energy intake from indigenous food sources is both practical and less costly (McLaren, 1974; Waterlow & Payne, 1975).

It is possible that these conflicting findings can be reconciled since most of the discussion of the relative importance of protein and energy has been concerned with infants and preschool children [as are the findings of Gopalan et al. (1973) and Martorell et al. (1978)] while the data from New Guinea (Lampl, et al., 1978; Malcolm, 1970) and Frisancho's data (this volume, Chapter 3) concern school-age children and adolescents.

In infants and young children the required level of dietary protein is usually reached when protein supplies 5–6% of the caloric intake (Payne, 1975), while protein requirements in adolescents may be as high as 15% of total calories (Guthrie, 1975). This difference in the ratio of protein-energy (P:E) with age is a consequence of the adolescent's high need for protein to support the pubertal growth spurt and relatively modest caloric needs as a consequence of a lower surface area to body mass ratio. These relatively low protein needs of the infant and toddler are likely to be satisfied by the protein content of local diets as long as energy intake is sufficient; however, the protein needs of children in the 10–16 year age range are relatively greater and protein itself, rather than energy, may here be the growth-limiting nutrient.

Frisancho's data, indicating that children with larger protein reserves showed better growth performance compared to children with greater calorie reserves during late childhood and early adolescence, provide clear support for this latter point, while the data from the INCAP group (Habicht et al., 1974; Lechtig et al., 1975; Martorell et al., 1978) support the primacy of caloric need early in life.

The policy implications of these findings should be clear. Caloric supplementation to pregnant mothers, infants, and toddlers is probably the most effective means of increasing birthweight early in life and decreasing the high rates of infant and toddler mortality and morbidity observed in many developing countries. This is the age period of greatest vulnerability and should have the highest priority. However, the data cited strongly suggest that protein intake in late childhood and adolescence is the limiting factor affecting physical growth during this period. Although mortality is not a significant risk factor at this time, the final morphological characteristics of the developing individual are molded during this period (see Haas, this volume, Chapter 11). Recent evidence (Viteri, 1976) suggests that work performance of adults is not only a consequence of caloric intake, but is strongly influenced by individual morphology. Thus attention to protein needs during adolescence may have a significant influence on worker productivity, and thus economic capability, later in life.

## BREAST-FEEDING, BOTTLE-FEEDING, AND DISEASE EXPERIENCE

While the first part of this volume is concerned with the anthropometric assessment of nutritional status, the second part (Stini, Chapter 4; Martorell, Chapter 5) deals with two of the major determinants of nutritional status early in life: type of feeding regime, and the interaction between dietary intake and infection that may alter nutritional status and consequently affect growth and development.

### Human Milk

Stini (this volume, Chapter 4) discusses the unique characteristics of human milk and how the choice to breast- or bottle-feed a child may have varying consequences under different environmental conditions. He points out that human breast milk is undoubtedly the product of very long-term natural selection for uniquely human needs. Its relatively high fat and lactose contents, in comparison to cow's milk, are probably associated with the high lipid needs of the rapidly myelinizing central nervous system early in life, while its relatively low protein content is a consequence of the comparatively leisurely rate of physical growth during human infancy and childhood in comparison with other mammalian species. Stini further discusses a number of the compositional, immunological, bacteriostatic, and bioavailability-related advantages of human milk as compared to cow's milk and formula. His basic points are two. First, that the consequences of bottle- versus breast-feeding are significantly different in developing as opposed to developed countries, and second, that there are changes in the composition and quantity of breast milk over time and that these factors have an influence on the growth-supporting qualities of this important food.

Data presented by Stini (this volume, Chapter 4), Martorell (this volume,

Chapter 5), Fomon (1974), Jelliffe and Jelliffe (1971), and others attest to the immunologic and bacteriostatic superiority of breast-feeding in comparison to bottle-feeding. Martorell notes that in developing countries sanitation is poor, sterilization is lacking, and the infective load is consequently great. He points out that some investigators have suggested that the role of dietary inadequacies has been overstated, while infection, especially diarrheal disease, probably has a very great impact on nutritional status and may actually be the primary cause of early malnutrition. The immunologic and bacteriostatic properties of breast milk are extremely important under these circumstances, and the data cited by Stini support the view that breast-feeding maintains a superior rate of growth under conditions encountered in most of the developing world. The data from industrialized countries also seem to indicate superior growth performance by breast-fed infants during the first 4 months of life (Stini, this volume, pp. 67–68), again as a consequence of a lower infection rate. However, sanitary conditions and the sterilization of bottles and nipples is more adequate in industrialized countries and the disease load is considerably lighter. Under these circumstances the immunologic and bacteriostatic disadvantages of bottle milk are less important, catch-up growth following mild infections is more than adequate, and the higher sodium, protein, and calcium contents of cow's milk (along with its ease of administration) tend to foster its overconsumption and a consequent excessive (or maximized) degree of growth by the latter part of infancy. Stini questions whether or not there is sufficient knowledge at this point to worry about the possible health hazards (i.e., obesity) that have been imputed to this phenomenon.

Stini also discusses the changes in composition and volume of human milk during the course of lactation. His main point, in addition to noting some quantitative and qualitative changes in human breast milk as a consequence of maternal malnutrition, is that long-term changes in the quantity and composition of breast milk in *well-nourished women* suggest that breast milk *alone* will not support adequate growth beyond 6–9 months postpartum. Thus, irrespective of the strategies employed in improving fetal and early infant nutrition, adequate supplements to breast milk should be made available to the infant by the ninth month of life.

## Diet, Infectious Disease, and Nutritional Status

Martorell (this volume, Chapter 5) discusses the important interactions between dietary intake, disease experience, and nutritional status, and how this then has an effect on child growth. As noted, he points out that some investigators believe that infectious diseases, especially diarrheal disease, may be a more significant cause of malnutrition than dietary deficiencies per se, and cautions us that malnutrition cannot be eliminated with dietary supplements alone. Adequate sanitation and health education are obviously necessary to break the synergistic link between marginal dietary intakes, infectious disease, and malnutrition.

Martorell also discusses the depressing effect of disease experience on nutritional status, as well as the effect of malnutrition on immunocompetence, especially the cell-mediated immune response. It is clear that the poorly nourished child is more susceptible to disease and that any disease experience has a detrimental effect on nutritional status, especially so in the inadequately nourished child. In the context of Stini's discussion, the nutritional and immunological advantages of breast-feeding in developing countries are even more patent.

Martorell (this volume, pp. 89–99) also presents an excellent summary of the data linking disease experience, nutritional status, and growth in both developed and developing countries. Just as breast-feeding has a clearer growth-promoting effect in developing countries, where the disease load is great, there is also a stronger epidemiological relationship in these countries between disease experience, particularly diarrheal disease, and physical growth during infancy and early childhood. Taken as a whole, the data presented by Martorell show a clearly depressing effect of disease experience on nutritional status and consequently on physical growth in environments characteristic of developing countries.

Martorell concludes by suggesting that the development and distribution of expensive high-protein foods, either through genetic modification of local grains or through supplementation programs, is probably unnecessary, and that a more appropriate strategy would be to increase energy consumption through an increased intake of locally grown food crops. Supplementation programs are obviously not long-range solutions. Martorell also suggests that improvements in sanitation and health and nutrition education must receive priorities as high as improvement in dietary intake if the problem of malnutrition in the developing countries is ever to be ameliorated on a widespread basis.

## BENIGN NEGLECT

The major conceptual issue facing the study of early childhood malnutrition is the question of why under similar environmental circumstances some children become malnourished while others do not. A corollary to this question is the issue of why early childhood malnutrition is more common in some societies than in others that exist under comparable ecological circumstances. In the second part of the volume Stini and Martorell (Chapters 4 and 5) discussed how breast- versus bottle-feeding, maternal malnutrition, and disease experience are associated with, or may be determinants of, early child malnutrition. In the following chapter, Cassidy (this volume, Chapter 6) introduces the concept of benign neglect in attempting to explain how weaning practices in some societies may contribute to the development of toddler malnutrition. The important issues that are raised by Cassidy should have a significant effect on our overall conceptualization of the problem of young child malnutrition under many social and environmental circumstances.

Cassidy notes that parents in some societies practice weaning customs which potentiate malnutrition among toddlers. She presents extensive crosscultural evidence indicating that these harsh weaning customs exacerbate the psychological stress of weaning, leading to a sense of rejection by the child and the development of a set of symptoms that have been grouped together under the rubric "maternal deprivation syndrome." Malnutrition is extremely common among weanlings in developing countries due to the loss of the nutritional, bacteriostatic, and immunological advantages of breast milk and the poor quality and unsanitary characteristics of the traditional weaning diet (see Stini, Martorell, Chapters 4, 5). The psychophysiological consequences of the maternal deprivation state lead to a potentiation, or exacerbation, of this already existing malnutrition among many toddlers. Cassidy also points out that in addition to customs which exacerbate the stress of maternal separation, many societies have practices which potentiate toddler malnutrition in a number of other ways: by prohibiting the toddler the use of certain foods; by forcing the toddler to compete with older siblings and adults for food; and by favoring one sex or the other (usually the male) in the provisioning of food.

Cassidy argues that the harsh weaning customs represent a form of "molecular rejection" that is specific to the weaning period and *not* a generalized "lack of affection" on the part of non-Western parents toward their children. She also rejects the suggestion that "ignorance" by non-Western parents of scientific nutritional practices, by itself, is a sufficient explanation of the "parental neglect" that has been imputed to many non-Western weaning practices.

The main argument of Cassidy's chapter is that the parental neglect associated with weaning practices in many non-Western societies is benign, as opposed to malevolent, not only because parents do not have a conceptualization of the relationship between food and what Western medical science calls nutritional status, but because the customs which produce malnutrition, and the effects of the malnutrition, both serve important group functions. Thus, institutionalized weaning practices which potentiate malnutrition may be conceived of as serving an important role in controlling population increase under conditions in which the carrying capacity of the subsistence system is constantly being strained. These same practices also assure the differential survival of those toddlers who are most likely to be able to make successful physiological and psychic adjustments to their physical and social environments. Since growth is plastic, weaning practices that produce malnutrition, and thus slow or restrict toddler growth, mold the phenotypes of developing cohorts of individuals in ways that reduce their nutritional requirements and maximize the adaptation of the *population* to its environment. Because these weaning customs which potentiate toddler malnutrition appear to enhance population adaptation they are, in Cassidy's terms, benign, although their effects on individuals may be detrimental.

Throughout her discussion Cassidy stresses the fact that Western nutritional interventionists bring an external, or etic, system of explanation to bear on the relationship between weaning customs, food habits, and toddler malnutrition. She chides them for focusing on the narrow, and sometimes detrimental, effect of these practices for individuals, and suggests that they develop an emic, or internal, appreciation of how these customs are interwoven into the cultural system of a population and how they apparently serve important functions (listed previously) in facilitating the adaptation of the group to its environment.

Cassidy's contribution has profound policy implications in that it suggests that all nutrition surveys and intervention programs be preceded by a thorough ethnographic evaluation of the population under study so that the program may develop an appreciation of the integrative and symbolic functions of traditional foods and dietary practices in defining membership within social groups, and in socializing the child so that it quickly learns the "rules of the game" of its particular cultural milieu. Nutritional interventionists must be aware of these important social functions of food and feeding in designing programs so as to assure that they are culturally congruent and therefore likely to find a reasonable degree of acceptance.

Cassidy also emphasizes the fact that many societies have developed complex and poorly understood ways of controlling population increase and that many of these practices are institutionalized in the guise of traditional weaning and feeding customs. Her exhortation that we consider nutritional intervention and the control of population increase as interrelated problems should certainly be heeded if we are to avoid creating greater problems than those that we are attempting to solve.

In summary, what Cassidy is suggesting is that there are strong social reasons maintaining weaning and food practices which potentiate toddler malnutrition in many societies. Therefore, any effort to deal successfully with the problem of young child malnutrition must be cognizant of these factors. The ethnographic, or anthropological, evaluation of study populations is thus a necessary component to an effective program of nutrition intervention and population control.

## EMPIRICAL STUDIES

In the first part of the volume we discussed various aspects of the problems involved in assessing nutritional status, and then followed in the second part with a consideration of several environmental, social, and biological variables which are important determinants of nutritional status, and thus child growth and development. In the fourth part of the volume we move to a more specific consideration of factors affecting nutritional status and physical and neuromotor growth and development in *particular* human populations.

### Correlates of Motor Development—An Overview

Although placed with the empirical studies, the first chapter in this part (Malina, Chapter 7) is actually an overview of the biological and social correlates of motor development during infancy and early childhood. Malina's discussion of the reflexes of infancy and the assessment of motor development during infancy and early childhood provide a useful framework for understanding the processes and measures which are the subject of the clinical and population studies which follow. What emerges from this discussion is an awareness of the extremely wide range of normal variability in motor development during this period. Although the *sequence* of developing events is reasonably uniform, the rate of development varies with normal children passing various developmental milestones at significantly different ages. Malina also cites data from Mead and Macgregor (1951) and Laughlin (1968) indicating that different child-rearing practices may lead to marked alterations in the sequential patterning of what is generally considered to be normal motor development. This great breadth of variation in normal motor development, and Malina's observation that children at this age often vary enormously in their repeat performance of a task (Malina, this volume, p. 151) makes it clear that most assessments of reflex and motor development early in life are extremely rough screening procedures, which are most useful in identifying the child whose neuromotor development is exceptionally lagging, and hence likely to be indicative of a subsequent neuromotor deficit. Less marked variation tends to have little predictive utility.

In his discussion of the biosocial correlates of motor development and performance Malina notes that twin studies show that there is a high degree of heritability for a number of different motor tasks, but he reminds us that the apparently strong inherited basis for these abilities reflects a genetic potential, the final expression of which involves the interaction of these genetic factors with the environment in which the individual is developing.

Malina also notes that a child's sex is a biological characteristic which does not seem to be clearly associated with differences in motor development in infancy, but which shows marked differences beginning in early childhood. Whether these later sex differences are a consequence of different rearing environments or the later unfolding of intrinsic genetic factors is unclear. It is not clear whether size, physique, or compositional factors affect motor development, nor is it certain whether any such associations reflect genetic differences or differences that arise as a consequence of differential parental expectations as a function of size and physique.

Birthorder, socioeconomic class, and ethnic and cultural factors all appear to have an effect on motor development and thus should be controlled in studies of child development. Malina (this volume, p. 161) suggests that the greater stimulation associated with the indulgence of first-born children may lead to earlier motor development, however, it can also be argued that the more permissive upbringing of later-born children should lead to greater exploratory behavior and more precocious motor development. This is the explanation put forward to account for the advance in motor development during the first year of life which has been observed among children from lower socioeconomic groups and some ethnic groups such as Black Americans (Malina, this volume, p. 161).

Socioeconomic status (SES) is often used as an indicator of the likelihood of a child having experienced malnutrition and is thus considered a useful predictor of neuromotor development in areas in which protein–energy malnutrition is common. However, investigators should be cognizant of the possibility that its predictive utility may be weaker during the first year of life, because the depressing effect of insufficient dietary intake on motor development among lower SES children may be compensated for by the influence of a more permissive rearing environment.

In sum, Malina's contribution indicates that there is a wide range of normal variability in motor development during infancy and early childhood and that a number of biological and social factors may influence the expression of the underlying genetic potential for motor development. The problem of this normal variability in development leads one to wonder whether greater emphasis should not be placed on longitudinal studies which follow cohorts of infants through adolescence to young adulthood, so that we may be able to assess better how nutrition and its various determinants affect the *final outcomes* of growth and development (physical, neuromotor, cognitive) without the confounding problem of normal variation in the rate of development.

## Clinical and Population Studies

The five remaining chapters in the fourth section are actual clinical or population studies evaluating the impact of a number of environmental, biological, and social factors on nutritional status, physical growth, and/or neuromotor development.

### Failure to Thrive

Chapter 8 by Pollitt and Leibel is a clinical psychosocial study of children with failure-to-thrive without an apparent organic basis. The subjects are 19-index and 19-matched control children 2–5 years of age who were selected from among the patients attending the Outpatient Pediatric Clinic at the Cambridge, Massachusetts Hospital. Index subjects were operationally defined as "failure-to-thrive" if they were below the third percentile for height and weight on the Boston growth standards, while contrast cases were children on or above the twenty-fifth percentile who were matched to the index cases for age, sex, and color of skin.

The purpose of the study was to develop a better appreciation of the characteristics of the social environment that was adversely affecting the growth and development of these children. The authors hypothesized that the most proximate mechanisms underlying the observed growth retardation were either (a) an insufficient intake of nutrients (undereating) as a consequence of emotional factors, and/or (b) a neuroendocrine disturbance, also as a consequence of emotional factors. Their study attempts to identify the socioeconomic, familial, maternal, developmental, and dietary factors which are the antecedents of this growth retardation. More specifically, they are attempting to identify and assign relative weights to these variables so that they may be used to discriminate between children experiencing "failure-to-thrive" and normal children. Ultimately, such variables might be used to predict whether a given child is likely to experience failure to thrive.

Most of the environmental and social data were collected through interview schedules and direct observations with the mothers in the subject's home over the course of a number of visits. From among the totality of nutritional, developmental, and social data collected, five variables were chosen to be used in a stepwise discriminant function analysis. These variables represented those which showed significant differences between the index and comparison cases. Among certain classes of data (i.e., SES) aggregate variables were created by entering component measures into a stepwise multiple regression and constructing the new variable from the beta weights of the most significant predictors. The final variables included in the discriminant function analysis were: (a) a Mother–Child interaction score; (b) the caloric intake of the child; (c) a measure of the help the mother received in caretaking; (d) an aggregate measure of socioeconomic status; and (e) the child's birthweight. The child's percentage of standard weight was the measure used in the analysis to classify children into the index and contrast groups.

The analysis was able to classify accurately 32 of the 38 children into either the index of contrast group with all of the independent variables except birthweight making statistically significant contributions to the maximization of differences between the groups. The measure of Mother–Child interaction was the strongest discriminator between groups, with the index mothers being less affectionate, relating less often to their children, and being more likely to use physical punishment.

Although the authors are aware of the fact that their statistical methods limit their ability to make causal statements (Pollitt and Leibel, this volume, pp. 194–195), they do suggest a neuroendocrine mechanism to explain the growth failure of the index cases since the dietary intake of the index children at the time of the study was apparently adequate.

The authors also suggest that the disturbances in Mother–Child interaction reflect a "restricted incompetence in childrearing" since the index mothers did not show an unusually high prevalence of psychopathology, and they relate this selective incompetence to stressful and traumatic experiences during the mother's childhood. They suggest that this difficulty in child care may have been exacerbated by the conditions of the immediate family environment, with the index mothers having had less aid in caretaking and a lower per capita income than the contrast mothers.

In summary, this study indicates that abnormalities in mother–child interaction, insufficient help in child caretaking, and a low per capita family income were factors which tended to discriminate children from low socioeconomic urban American backgrounds who were experiencing growth retardation ("failure-to-thrive") from contrast subjects from similar backgrounds whose growth was adequate. These data are particularly interesting in the light of Cassidy's discussion (this volume, Chapter 6) of benign neglect. Without becoming involved in a consideration of whether the failure-to-thrive children are experiencing benign or malevolent neglect, it is still instructive to note how the quality of parenting may have a profound effect on physical growth (and possibly neurological development and cognitive functioning), and how this effect may be mediated through nutritional or, as apparently in these cases, neuroendocrine mechanisms. In this study the growth retardation is taking place among children in a developed society with an adequate dietary intake (except iron) who are probably experiencing a relatively light disease load. With these findings in mind it should not be difficult for us to conceive of how in developing countries, where the dietary intake and disease loads are much less favorable, the benign neglect described by Cassidy (this volume, Chapter 6) may not only affect nutritional status and physical growth, but may also have a profound influence on the high rate of toddler mortality observed in these populations. Data from Mexico (Cravioto & DeLicardie, 1976) appear to support this view that the quality of maternal–infant interaction is the major discriminator of infants who experience malnutrition from those of entirely comparable backgrounds who do not.

## Dynamics of Malnutrition in Jamaica

Marchione and Prior in Chapter 9 discuss the dynamics of malnutrition in Jamaica. Their major focus is an attempt at understanding how economic changes (resulting from the world food crisis of 1973–1974 and the consequent policy responses of the Jamaican government) had an effect on the microenvironments, nutrition, and growth of 1-year-old (12–24 months) Jamaican children. What is particularly interesting about this study is that it is diachronic—involving two separate surveys of 1-year-olds and their households, one in 1973 before the impact of the world food crisis, and the second in 1975 immediately after the crisis. Although the samples are different, they were selected by identical procedures from the same areas. On the basis of their data, the authors attempt to determine which of a number of social and environmental variables were significant predictors of child growth in 1973 and 1975, and then try to explain how social and environmental changes (brought about as a consequence of the world food crisis and the consequent programmatic responses of the Jamaican government) altered the predictive strengths of these variables.

The study was carried out in St. James Parish, Jamaica, on 128 1-year-olds and their households in 1973 and 119 subjects and their households in 1975. Nutritional status was defined in terms of height and weight for age as a percentage of the fiftieth percentile of the Boston standards, and a high prevalence of mild to moderate malnutrition was observed on the basis of the Gomez classification. Data were collected on 31 social and environmental variables that were hypothesized to be associated with child growth. These variables were reduced by factor analysis to produce eight orthogonal factors for both the 1973 and 1975 samples. Factor scores were constructed and the ability of the eight factors to predict height and weight for age was then evaluated.

The analysis showed that the eight factors were not consistently associated with nutritional status (percentage standard weight and height for age) among 1-year-olds over time. However, two of the factors, Agricultural Subsistence Stress and Maternal/Guardian Maturity, were consistent predictors of weight for age in 1973 and 1975. The variables "Home Food Use" and "Food Expenditure" loaded heavily on the first factor and indicate that children from households with limited cash food expenditures and a high dependence on home-grown foods showed an inferior nutritional status. The authors suggest that this factor identifies households with limited resources except an inadequate parcel of land.

The second factor merely reflects the age of the mother or caretaker and indicates that the children of younger mothers, especially those under age 20, showed an inferior nutritional status. Whether the poor nutritional level of these children is a consequence of inadequate lactation by the young growing mother, or the result of a deficiency in caretaking, is unclear from the present analysis.

In their discussion the authors indicate how the interactions between different variables change with time and circumstances, thus influencing the predictive strengths of the supposedly independent factors. In the first case they note how Agricultural Subsistence Stress is a strong predictor of both weight and height for age in 1973, but has a weaker association with weight and no association with height in 1975. They suggest that this is the consequence of an increased use of home-grown foods in response to the 1974 food crisis by a more heterogeneous group of households than the poorest households that rated high on this factor in 1973. In a similar fashion, a child's age (from 12 to 24 months) was not associated with his/her weight or height for age in 1973, but was significantly associated with these indices of nutritional status in 1975. The authors point out that the availability of food had been relatively uniform through the lives of the 1973 sample, while the *older* children in the 1975 sample had experienced the greatest stress during the food crisis of the previous year. A somewhat more speculative explanation is put forward to account for the strong association between the Family Demographic Stress factor and young child nutritional status in 1973, and the lack of association in the 1975 survey.

In summary, this study provides an overview of the articulation between distant and proximate causes of young child malnutrition. The study is somewhat unique in that it is diachronic and thus able to evaluate the interactions between these variables over time. It is also distinguished by the fact that it is a dynamic rather than a static statistical approach. The authors are particularly familiar with the ethnographic setting of the population which they are studying and also attempt to articulate findings and changing relationships to the larger national and international setting within a particular theoretical framework. The importance of an ethnographic appreciation of the study population is also emphasized in the subsequent chapter.

### *Iodine Malnutrition and Development in Highland Ecuador*

In Chapter 10, Greene evaluates the interrelationships among a number of social and biological factors and physical growth and neurological development in an area in highland Ecuador where both iodine malnutrition and protein–energy malnutrition are common. Three facets of the study distinguish it from the others that are reported in this volume: (a) that the major nutritional stress is iodine malnutrition, with protein–energy malnutrition being less common; (b) that the nutritional stress (or combined effect of the nutritional stresses) is severe, compared to the mild to moderate protein–energy malnutrition affecting some of the subjects in several of the other studies; and (c) that it is primarily concerned with predictors of neurological development. The major purpose of the study is to attempt to ascertain which of a number of social and biological variables are the major predictors of neurological development in two populations in which cretinism is endemic and in which there is an extremely high prevalence of individuals with moderate to severe neurological deficits. The author is particularly interested in understanding the reasons why some individuals are retarded and others living under similar environmental circumstances are not.

The study involves 313 adults, 15–64 years of age, and 348 children, 6–15 years of age, in two predominantly indigenous communities in highland Ecuador where goiter and cretinism are endemic. Data on the adult subjects are used to reject the hypothesis that the high prevalence of developmental deficits observed in the populations is a consequence of inbreeding depression. A comparison of estimates of inbreeding from three different social segments of the indigenous population occupying different altitudinal ecological zones indicated that physical growth and neurological development varied as a function of ecological and socioeconomic factors, and that the significant differences in inbreeding, as measured by the frequency of marriages between persons of the same surname, among these subpopulations had no detrimental effect on physical growth or neurological development. These data are particularly important because it is often implied that the high frequency of developmental deficits observed in some human populations is more likely to be a consequence of inbreeding depression than of environmental factors.

The utility of the various independent social, nutritional, and biological variables as predictors of physical growth and neurological maturation was evaluated in the sample of children through a stepwise multiple regression analysis. The analysis indicated that individuals with a genetically determined limited ability to detect the bitter taste of naturally occurring antithyroid compounds of plant origin (PTC nontasters and insensitive tasters) were more likely to manifest visual–motor deficits, as were females, possibly due to hormonal factors. These two biological factors are highlighted as significant determinants of visual–motor development under these particular environmental circumstances.

A subjective rating of socioeconomic status by native informants was the other significant predictor of visual–motor maturation. Greene interprets this variable to include economic factors that may be associated with the likelihood of the child having experienced protein–energy malnutrition, and also with dimensions of the home environment and with aspects of parenting that may also have had a direct effect on visual–motor development. He also discusses some of the possible advantages of this subjective measure of socioeconomic status by an "informed other" in comparison to a more quantitative Total Resource Index which was not a significant developmental predictor.

In a separate partial correlational analysis the author demonstrates that height-for-age (as an index of long-term nutritional status) is a significant predictor of visual–motor maturation, thus illustrating the cumulative effect of nutritional factors on visual–motor development, and discusses why any measure of this association necessarily *underestimates* the influence of nutrition on neurological development.

An important point which Greene raises is the apparent interaction between protein–energy and iodine malnutrition, whereby a restriction in food intake leads to an increased extrathyroidal production of reverse $T_3$ which, since it is metabolically inactive, exacerbates the iodine deficient state. Greene (this volume, pp. 228, 247) suggests that the simultaneous occurrence of protein–energy and iodine malnutrition early in life may be one of the major factors accounting for the extremely high prevalence of individuals with *severe* neurological deficits in these communities.

Like the study by Marchione and Prior (this volume, Chapter 9), Greene's work has a strong ethnographic focus on the communities under study and their synchronic and historical articulation with the larger sociopolitical and economic settings. Greene utilizes this ethnographic perspective to interpret statistical relationships which would otherwise be unclear, and in his concluding section he strongly urges that all future population studies evaluating the interrelationships between nutrition and growth and development be carried out within the context of an ethnographic evaluation of the population that is being investigated.

## Maternal Adaptation and Fetal Growth at High Altitude in Bolivia

In Chapter 11, Haas evaluates the influence of high-altitude hypoxic stress on maternal adaptation and fetal growth. He argues that natural selection has worked to optimize the efficiency of the maternal–fetal unit under certain environmental conditions such as those encountered at high altitude, and suggests that we can expect a certain degree of interpopulation variation in the characteristics of the maternal–fetal unit when high-altitude populations are compared to those *not* living under hypoxic stress.

In his discussion of the mechanisms underlying this adaptation he notes that hypoxic stress is thought to be the major factor explaining the slow growth, small body size, delayed puberty, and late attainment of adult body size observed at high altitude, and suggests that growth during adolescence may be a particularly crucial period in that events taking place at this time have a direct effect on the ultimate female phenotype. He then hypothesizes that women whose pattern of growth has optimized their adaptation to high-altitude hypoxia would have an adult phenotype that would be favored by natural selection in that they would have a relatively greater ability to produce offspring that are developmentally more mature, and thus differentially more viable. The study which he presents attempts to predict fetal growth and newborn nutritional status from maternal phenotypic characteristics.

In order to evaluate the relationships between maternal phenotype and pregnancy outcome Haas uses a study design that compares sample populations of indigenous and European ancestry living at high and low altitudes in two Bolivian cities, La Paz and Santa Cruz de la Sierra. The design consists of four sample populations from both ethnic groups each varying in the lengths of residency and age of first exposure to either high or low altitude. By the use of such a design he is able to evaluate whether observed differences in pregnancy outcome are the consequences of cross-generational genetic adaptation, irreversible developmental acclimatization, or reversible acclimatization.

The results of his findings on maternal biological characteristics show that high-altitude dwellers of both ethnic groups tend to be shorter and lighter than their low-altitude ethnic comparisons, and that indigenous women tend to be shorter than nonindigenous women living at the same altitude with socioeconomic factors being controlled.

The relationship between maternal phenotypic characteristics and fetal growth and nutritional status, which is the main focus of his study, was then evaluated through two multiple regression analyses—with birthweight and crown–heel length being the dependent indicators of fetal development. The analyses indicated that after gestation age, ethnic group was the strongest predictor of infant birthweight with infants born to indigenous mothers being 155 gm heavier at high altitude and 184 gm heavier at low altitude, even though socioeconomic differences tended to favor the mothers of European ancestry. Haas interprets this finding as indicating a more favorable maternal–fetal supply line in the indigenous population and suggests that this is probably associated with a superior oxygen transport system. He notes that this greater birthweight was also observed among infants of indigenous women who were low-altitude residents, and hypothesizes that this more favorable pregnancy outcome under the low-altitude conditions may be a consequence of a greater ability on the part of the indigenous women to provide oxygen to the fetus during the last months of gestation when the oxygen transport system and fetal supply line are particularly stressed.

A second significant finding was that maternal hemoglobin levels were significant predictors of infant birthweight at high, but not low altitude, and that the relationship was inverse with mothers having higher hemoglobin levels giving birth to lighter infants. Haas explains this apparently paradoxical finding quite convincingly. He argues that better adapted women should be able to transport more oxygen to the fetus with greater physiological efficiency. Such an efficient oxygen transport system, and a reduced demand for hemoglobin synthesis, would be especially adaptive if iron or folic acid intake is limited—a situation that is quite common at high altitude and under many other environmental circumstances.

Another important finding of the multiple regression analyses was that the infant's sex was a significant predictor of its birthweight at low, but not at high altitude. Haas notes that male infants are usually larger than females at birth, but tend to be more vulnerable to nutritional and other environmental stresses. He suggests that the lack of sex difference in birthweight at high altitude may be a consequence of this greater vulnerability of the male and a more "canalized" female fetal growth pattern.

In summary, although he is not studying malnutrition per se, Haas has utilized the effect of high-altitude hypoxia on the maternal–infant supply line to design a naturalistic experimental study that evaluates the influence of maternal phenotypic characteristics on oxygen and nutrient delivery and fetal growth. The results of his analysis indicate that three biological characteristics (maternal ethnic group, maternal hemoglobin level, and the infant's sex) all are significant predictors of infant birthweight (nutritional status), with these predictors having different effects in the high- and low-altitude environments. This study thus illustrates how maternal biological characteristics affect infant nutritional status and growth, just as Pollitt and Leibel's study (this volume, Chapter 8) demonstrates how maternal psychosocial characteristics and child caring competency influence the growth of young children. We also see how a biological variable, such as a child's sex, may be a significant developmental predictor in some environments (low altitude, but not high altitude), just as Greene (this volume, Chapter 10) has shown that this variable was a predictor of visual–motor maturation in his noniodized, but not in his iodized population. Although not conclusive, the explanations offered by the author for these associations can obviously be utilized to generate hypotheses that can be subjected to further experimental validation.

## Correlates of Nutritional Status among Children in
## a Mexican Community

In the final chapter of this section, Johnston, Newman, Cravioto, De-
Licardie, and Scholl present a methodologically sophisticated analysis of
predictors of nutritional status among a cohort of 276 children in a Mexican
community in which malnutrition is common. The data presented cover ages
birth to year 3 in a longitudinal study of children born into the community
between February 1966 and February 1967, and is a continuation of Cravioto
and DeLicardie's extensive research in this area (Cravioto & DeLicardie, 1972, 1975, 1976; Cravioto, DeLicardie, & Birch, 1966; DeLicardie &
Cravioto, 1974).

The analysis evaluates the relationships among 40 social, biological, environmental, and health-related variables and nutritional status from birth to
age 3, at 6-month intervals. Nutritional status was defined anthropometri-
cally by length, weight, upper arm circumference, upper arm muscle area,
and triceps skinfold.

The authors reduced the independent variables to five factors by a principal component analysis, and then retained three of the factors (SES, father's
size, mother's size) and three of the dependent indicators of nutritional
status (length, weight, upper arm muscle area) on the basis of an analysis of
the intercorrelations of all of the factors and all of the anthropometric indicators over the 3-year period. These three independent and dependent variables were then utilized in a series of path analyses to determine the amount
of variance in each dependent anthropometric variable that was accounted
for by the direct effect of each independent factor as well as the joint effects
of the various combinations of factors.

The analyses found that there was a differential effect of the various factors
on growth (nutritional status) at different ages. Thus, at birth the factor
reflecting mother's body size accounted for approximately 70% of the accountable variance in infant length, while the SES factor and the factor
reflecting the father's body size had much smaller contributions. However,
by 3 years of age the mother's body size explained only 10% of the variance
in child height (length), while the SES variable now accounted for nearly
40% and the father's body size around 20% of the accountable variance in
child height. This observation quantifies the growing importance of social,
economic, and environmental factors in affecting child growth during the
period of early childhood (toddlerhood) and the diminishing influence of the
maternal biological factors which were the best predictors of growth (nutritional status) very early in life.

The authors also note that the path analyses accounts for only a small
portion of the variance in infant length at birth, but seems to reach a stable
point of accounting for about 28% of the variance in this measure between 2

and 3 years of age. The proportion of variance in weight and upper arm muscle area which was explained by the analyses was much lower.

A particularly important observation made by the authors is that the joint effects of the factors accounted for a relatively small percentage of the variance in the dependent measures. They thus suggest that in future analyses it may be possible to dismiss these joint effects and evaluate the contributions of the independent variables as direct causal agents.

This study is particularly interesting and important because it is longitudinal in nature. It is thus able to evaluate the changing pattern of influence of the independent variables on nutritional status and child growth at different points in the life cycle. This analysis and future evaluations of the later age periods, together with the INCAP data, should provide us with some of the most unique perspectives on the determinants of nutritional status and child growth in areas where malnutrition is common.

## SUMMARY AND METHODOLOGICAL COMMENTS

### Indicators of Nutritional Status

A review of the chapters in this volume indicates that nutritional status is almost uniformly defined in anthropometric terms. Height and weight for age are the values most commonly employed, often as a percentage of the fiftieth age and sex-specific percentile on the Boston standards. It is generally agreed that height provides the best indication of cumulative nutritional status over time, while weight or weight-for-height indicates current nutritional status. Himes' chapter (this volume, Chapter 1) discusses the utility of a measure of subcutaneous fat thickness as an anthropometric indicator of current caloric nutriture, and Frisancho (this volume, Chapter 3) uses this measure and a measure of the upper arm muscle area as indicators of caloric and protein nutriture. It is strongly suggested that these measures be utilized in future studies to attempt to elucidate information about the specific components of nutritional status. The chapters by Haas and by Johnston *et al.* (this volume, Chapter 11, 12) both illustrate the utility of using anthropometric data on the parents of subject children as indicators of their past nutritional status and as possible predictors of infant nutritional status and growth and development.

### Predictors of Nutritional Status, Physical Growth, and Neurological Development

Table 13.1 provides a *rough* summary of some of the biological, social, and environmental factors that have been found, or are hypothesized, to have an

**TABLE 13.1**

Biological, Social, and Environmental Factors That Have Been Found to Be Predictors of Nutritional Status, Physical Growth, and Neurological Development by the Contributors

| Biological | Social | Environmental |
|---|---|---|
| Sex | Culture-specific child-rearing attitudes | Disease experience |
| PTC taste sensitivity | Maternal maturity | Hypoxic stress |
| Ethnic group | Pattern of Maternal–Infant interaction | |
| Maternal hemoglobin level | Adequacy of help with child care | |
| Mother's body size | Per capita income | |
| Father's body size | Socioeconomic status | |
| | Breast- or bottle-fed | |

effect on nutritional status, physical growth, and/or neurological development by the contributors to this volume. This list is not exhaustive, but it does suggest some major areas of agreement.

### General Genetic Factors

We should first note that underlying genetic factors probably account for much of the variance in both physical growth and neurological development under most environmental circumstances. Cavalli-Sforza and Bodmer (1971) cite data estimating the heritability of growth in stature at around .80 and Malina (this volume, Chapter 7) suggests that the heritability of some motor abilities may be fairly high.

### Specific Biological Factors

The biological factors listed in Table 13.1 appear to have an effect on growth and development which may, or may not, be mediated through nutritional status. Thus males usually weigh more at birth and tend to be taller and heavier than females (which reflects underlying genetic differences between the sexes), but Haas (this volume, Chapter 11) suggests that the disappearance of the sex difference at birthweight at high altitude reflects a greater susceptibility on the part of males than females to hypoxic and nutritional stress, and Greene (this volume, Chapter 10) noted that females may be more susceptible than males to the effect of iodine malnutrition.

The relationship between PTC taste sensitivity and neurological development in areas where iodine malnutrition is common and goitrogens of plant origin are consumed in the diet was discussed by Greene (this volume, Chapter 10). Ethnic differences in stature, noted by Greene (this volume, Chapter 10) between and within *blanco* and indigenous subpopulations in Ecuador seem to be due to nutritional factors, while ethnic differences in birthweight among indigenous and nonindigenous infants in Bolivia seem to be a consequence of differential fetal nutriture (Haas, this volume, Chapter 11). The maternal phenotypic characteristics that predict infant and child growth in the study by Johnston *et al.* (this volume, Chapter 12) probably represent a combination of nutritional and genetic factors, while the increasing predictive strength of the paternal phenotypic characteristics with age (between birth and 3 years) may be a consequence of the paternal physical characteristics reflecting differential economic capabilities (thus better child nutrition) that were not measured in the socioeconomic variable. Greene's chapter clearly indicated that inbreeding had no depressing effect on physical growth and visual–motor development in the populations under study.

## Social Factors

The chapters by Cassidy, Pollitt and Leibel, and Marchione and Prior (this volume, Chapters 6, 8, 9) all indicate how aspects of the home environment, especially the mother–infant relationship, have a strong influence on child growth and development. Pollitt and Leibel (this volume, Chapter 8) show how abnormalities in the pattern of mother–infant interaction is the main discriminator of children experiencing growth failure in an urban United States setting, and the authors suggest a neuroendocrine, rather than a nutritional, mechanism of mediation. Marchione and Prior's (this volume, Chapter 9) Maternal/Caretaker Maturity factor also indicates an important maternal/caretake effect on child growth mediated either through nutritional, disease, or psychophysiological pathways; while Cassidy's hypothesis about "benign neglect" (this volume, Chapter 6) suggests the widespread influence of child caring and feeding practices on nutritional status, child growth and development, and toddler morbidity and mortality in many non-Western societies. Her ideas are extremely provocative and call for a fundamental reevaluation of the traditional approach to nutritional intervention.

The chapters by Pollitt and Leibel, Marchione and Prior, Greene, and Johnston *et al.* (this volume, Chapters 8, 9, 10, 12) all have some measure of socioeconomic status that was a significant developmental predictor. Greene (this volume, Chapter 10) found that a subjective measure of socioeconomic status by his main informants was a better predictor than a more quantitative index, while Pollitt and Leibel (this volume, Chapter 8) found that lack of help with child care and low per capita income were two more specific social indicators.

The chapters by Stini and by Martorell (this volume, Chapters 4, 5) both indicate how the choice between breast- and bottle-feeding may have important but variable effects on nutritional status and child growth depending on the environmental circumstances.

## Environmental Factors

Martorell's chapter (this volume, Chapter 5) reviews the important inter-relationships between dietary intake, disease, and nutritional status, and shows how the effect of disease experience on nutritional status and child growth may differ in developed and developing countries. The only empirical study in this volume that evaluates the effect of disease experience on nutritional status and child growth is that of Johnston *et al.* (this volume, Chapter 12) which, surprisingly, did not find this variable to be a significant predictor.

Haas (this volume, Chapter 11) discusses the effect of the other major environmental factor, high-altitude hypoxia, on the maternal fetal supply line and consequently on nutritional status and child growth. The cross-generational genetic adaptation of the indigenous ethnic group to this stress has been discussed, as has the importance of maternal hemoglobin levels and sex as developmental predictors under these environmental circumstances.

## Some Methodological Comments

All of the empirical studies presented in this volume use some form of multivariate analysis. The discriminant function analysis (Pollitt and Leibel, this volume, Chapter 8) is basically a procedure for choosing which of a number of independent variables are best at classifying subjects into distinct categories, in this case "failure-to-thrive" and normal, while the multiple regression analysis (Greene, Chapter 10; Haas, Chapter 11) evaluates the relative ability of a number of independent variables to account for changes in a dependent variable. In these studies factor analysis (Marchione and Prior, Chapter 9; Johnston *et al.*, Chapter 12) has been used as a data reduction tool. Thus, a number of independent variables are reduced down to a smaller number of factors that account for a large portion of the interrelations between the original variables. These factors are then employed as independent variables in correlational, multiple regression, or path analyses. Path analysis (Johnston *et al.*, this volume, Chapter 12) is essentially the solution of a set of simultaneous equations that attempts to determine the effects of a series of hypothesized causal variables. Its advantage lies in the fact that it permits an estimation of the proportion of the variance in the dependent variable that is accounted for by both the direct and joint effects of the independent variables, thus avoiding the problem of multicollinearity which is a common difficulty in standard multiple regression analysis.

Although these techniques can be powerful descriptive and inferential tools, they are based on a number of assumptions concerning random sampling, linearity of relationship between the independent and dependent variables, and the normality of distribution and homogeneity of variance of the variables. Different assumptions also underlie the various methods of factor analysis. Serious violations of these assumptions will produce spurious results. Similarly, violation of the assumption of causal closure in path analysis will also produce spurious findings.

Other methodologically noteworthy procedures used in the studies in this volume are Himes and Frisancho's use of *summed* subcutaneous fatfold thickness (this volume, Chapters 1, 3), Harrison's use of age and sex-adjusted percentiles in comparing her data to the National Center for Health Statistics standards (this volume, Chapter 2), and Frisancho's adjustment of his data to an equal projected age (this volume, Chapter 3).

## CONCLUSIONS

The data presented throughout this volume indicate that several anthropometric measures are useful indicators of different aspects of nutritional status, and that a number of social, biological, and environmental factors are significant statistical predictors of nutritional status, physical growth, and neurological development. Further, causal relationships can frequently be posited for these variables via their effects on nutritional status or through other direct mechanisms. The chapters presented in this volume also demonstrate how a number of different multivariate statistical techniques may be utilized to evaluate such data in human population or clinical studies. Finally, the chapters suggest that an ethnographic appreciation of the study population is essential for the design of intervention programs and for the proper interpretation of the data that are collected.

## REFERENCES

Beaton, B., & Swiss, L. Evaluation of the nutritional quality of food supplied: Prediction of "desirable" or "safe" protein:calorie ratios. *American Journal of Clinical Nutrition,* 1974, 27, 485–504.

Calloway, D. Nitrogen balance of men with marginal intakes of protein and energy. *Journal of Nutrition,* 1975, 105, 914–919.

Cavalli-Sforza, L., & Bodmer, W. *The genetics of human populations.* San Francisco: Freeman, 1971.

Cravioto, J., & DeLicardie, E. Environmental correlates of severe clinical malnutrition and language development in survivors from kwashiorkor or marasmus. In *Nutrition, the nervous system and behavior.* Pan American Health Organization Scientific Publication No. 251. Washington, D.C.: Pan American Health Organization, 1972. Pp. 73–94.

Cravioto, J., & DeLicardie, E. Longitudinal study of language development in severely malnourished children. In G. Servan (Ed.), *Nutrition and mental functions.* New York: Plenum, 1975. Pp. 143–191.

Cravioto, J., & DeLicardie, E. Microenvironmental factors in severe protein–calorie malnutrition. In N. Scrimshaw & M. Béhar (Eds.), *Nutrition and agricultural development*. New
York: Plenum, 1976. Pp. 25–35.

Cravioto, J., DeLicardie, E., & Birch, H. Nutrition, growth and neuro-integrative development: An experimental and ecologic study. *Pediatrics*, 1966, *38*, 319–372.

DeLicardie, E., & Cravioto, J. Behavioral responsiveness of survivors of clinically severe malnutrition to cognitive demands. In J. Cravioto, L. Hambracus, & B. Vahlquist (Eds.),
*Early malnutrition and mental development*. Stockholm: Almqvist & Wiksell, 1974. Pp.
134–154.

Dugdale, A., Chen, S., & Hewitt, G. Patterns of growth and nutrition in childhood. *American
Journal of Clinical Nutrition*, 1970, *23*, 1280–1287.

Fomon, S. *Infant nutrition* (2nd ed). Philadelphia: Saunders, 1974.

Gopalan, C., Swamminathan, M., Kumari, V., Rao, D., & Vijayaraghavan, K. Effect of calorie
supplementation on growth of undernourished children. *American Journal of Clinical
Nutrition*, 1973, *26*, 563–566.

Guthrie, H. *Introductory nutrition* (3rd ed.). St. Louis: Mosby, 1975.

Habicht, J.-P., Lechtig, A., Yarbrough, C., & Klein, R. Maternal nutrition, birth weight and
infant mortality. In K. Elliott & J. Knight (Eds.), *Size at birth*. Amsterdam: Associated
Scientific Publishers, 1974. Pp. 353–377.

Jelliffe, D., & Jelliffe, E. The uniqueness of human milk. *American Journal of Clinical Nutrition*, 1971, *24*, 968–969.

Lampl, M., Johnston, F., & Malcolm, L. The effects of protein supplementation on the growth
and skeletal maturation of New Guinea school children. *Annals of Human Biology*, 1978,
*5*, 219–227.

Laughlin, W. Hunting: An integrating biobehavior system and its evolutionary importance. In
R. Lee & I. Devore (Eds.), *Man the hunter*. Chicago: Aldine, 1968. Pp. 304–320.

Lechtig, A., Yarbrough, C., Delgado, H., Habicht, J.-P., Martorell, R., & Klein, R. Influence
of maternal nutrition on birth weight. *American Journal of Clinical Nutrition*, 1975, *28*,
1223–1233.

Malcolm, L. *Growth and development in New Guinea: A study of the Bundi people of the
Mandang district*. Mandang: Institute of Human Biology, 1970.

Martorell, R., Lechtig, A., Yarbrough, C., Delgado, H., & Klein, R. Energy intake and growth
in an energy deficient population. *Ecology of Food and Nutrition*, 1978, *7*, 147–154.

McLaren, D. The great protein fiasco. *Lancet*, 1974, *2*, 93–96.

Mead, M., & Macgregor, F. *Growth and culture: A photographic study on Balinese childhood*.
New York: Putnam, 1951.

Payne, P. Safe protein–calorie ratios in diets. The relative importance of protein and energy
intake as causal factors in malnutrition. *American Journal of Clinical Nutrition*, 1975, *28*,
281–286.

Seltzer, C., & Mayer, J. A simple criterion of obesity. *Post Graduate Medicine*, 1965, *38*,
A101–A107.

Viteri, F. Definition of the nutrition problem in the labor force. In N. Scrimshaw & M. Béhar
(Eds.), *Nutrition and agricultural development*. New York: Plenum, 1976. Pp. 87–98.

Waterlow, J., & Payne, P. The protein gap. *Nature (London)*, 1975, *258*, 113–117.

# Subject Index

## A

Acclimatization, 258, 266–287

## B

Benign neglect
  defined, 129–130
  and developmental plasticity, 123, 133,
    320–322
  explanations, other, 122–130
  expressions, 113
  and malnutrition, 110, 130–136, 320–322
  and maternal deprivation syndrome, 113–
    115, 325
  and molecular rejection, 114–118, 320
  policy implications, 134–136
  and population control, 123, 131–133,
    320–322
  and weaning, 109–122, 320–321
Birthweight
  and calorie supplementation, 49–50, 56
  and cigarette smoking, 44
  genetic and environmental factors, 43–45,
    257–287, 329–331
  and hypoxic stress, 257–287, 329–331
  and maternal phenotype, 258, 262–265,
    268–269, 275–287, 330–331
  and maturity, neonatal, 261
  and motor development, 154–155
  population differences in, 35–36, 257–287,
    329–331
  and supplementation, 86

and weight for length in the second year,
  37–38, 43
Bottle-feeding
  cow's milk, 71–74
  and growth, 66–70, 318–319
  and infectious disease, 66–70, 318–319
  nutritional adequacy, 66–67
  and obesity, 68–70
Brain growth, 157–158
Breast-feeding, *see also* Human milk
  duration, 62–63, 74–75, 318
  and growth, 66–70, 73–75, 318–319
  and infectious disease, 87–88, 317–319
  and malnutrition, 67
  social attitudes toward, 75–76
Bundi, 13, 14, 313–314

## C

Calorie reserves and growth, 49–56, 312–313,
  315–317
Chilean nitrate, 226
Colostrum, 62, 68
Cow's milk, *see* Bottle-feeding
Cretinism
  in Ecuador, 225, 232–233, 328
  and malnutrition, 247, 328
  and phenylthiocarbamide (PTC) taste sen-
    sitivity, 237–238, 242, 328
  prevalence, 231
  and thyroid hormones, 230–231
Culture change agents, 109, 123, 134–135